21st Century Radionics

NEW FRONTIERS IN VIBRATIONAL MEDICINE

NICK FRANKS

THE FRONT ROOM PRESS

First Edition
Published in the UK in 2012 by
The Front Room Press
9 ALBERT ROAD
WILMSLOW
CHESHIRE SK9 5HT
email: nick.franks@radionics.co.uk
www.radionics.co.uk

ISBN 978-0-9573111-0-7

The cover illustration is a Radionic coding by the author
of the homoeopathic remedy Kalium Phosphoricum.
Typeset in Calibri. Title page in Bookman Old Style.

The Front Room Press

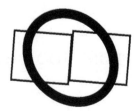

About the author: Nick Franks was born in Manchester (UK) in July 1951. He was educated at Manchester University where he received an Honours degree in Economics. In 1973 he co-founded AMEK SYSTEMS & CONTROLS LTD (later AMEK TECHNOLOGY GROUP Plc) with Graham Langley. AMEK manufactured professional audio mixing consoles and its large customer base included many of the world's leading broadcast, recording, and sound reinforcement companies and also numerous multi-platinum recording artists. AMEK and subsidiary companies were awarded the Queen's Award for Export for three consecutive years in the 1980s. In 1997 Nick departed the professional audio industry and began to develop an existing interest in Radionics and Homoeopathy. Almost entirely self-taught in both disciplines, his current main line of work is the development of Radionic instruments and codes.

WARNING AND DISCLAIMER

Contents

Figures and Tables

PREFACE

EVERYTHING YOU KNOW IS WRONG

Although some years previously I had had successful acupuncture treatment for tinnitus, my real introduction to the world of vibrational medicine came at the very beginning of 1994. I returned home from a New Year's party with friends in Denmark and developed (yet another) dreadful bout of flu. This time, I thought I would try something different to the usual routine of pain killers and cough medicines. I went to the local health food store and read through a pamphlet about the uses for a range of common homoeopathic remedies. I studied this leaflet for a very considerable amount of time while gagging on snot, running a temperature and generally feeling, as we jovial British say, 'like death warmed up'. I was equipped with two decisive weapons to help guide me towards making my selection - ignorance and disbelief. Having absolutely no idea about homoeopathic concepts and methods, there was no preconception to stop me using it in any way I wanted. Having a total disbelief in the idea that it could work, I felt that there was nothing to lose but a few quid. Purchasing a number of remedies which looked relevant to the situation, I went home and took them in combination, dose as per the instructions. Much to my amazement, within just a few days I was better - really better. How could this be? What was happening here? Was everything I knew wrong?

With the benefit of some years of experience I now know that sceptics would simply say that this was a self-limiting disease. The limit was concurrent with taking the remedies, so I was fooled into mistaking one thing for another. However, what needs to be understood is that I used to get violent attacks of flu with many dire symptoms at least four times a year. These attacks would often go on for weeks if you include the sequelae (cough, bad chest, etc). Getting better within two days was not the rule and so in my case I discard the 'self-limiting' explanation. I also rule out placebo effect. When you are lying on your back feeling so ill that you think that death might be the better option, you are not in a mind to wish yourself better at the sight of a sugar pill.

Following this experience I began to teach myself Homoeopathy, and in 1995 I came across Radionics. Here I thought I had reached a new level of lunacy. Again, it is true that I had read books by Bhattacharyya (of whom more later) prior to this, but he referred to his methodology as Teletherapy, so I did not relate the two concepts. Now you will bear in mind that at that time I was deeply involved in the professional audio industry, manufacturing high technology audio consoles using both analogue and digital signal processing techniques. So you look at a Radionic instrument of that time, in this case those manufactured by the late Bruce Copen, and you wonder what something which looked like a relic from the 1950s or even the 1930s could possibly be or do when compared with fabulous precision modern electronics. The only responses I could find in myself were either 'ignore' or 'get in deeper', so I chose the latter and bought one. This weird box was delivered to my office. I took it home and handled it gingerly, as only a true pro-audio snob could do, clothes-peg on my conceptual nose to cut out the metaphorical stench. I thought I had wasted my money, but after some persistent experimentation I started to get the idea that this 'box' worked to some extent and in some incomprehensible way. It did do something. How could this be? What *was happening here*? How wrong was this? In this book I will draw from the extensive research I have done since that time, and try and give you a viable answer. This may provoke a few thoughts, and explain something of what I think is happening *here*.

Since its beginnings in the work of Abrams more than a century ago, Radionics has been neck-deep in controversy. The situation today remains the same, although as a healing art it is now not so very well-known and has been eclipsed in the public mind by the rise to prominence of disciplines such as Homoeopathy and TCM - Traditional Chinese Medicine. In a sense, however, Radionics exemplifies, in a very condensed form, the whole debate about complementary and alternative medicine. Some, such as the writer Upton Sinclair, thought Abrams a genius; others labelled him a fraud of the highest order. Wikipedia, in its entry for Abrams, reports:

'**Albert Abrams** *(1863–1924) was an American doctor, well known during his life for inventing machines which he claimed could diagnose and cure almost any disease. These claims were challenged from the outset. Towards the end of his life, and again shortly after his death, his claims were conclusively demonstrated to be both false and intentionally deceptive. Radionics is not based on any scientific evidence, and contradicts the principles of physics and biology and as a result it has been classed as pseudoscience and quackery by most physicians.....'*

In its entry for Radionics, Wikipedia further reports that:

'*Radionics* is the use of blood, hair, a signature, or other substances unique to the person as a focus to supposedly heal a patient from afar....According to radionics practitioners, a healthy person will have certain energy frequencies moving through their body that define health, while an unhealthy person will exhibit other, different energy frequencies that define disorders. Radionic devices purport to diagnose and heal by applying appropriate frequencies to balance the discordant frequencies of sickness. Radionics uses "frequency" not in its standard meaning but to describe an imputed energy type, which does not correspond to any property of energy in the scientific sense....The claims for radionics devices contradict the accepted principles of biology and physics. No scientifically verifiable mechanisms of function are posited. In this sense, they can be described as magical in operation. No plausible biophysical basis for the "putative energy fields" has been proposed, and neither the fields themselves nor their purported therapeutic effects have been convincingly demonstrated. No radionic device has been found efficacious in the diagnosis or treatment of any disease, and the U.S. Food and Drug Administration does not recognize any legitimate medical uses of any such device. According to David Helwig in The Gale Encyclopedia of Alternative Medicine, "most physicians dismiss radionics as quackery."'

Here is a different point of view. Richard Gerber, M.D., concludes a lengthy Chapter on Radionics with the following:

'*Radionics is certainly the strangest of all vibrational-medicine approaches, but is one that may ultimately teach us the most about the vibrational nature of healing and human consciousness itself. To the uninitiated, radionics will forever seem like magic. Yet to those with an open mind, radionic technologies may provide a healing answer when all other treatment modalities have failed. It is certainly an approach to diagnosis and treatment worthy of further study and research, both to verify the claims of its proponents and to discover how this technology may aid us in releasing our own inner capacities for self-healing and healing a distance.*' (Vibrational Medicine for the 21st Century, p. 401)

Here, then, we have two typical and diametrically-opposed views of Radionics. In this book I neither make claims nor present evidence; I describe Radionics as I have come to understand it after some 18 years of research. This understanding is presented here in as coherent a manner as I could manage. After reading it you will then, hopefully, be able to come to your own conclusions as to whether the matter has any validity or not. You may then be able to look into the mouths of both proponents and sceptics and see which of them, if any, holds teeth.

The central problem to be dealt with can be summarised in the question *'but how can it possibly work?'* This I have been asked so many times and it therefore seemed essential to provide some kind of answer. In order to do so I found myself pushed into various areas of inquiry for which I have little formal training. I did not allow this to stop me, but there is the possibility that I have made gross errors of understanding or interpretation; equally, there is the possibility that I have come up with something new. Whatever may be the outcome, I did not consult any accredited scientists on the way. In retrospect I think that this was a fairly wise decision, in that any blame for what might be wayward interpretations of science can be laid squarely at my feet and no-one's career path or reputation will be sullied or even destroyed by their involvement with this project. Even though I am fairly certain, from many discussions, that 'most physicians' and by extension, 'most scientists', and, for that matter, 'most of the general public', have never heard of Radionics, let alone come to any form of conclusion about its validity, from the above Wikipedia quotes we can readily see that it still stinks to high heaven in some noses. It is still necessary to beat it senseless, and this by the simple method of further battering the body of a man long dead? A character assassination of Abrams is one thing, but what about a balanced assessment of those who followed him, such as Drown, Boyd, de la Warr, Bhattacharyya, Guyon Richards, Hieronymus, Rae, Tansley, Copen, Butcher, Upton and Knuth, and the Servranx brothers to name but a few? Of them, nothing. We are gleefully told that there is no evidence for Radionics, but (for example) Russell in *Report on Radionics* reproduces some pages of statistics on its success in agricultural work. Rather than provide the public with any kind of balanced viewpoint - balance certainly being a major requirement of reporting, at least in the UK - the author of these articles is content to peddle the old prejudices without any further investigation of the matter.

My broad conclusion, however, is that I think that there is a certain degree of explanation for Radionic actions to be found in science. This conclusion might be inconvenient or, more likely, inconsequential, to the edifice that is the modern scientific-technological complex, but it might be of value to some readers. Others might ask me why I have bothered to go down such a path. Why bother with science? If Radionics seems to work, tell us how it is done and leave us to do with it what we will; on our heads be the responsibility. In this book you will find a broad description of Radionic and Radiesthesic techniques, and therefore the second main aspect of this work is to describe what the practitioner does and how he or she tries to do it. There is a considerable dearth of books on Radionics; perhaps two or three have been published so far this century and there are only a few remaining in print from the last, those of Tansley holding pole position. In all of these, there are relatively few descriptions as to how Radionic work is actually done, so I have tried to accrue something additional to methodology in this book, but without turning it into a textbook. The matter of science is important because, considering the balance between good and ill, it has done many great things for us. What is important to distinguish is the difference between science and scientism. This latter is described in Wikipedia as follows:

'Scientism refers to a belief in the universal applicability of the scientific method and approach, and the view that empirical science constitutes the most authoritative worldview or most valuable part of human learning to the exclusion of other viewpoints...the reduction of all knowledge to only that which is measurable.'

As can easily be observed from history (a non-measurable, non-repeatable, non-quantifiable phenomenon), triumphalism usually leads to hubris, closely followed by catastrophe. There is a clear difference between a close-minded, dogmatic, triumphalist science and a science governed by free and unprejudiced enquiry, which how it started. Therefore I look to what is in science which might help answer the question as to how Radionics works, and not to that part of science which seeks to promote itself as an ideology to the exclusion of all other ways of looking at the world. I also do something else, which is to try and show that science and its inherent materialism are not one thing and everything else is some other thing. I try to show you that everything is an aspect of *one* thing, and that we cannot dissect the world into components and thereby hope to have a viable understanding of the totality.

The initial impetus for *21st Century Radionics* came from Rebecka Blenntoft and Geoffrey Bourne, who visited me some years back and requested an exposition of Radionic techniques and principles. After some two hours of discussion they both informed me that I should 'write it down'. For some reason, such as not knowing what I was letting myself in for, I thought that this was a good idea. As the classic expression goes, 'it seemed like a good idea at the time.' Some years later, having driven myself half round the bend (and back), I have now completed this book and, right, wrong or deluded, I find it satisfactory. It is neither a seamless exposition nor a complete theory; there are many points which I have deliberately left hang simply because it seems to me that the plain fact is that no-one, least of all I, knows the answers to some of the questions I consider. It would therefore be either immensely egotistical or dogmatic of me to presume upon the reader. Nevertheless, if you read this book through, you should have a decent understanding of the central elements of the Radionic endeavour. Irrespective of more trivial aspects such as the amount of work required, certain elements of writing this book have been a mind-blowing experience and for this I have to extend my gratitude to Rebecka and Geoffrey for their initial encouragement.

Many others have been involved, and in the first place I would like to thank Elise Dijkstra for her continued and deeply enthusiastic support and encouragement over the years we have been working together. I also have to extend sincere thanks to Charles Bourne (not related to Geoffrey) and Fay Wertheimer, both of whom read the manuscript as it was written and roundly encouraged me to keep going.

I would also like to extend my thanks for their generous help, support and encouragement to Asger and Marie Bak; Sheila, Ben and Owen Bourne; Jim Beal; Roberta Shoemaker-Beal; Nicholas Biggins RS (Hom); Amanda Erstling; Jan Freeman; Tim Franks; Marcus Gitterle M.D; Don Hardyman Dip HOM L.R.A.M.; Frank Hinton; Graham Langley C. Eng. MIET; Michael Leger; Stella and Francis Linon; Tim Merlin-Davies; Antoinette Pernetta; Neil Prosser; Luc Sala; Ian Sanders; Dr Tony Scofield; Joshua Thomas and family; Agnès Wagermans; Katherine Wells; Jeremy Wilson; and Tim Wheater. The omission of the name any other person who has been of significant help to me should be taken as a sin of negligence, not an act of discourtesy. Finally I must mention the late Paul Fik, a probable genius whose most regrettable early death cut short the realisation of his full potential, and whose insights helped me greatly at the beginning of my Radionic investigations.

1: WHAT IS RADIONICS?

Simply put, the basic concept underlying Radionics is that all living organisms, including humans, have a complex energy field which must function in an ordered matter for health to result. If this functioning is disturbed then illness may occur, and the symptoms experienced are for the most part a reflection in the physical body of the disturbance to the energy field.

This complex energy field is considered to be an exact correspondence to the physical body in every aspect down to the minutest detail. The quality and condition of this energy field, and the quality and calibre of its links to the structures of the physical body, are the main determinants of health. Consequently, any deterioration in the state of this field, whether the impact comes from *outside*, in the general sense of some kind of impact or interaction with other beings or objects in the physical world, or from *inside*, in the general sense of some problem in the psyche of the individual, or with his or her relationship with the psychic continuum of humanity - some part of which is known as the *collective unconscious* - may, according to the seriousness of the problem, result in a weakening of the health of the individual. In short, correcting disturbances to the field leads to the possibility that the symptoms may be alleviated or removed.

Radionics contends that, potentially, this energy field, when disturbed, can be repaired and its relationship to the physical body restored. In short, correcting disturbances to the field leads to the possibility that the symptoms may be alleviated or removed. The anticipated result is an improvement in the individual's health. To try and achieve this objective, Radionics has developed a methodology which sets it apart, in many respects, from other forms of healing modality. In doing so it has acquired a distinct character and quality.

Radionics is a healing art and therapeutic discipline which uses forms of *instrument-mediated dowsing* to analyse the health of the patient and to discover and give treatments which may assist in resolving or reducing the patient's health problems. The practitioner uses the instruments in connection with a *witness,* so-called - a sample from the patient such as a small snip of hair, sometimes a spot of dried blood - this being used to link the practitioner and the patient. The Radionic practitioner and patient are very often physically distant from each other. The two may be separated by any distance; they may even be on different sides of the planet - but the witness, as a unique identifier for the patient, 'stands in' for his or her physical presence throughout the whole process.

Many such unique identifiers are known to, and accepted by, orthodox science - fingerprints, DNA sequences, the contours of the iris of the eye, voice print, face structure, handwriting, and so on - and some or any of these play central roles in forensics, security, criminology, and medicine, to give but four examples of widely-accepted applications. In these contexts, the concept of each individual being unique, and the idea of using or finding something from the patient which uniquely identifies him or her is not foreign even to the most mainstream of scientific thought.

RADIESTHESIA

The basic idea behind dowsing - also known as *divining*, or perhaps more technically, *Radiesthesia* - is that certain things - effectively, different types of information - can be discovered which are concealed from the five ordinary senses. The radiesthesic sense has been known for hundreds of years and is nothing new. It is documented in a large number of books and dowsing is regularly used by large numbers of people, with varying degrees of success. The most basic form of dowsing is probably water divining, whereby underground water can be located with considerable accuracy with regard to depth, flow rate, and even purity, by a good dowser. Some examples will be given in the following Chapters.

In Radionics, the application of the radiesthesic sense has a much wider range. Living organisms, and human beings in particular, are complex and the energy field is usually subdivided into a number of regions for analytical purposes. Furthermore, the practitioner has a large palette of potential treatments at his or her disposal. Thus the process of analysis and treatment may be quite demanding on the practitioner's psyche and the instruments are intended to assist with the procedures by providing a support to the intentional and intuitive mental processes involved.

Radionic methods give rise to a number of fundamental conceptual difficulties for many people. I have already mentioned the basic question in the Preface - *'but how could it possibly work?'* The problem divides into two general areas. First, the idea that practitioner and patient can connect at any distance via the witness and that useful information may be gained using Radiesthesic means. Second, the idea that useful treatments may, in turn, be applied to the patient through it - in short, the seemingly-incredible concept of analysis and treatment at any distance. It is very common to suggest that Radionics is a form of magic, in this context meaning, presumably, the use of techniques such as the control and manipulation of supernatural agencies and not the creation of illusions through prestidigitation and other conjuring tricks. It is a primary contention of this book that Radionic actions have no supernatural element to them, and are an aspect of a relatively unexploited natural human capability which has its roots in the deeper structure of what we superficially perceive to be reality.

If the idea of interconnectability at a distance can be accepted *pro tem*, however, some means through which the connections can be made may be proposed. To the author's mind this means is what, for the sake of brevity, we may call for the moment a *universal information field*, which enables practitioner and patient to link together, and which is to a certain degree beyond the bounds of 'normal' time and space. In one sense it might be thought of as a kind of holographic[1] information field, which can be accessed from any point in physical space to yield the required information, in much the same way as a computer memory can be accessed from many points in physical space for the same purpose.[2]

---

1. Each part of a hologram contains the same information as the whole. 'Since each point in the hologram contains light from the whole of the original scene, the whole scene can, in principle, be reconstructed from an arbitrarily small part of the hologram. To demonstrate this concept, the hologram can be broken into small pieces and the entire object can still be seen from each small piece. If one envisions the hologram as a "window" on the object, then each small piece of hologram is just a part of the window from which it can still be viewed, even if the rest of the window is blocked off.' Article in wikipedia at http://en.wikipedia.org/wiki/Holography Note, however, that same article also points out that 'One does, however, lose resolution as the size of the hologram is decreased—the image becomes "fuzzier."' This is not so with any putative 'dowsing information field'. Each point of entry to the field can yield the same calibre of information. The problem in Radionics is, more realistically, to accurately tune the dowser's consciousness so that what is perceived through the "window" is understood and interpreted. See also Susskind (2008), Chapter 18, which refers to the idea of an information field from the point of view of advanced physics.
2. E.g. via the Internet. Although analogies with computing, music etc can be useful to help the reader understand concepts which I think may lie behind Radionics, I am nevertheless somewhat wary of using them. Cyberspace, for example, should not be taken as a *real* analogy for what I am describing. A simple but crucial difference would be that if all the computers were to be switched off, cyberspace would disappear. If all life were to vanish from the face of the earth, the universal information field itself would *not* disappear although its action would become a potential, rather than an actual, at least as far as this planet is concerned. For other planets or life forms which may exist across the Universe, I cannot say.

Thus it could be suggested that three central points characterize Radionics in this regard. The first is that strictly speaking, Radionics is not, for the most part, an electromagnetic process and may not to a presently-undetermined degree generally be governed by the routinely-accepted laws of physics, such as the Inverse-Square Law.[3] Second, it is considered possible to 'read' certain characteristics of this field using dowsing techniques, this including the condition of the patient and the identification of treatments which may benefit him or her. Third, that this field can be activated by the practitioner to entrain the patient with the 'energy pattern' of the selected treatments, in other words, the field can be actively manipulated in certain ways by human actions to achieve a therapeutic objective.

By inference, therefore, Radionics proposes that the 'energy patterns' of its treatments - for example, minerals, crystals, herbs, medicinal plants, flowers, homoeopathic remedies, the elements, and so forth - exist as discrete and identifiable vibrational quanta, or information, or a combination of both - basically - 'energy patterns' - within the universal information field. These may be evoked by the practitioner using appropriate codes and this irrespective and independent of whether the physical material corresponding to the patterns selected is present. Therefore you might invoke the 'energy pattern' of the crystal quartz without actually having any quartz physically present; and the same goes for any number of other substances. However, just as quartz, iron or lotus flowers exist as discrete objects in the physical world, so it is considered that they also exist as discrete energy patterns in the information field.

Furthermore, there is the additional possibility that *new* patterns may be created within the field in order to help bring about a desired result, these being typically known in Radionics as *therapeutic commands*,

---

3. This Law describes, for example, the amount of energy required to propagate an electromagnetic wave through space. Most readers will be familiar with the signal strength of an FM radio station falling off and finally disintegrating with distance from the transmitter; the amount of energy required to broadcast the signal is generally governed by the Inverse-Square Law. See also Jahn and Dunne (2011) for similar comments drawn from their experimental results using techniques somewhat similar to those used in remote viewing, e.g. 'Perhaps most instructive....was the evidence that the statistical scores of the remote data were essentially independent of the magnitudes of the intervening distances, thereby laying the axe to any conventional signal hypotheses wherein typical $1/r^2$ or exponential decays would have been expected.' (p. 164) Although I was basically aware of the PEAR (Princeton Engineering Anomalies Research) experiments from reading McTaggart (2001), I did not read Jahn and Dunne's book until I had completed Chapter 11 of the present work.

or simply *commands*. Examples might be *'co-ordinate [functioning of]* *stomach and duodenum'* or *'normalise functioning of the digestive tract'* or *'detoxify respiratory system'*, and so on. Needless to say, creating a viable code which will enable such commands to work effectively is no easy matter.[4]

As noted, instruments are crucial to Radionic operation; there are many designs of such instruments, but there are three basic functions which may be performed. Some instruments may be dedicated to one function, others may be able to perform all three.

The first of these is *analysis*: to help attune the practitioner's mental focus on the patient in order to improve the accuracy of the practitioner's dowsing;

the second is *treatment*: to enable the practitioner to treat the patient;

the third is *remedy synthesis*: to enable synthesis of remedies, such as homoeopathic medicines, in carrier materials such as water.

INSTRUMENTS AND CODES

In the first two functions the patient's witness is located somewhere in or on the instrument, and intermediary codes are used to 'tune' the instrument and by this means link or, perhaps more accurately, *entrain* the patient with the energy patterns being used in the treatment. Remedy synthesis is performed locally, i.e., not at a distance; the whole

---

4. Note that the patient's consent to Radionic treatment is required, and can, of course, be withdrawn. Treatments cannot be forced on an unwilling person. See for example McTaggart, 2001 - *The Field*. This useful book examines efforts by various scientists to subject a range of anomalous phenomena, such as 'healing', to scientific tests. In Chapter Seven, *Sharing Dreams*, concerning the remote influence of one mind upon another (e.g. the sense of being stared at), she reports 'Thoughts about the significance of his work percolated up in Braud's mind to a disquieting realisation. If we could intend to make good things happen to other people, we might also be able to make bad things happen....(i.e.) given the experimental results he'd been getting, that bad intentions could have an effect. Was it possible to protect yourself from them? Some preliminary work of Braud's assured him. One of his studies showed that it was possible for you to block or prevent any influences you didn't want. This was possible through psychological 'shielding strategies'.....at the end of the experiment, the shielded group showed far fewer physical effects than those who just allowed themselves to be affected.' (p. 136) Nevertheless, two points are substantial. In the first place, the ethical character of the practitioner (as in any other profession) is paramount. Secondly, as I will describe later in the book, occult attacks of various types and their malign effects on the victim are serious matters which sometimes need to be dealt with in Radionic practice.

operation is carried out within the instrument, with the carrier material replacing the patient's witness as the focus of the procedure.

An advantage of the Radionic instrument is that it can be used as what may be termed a *sample-and-hold device* for the practitioner's *precisely-tuned intention*. The instrument, set up with appropriate codes, allows him to devote time to other matters while the treatment proceeds. Some patients, such as the chronically-ill, may require a lengthy period of treatment - in some cases, months - and by using instruments the burden of concentration is removed from the practitioner. Distant treatment has traditionally been referred to as *broadcasting*, but as will become more and more apparent, there is nothing similar to electromagnetic broadcasting, e.g. radio or television, in it at all. The same 'signal strength' (analogously speaking) is used no matter where the location of the patient. Generally speaking no radio or other electromagnetic waves are being emitted by the instrument - but, if some instrument designs do emit such waves, they are not, in my opinion, much relevant to the treatment process.

Historically, codes have been referred to as *Rates*, but more generally I will refer to them as codes, since there are in fact various possible methods of coding and some of them do not at all resemble Rates.

Radionic codes emerged from the experiments of Dr. Albert Abrams (1863 - 1924), the founder of Radionics[5], and were greatly developed in the work of Dr. Ruth Drown (1892 - 1962). In its basic form, a Rate is a chain or string of numbers which is used to represent what I have called above an *energy pattern* or *vibrational quantum*. To repeat, it is considered that everything, from elements and atomic particles via the entire contents of the kingdoms of nature to emotional, psychological and spiritual states can, potentially, be conceptualised as a vibrational quantum which can be identified and evoked using a Rate or other Radionic code. The fact that there are different possible types of code is in principle no different from the fact that there are different human languages. Language itself might be considered to be an audio-visual coding system which describes an underlying state of consciousness. The fact that humanity has not one language but many suggests that the same thing or experience may be represented by any number of different such

---

5. As far as I know the word 'Radionics' was not in use by Abrams, who used the name ERA - Electronic Reactions of Abrams. According to Scofield (2003) p. 23, the term was first seen in print in a paper by one Mary Senseman in 1931, some seven years after Abrams' death.

coding systems (languages), some of which may have a greater degree of accuracy or expression than others. Further in this regard, the fact that one language may be translated into another suggests a common experiential basis which underlies the creation of languages; an *experiential ground which pre-exists language*. And finally, we note from science the need to create precise languages - notably mathematics - which attempt to go beyond interpretation and allow absolute specificity, which human languages often do not.[6]

Equally, Radionic codes can be thought of as an attempt to create a precise language which can be used to identify and evoke a supra-physical order of reality - supra-physical, but not supernatural. From the viewpoint of materialism this order is not considered to exist, but from the Radionic viewpoint it is intrinsic to, and indivisible from, the structure and function of physical reality - of the material Universe. Codes, therefore, are used in Radionic instruments to describe, evoke and entrain selected energy patterns with the patient. Accordingly - at least in principle - just as the witness represents the patient, so the Radionic code represents the energy pattern with which the practitioner is working; and each code is in principle uniquely related to the pattern in the same way that the witness uniquely represents the patient. A code does not represent two different things. As I have noted, various rates and other coding systems have been used over the last century of Radionic development, and, to give but one example, the Magneto-Geometric Applications (MGA) system contains around 28,000 coded cards at the present time. The problem of effective and accurate coding in Radionics is, however, substantial. The fact that different coding systems exist which may be used to identify the same vibrational quanta suggests that the matter is not cut-and-dried and that coding systems are not yet, as it were, a completed technology - an *absolutely precise and comprehensive language* which completely describes all relevant aspects of the vibrational patterns being used.

DOWSING
It is important to understand that good dowsing requires both so-called intuitional and intellectual skills. Dowsing in Radionics is notably Q & A dowsing - Question & Answer. The practitioner works from a basis of

---

6. For example interpretation of the law. We may think we know what a law means, but many clever lawyers have made large amounts of money by capitalising on what we might call the imprecision of language, or perhaps *the 'intention' gap* - variances between what is intended and how it is expressed.

intelligence and knowledge in order to know what questions to ask about the patient, and to interpret the meaning of the pendulum movements which appear in response to the questions. But the information which makes the pendulum respond is gleaned from the practitioner's *subconscious;* the subconscious reaction. From this standpoint dowsing gives access to a type, or level, of comprehension not immediately available to the conscious mind, and the Q & A process may be typified as a left brain ⟷ right brain interplay (sometimes described as intellect versus intuition). However, it is debatable whether the discovery process is in fact truly or only intuitional; if the practitioner is 'reading' selected aspects of the information field, then this implies the use of some unusual sensory faculty, which I have heard described as ESP - that is to say, *Extended* Sensory Perception (as opposed to the more usual 'Extra-Sensory Perception'). The end result is that the ESP faculty produces a subconscious reaction which in turn generates a response in the nervous system; this is transmitted to the relevant muscles, which move the pendulum in specific ways. Each pendulist has his or her typical movements which may be interpreted as *yes* or *no*, and so forth. Consequently this so-called 'intuitive' process may be basically no more intuitive than reading the page of a book, and by way of analogy the well-educated and highly-literate reader reads quickly and understands more than the barely-literate, poorly-educated reader.

The pendulum, therefore, seems to be a means of amplifying and making visible that which is hidden, in short, the dowser's subliminal reaction - a *state* precipitated in the dowser's subconscious resulting from a question posed in the dowser's conscious mind which enables him to query the relevant region of the information field. However, the pendulum is sometimes thought of as having properties of its own, some of which may be considered magical or supernatural, but as far as I am concerned it is not so - or, if it *is* so, such properties are not relevant in the Radionic application. A *real* and far more serious problem, however, is the improper use of the pendulum resulting from *mentally driving* it to give the answers you want to have. Dowsing requires much self-discipline, neutrality of mind, and absence of expectation of any particular outcome to a given question. If you believe the patient has a certain type of problem, or that a certain type of treatment is suitable, then you can certainly drive the pendulum to produce motions which confirm your prejudices. But there is no 'right answer' to any dowsing operation; there is only *the* answer indicated by the pendulum movement. Such movements may, however, be equivocal if the answer to the question is potentially equivocal, or the question is improperly formed. Usefully interpreting the meaning of the answer within the context of the enquiry may also require considerable effort and knowledge if the patient's situation is complex.

It should also be noted that the pendulum is not the only means by which the subconscious reaction can be externalized - the *stick pad* and other methods are employed by some. The general usage is the same, although I find the pendulum to be faster and more flexible than the pad. The stick pad, or *rubbing plate*, for example, is a panel located in certain designs of Radionic instrument. The operator rubs his finger across the pad while tuning the instrument, and when it comes into balance (into tune), the operator experiences a definite 'stick' of the finger on the pad at a certain point; otherwise the finger will rub across without sticking. The sticking sensation is quite singular and unmistakeable. Perhaps the ultimate, however, is to go beyond dowsing, to *direct conscious perception* without the use of dowsing tools - i.e. 'knowing' the answer, but this is very hard to do, although it might be an *evolutionary goal* or an *undeveloped* or *suppressed* human faculty.[7] Jung (1875 - 1961) comments on the unknown nature of the psyche:

'...should it turn out that the psyche does not coincide with consciousness, and, what is more, that is functions unconsciously in a way either similar to, or different from, the conscious portion of it....it is no longer a question of general epistemological limits, but of a flimsy threshold that separates us from the unconscious contents of the psyche. The hypothesis of the threshold and of the unconscious means that the indispensable raw material of knowledge - namely psychic reactions - and perhaps even unconscious "thoughts" and "insights" lie close beside, above or below consciousness, separated from us by the merest "threshold" and yet apparently unattainable. We have no knowledge of how this unconscious functions, but since it is conjectured to be a psychic system it

---

7. Science tends to dismiss dowsing. But simple tools and simple observations can bring about profound results. Sir Isaac Newton (1643 - 1727), we are told, with neither a high-energy particle accelerator nor low-earth orbit space station to hand, observed an apple fall from a tree and this brought him to his concept of gravity. So what's the falling of an apple compared to a pendulum? The fall of an apple is the simple thing that brought about a profound result - because Newton's *mind* was prepared and knew what to do with the observation. Thus the pendulum - an apple on a piece of string, as it were - may help trigger a reaction in the mind of the dowser. *'Fortune favours the prepared mind'* (Louis Pasteur, 1822 - 1895).

may possibly have everything that consciousness has, including perception, apperception, memory, imagination, will, affectivity, feeling, reflection, judgment, etc., all in subliminal form.' [8]

In short, I suggest that dowsing may be a method which allows a certain form of access to various regions of the unconscious, a means of breaking through the 'flimsy threshold'. Since we do not know the contours and extent of the unconscious, there is no reason to assume until proven otherwise that there are not some contents which correspond to, contain, or give access to, the information potentially gained from dowsing operations.

SUBTLE ANATOMY

As noted above, central to Radionic thinking is the idea that every living organism has an 'energy field'. In the case of the human being, this *field* is considered to be extremely complex and is composed of a number of layers or levels, which are often referred to as *bodies*; and the *energy* is referred to as 'subtle' energy (or 'life force'), to differentiate it from the forms of chemical or electrical bio-energy recognized by orthodox science. The whole construct of the various fields of the living organism is referred to as the *Subtle Anatomy* and the flow of energy through, and interchange between, different locations in the Subtle Anatomy may be referred to *Subtle Physiology*; but for the sake of brevity I shall mainly use the term Subtle Anatomy to refer to the system as a totality.

These fields and energies are considered to be fully integrated with the material of the physical body proper in a continuous and intimate exchange of energy and information. It is indeed the information contained in the Subtle Anatomy which is immediately registered in the universal information field where it can be 'read' by the skilled practitioner-dowser and interpreted in terms of various energetic deficits which may correlate to the symptoms described by the patient. For example the presence of an infection may be indicated by the pendulum reading, but the idea is that it is the presence of the energy pattern or *energetic envelope* of the pathogenic micro-organism in the Subtle Anatomy which is detected, not the physical presence of the organism in the tissues or other structures of the physical body. The presence of the pathogen will alter the normal vibration (and spectral output, i.e. the colour spectrum in the supra-physical field) of the infected region,

8. Jung, 2001, p. 96

potentially rendering it detectable by the dowsing method. It could also be proposed, and rather controversially perhaps, that if the pathogen cannot successfully integrate its energetic envelope into that of the host, then it cannot successfully infect on the physical level, since it would not be able to access its own specific quantum of life force and hence would be, as it were, like a tree without roots.

However, just as the physical body proper is in an intimate relationship with the underlying Subtle Energy fields - which we may also call the *paraphysical level* - so the regions of the Subtle Anatomy which correspond to the emotional and psychological components of the individual are just as equally in a continuous reactive and responsive interchange with the individuals' self and its functions. Jung defines the self as:

'*a quantity that is superordinate to the conscious ego. It embraces not only the conscious but the unconscious psyche, and is therefore, so to speak, a personality which we also are.... there is little hope of our ever being able to reach even approximate consciousness of the self, since however much we may make conscious there will always exist an indeterminate and indeterminable amount of unconscious material which belongs to the totality of the self.*' [9]

In Radionics it is proposed that the self manifests through various Subtle Bodies, or 'energy bodies' which are conditioned by, and may also condition, the quality, calibre and expression of the self, or *psyche*. Thus emotional and psychological impacts result in disturbances to the corresponding fields and it is these vibrational changes, again, which the practitioner can, potentially, read and treat by Radiesthesic means. More fully, symptoms and pathology in the physical body or in the ordinarily-discernible components of consciousness - i.e., disturbances to the *experienced* mental and emotional states - are, equally, considered to be clearly-identifiable impacts of various kinds to the Subtle Energy system. Considering that the whole of the Subtle Anatomy forms a totality with the mind, emotions and physical body (the term *bodymind* expresses a

---

9. Jung 1995, p. 417. One suspects that the rest of Science will probably find that a similar relationship exists between it and reality, i.e. however much we discover, there will always be more.

part of this totality [10]) with many linking and interlinking pathways, such impacts may impede or prevent the organised, balanced, structured and rhythmic flow of energy necessary to maintain health. In Radionics the body is not in principal some form of autonomous system which develops diseases by itself; in most cases there is a background context to be considered. For example, your mental and emotional state can have an effect - and in fact a very strong effect - on your body. This does not mean that your health problems are necessarily 'your fault'. Life can be difficult, things do not go smoothly, and there is much to contend with, often, seemingly, beyond your control. It is the analysis of, and possibility of correction of these disturbances to the Subtle Anatomy which gives Radionics its singular range of therapeutic actions. The hope is that normalisation of problems in the Subtle Anatomy will produce a reduction or removal of the corresponding symptoms or pathology at whatever level it may occur in the physical body or the psychological-emotional domain.

Radionics places the individual's *consciousness* and *conscious awareness* at the centre of the human system and views the human being as a living, self-conscious, reactive and responsive organism in a dynamic relationship with the environment. This includes not only the *external physical environment* of cosmos, planet, air, earth, and water but also the *relational environment*, by which I mean the individual's relationships with others on an *interpersonal, social* and *group* level. Problematic close relationships such as those between parents and children (interpersonal), negative interactions between friends and work colleagues (social), the adverse effects of mass relationships (group) - the mass emotional and psychological currents, and mass programming to which society is ceaselessly subjected - may all impact the individual in many negative ways which can produce deficits in the Subtle bodies. These deficits may lead to illness. In short,

'....what we try to do in Radionics is present information to the patient which hopefully enables them to reorganise their energetic makeup along more coherent lines. We can view illness as incoherence and the breaking-down of order, if you will, the entropic force, which brings everything towards disorder and a lower level of organisation, eventually disorganisation and destruction, for example as found in cancers and necrotic processes, heart attack, overwhelming infection leading to death,

---

10. See for example Jawer and Micozzi, 2009, for a lengthy exposition on contemporary research into the interrelationship of mind and body.

and so on. On the other hand biological entities may be considered to be generally attempting to attain or maintain a higher or proper state of order (i.e. negative entropy). In a healthy system this growth has its own intrinsic coherence and can be characterised, for example at the physiological level, by processes such as ordered cell division and reproduction....These processes maintain the physical being in its intended and appropriate form; they build the growing infant into the adult and maintain the adult in a healthy state. Thus we may not unreasonably consider that form, order and organisation are closely entwined.' [11]

Finally, I propose the idea that the Subtle Anatomy in all its aspects may correspond to some degree, or even entirely, to what Jung denotes the collective unconscious. If this is correct, then Radionics is a means by which the subconscious and unconscious states of living organisms may be explored. Simple organisms or organisms such as plants are not considered to be conscious in the normal sense, but there is evidence in the work of Burr (of which more in Chapter 7) and Backster[12] that they are in fact reactive and responsive to stimuli, which implies consciousness at some level. Consequently, I append that Radionic work may be grouped into four general areas of analysis and treatment:

1. Humans (Human Radionics)
2. Animals (Veterinary Radionics)
3. Crops, Plants and Soils (Agricultural Radionics)
4. Environment and Ecosphere (Environmental Radionics)

Of these, the last in particular is not well-developed and there is much scope for exploration by the determined researcher. This book is primarily concerned with Human Radionics, but the methods and concepts described herein have many characteristics which are relevant to whichever branch of Radionics is being studied.

BASICS OF THE WORKING METHOD

It is often necessary to take a wide spectrum of factors into account in Radionic analysis. In short what is tested is *the deviation from functional normality for the Location under question*. I shall give at this

---

11. Originally from the author's article "Genesis of the ANT" (Alpha-Numeric Transducer, a Radionic instrument designed by the author), published in The Radionic Journal 48(2): 5-11.
12. Backster (2003)

point the briefest idea of the process. Using a suitable dowsing chart, various points in the Subtle Anatomy (*Locations*) are tested and qualitatively[13] measured as the degree of deviation from 0 (zero) as a percentage.

If we check the Respiratory system of an individual - i.e. at the energetic (paraphysical) level - and find that the reading is 0% then it may be assumed for the time being that all is well. If, however, the reading is 50% or 83%, and so on, we may then look for some form of impact - in general denoted a *Factor* - to the Respiratory system, such as infection or inflammation. We may find a reading which gives Respiratory System: Infection, 83%. This implies that the Respiratory System is stressed on account of the presence of some form of pathogen.

From this point we may investigate further by testing subdivisions of the Respiratory System, e.g. Lungs, Bronchi, Upper Respiratory Tract, and so on, and then which side - left, right, or both. Obviously one would ask the patient, or study his case history, to see if this test corresponds to any symptoms; it may, or may not - many infections and other problems are asymptomatic until triggered into action by appropriate conditions. Herpes virus infections are a well-known example, where the virus awaits suitable conditions under which it may erupt. Another typical situation is that the patient comes with one complaint and has forgotten to mention others, and analysis brings the matter to light.

It should be noted that there are alternative measuring techniques. In some approaches 100% may be considered fully and normally functional; any lower reading, such as 47%, indicates the presence of an inimical Factor. In other approaches, an under/over system is used. Here 0% is considered normal and readings may be taken over a scale +/- 50% or +/-100%. Here a reading over zero, such as +37%, would indicate that the Location is energetically overexcited by a Factor, such as

---

13. This question, and the Location - Factor system, were proposed by Malcolm Rae (1913 - 1979), one of the great pioneers of Radionics. Rae also developed the Magneto-Geometric encoding system, which is used to create specific coding patterns which are printed out on standard cards (commonly referred to as Rae cards). Orthodox medical science measures quantitatively and has many techniques to do so. Some readings taken Radionically could probably be interpreted comparatively with medical readings and an appropriately-qualified group of researchers may care to make a study at some point. For the moment we will consider Radionic readings to be qualitative, indicating the degree of impairment to the quality (normal functioning) of the Location under question and not equivalent to objective analysis by laboratory techniques.

Inflammation. A negative reading, such as -45%, would indicate that the Location is energetically depleted.

Corresponding examples may be found in the psyche of the individual, where readings may be taken to try and establish the presence of any stressors. These include neuroses, complexes, repressed and delusional states, and so forth. When a situation arises which aggravates the unresolved psychological conflict, the compensatory activity in the psyche becomes visible as the neurosis. Equally, all of these conflicts are qualitatively measureable as impacts to the appropriate Subtle Bodies. Thus, for example, a neurosis may be seen a *congestion*, since the normal flow of psychic energy is impeded because of the unresolved state which must be worked around in order to avoid the unacceptable feelings resulting from a triggering of the conflict. It is also an *overstimulation*, since an over excitation of the relevant regions of the Subtle Anatomy, resulting from efforts to deal with the conflict, may be detected. Therefore a specific fear (congestion) might be the trigger and the reaction is anxiety (overstimulation).

In general, such readings are made by using the pendulum or other Radiesthesic device in connection with suitable Charts and related instruments.

PROCEDURE

Considering any medical or therapeutic procedure, as a generality it might be suggested that there are four basic stages:

Presentation of the patient to the medical practitioner, and a description by the patient of his complaints;

Analysis of the patient's complaints in terms of some model of the human system;

Selection and administration of treatments;

In due course, assessment of the results and a decision as to what extent the treatment has been successful, and given this, whether further treatment is necessary. If *yes*, we return, more or less, to stage one and so the cycle is repeated as required.

Now the relationship between patient and practitioner, implied in 1. above, is of course important. Obviously, the nature of the problems for which the patient seeks treatment needs to be understood - the digestive complaints, the sleeping problems, the skin eruptions, the chronic respiratory infection, the poor self-image, and so on. The patient must have confidence in the practitioner, and the practitioner must come to an understanding of the patient, in order to help him attune to the patient's state. Of course, human to human, the practitioner may empathise or sympathise with the patient; but if all of the problematic states of all patients are taken on board or internalised then the practitioner stands the risk of becoming unwell himself. There are many who give all to help others while neglecting themselves and in the end may become yet another patient, incapable of fulfilling their calling - and not only in the *un*orthodox healing disciplines.

Presentation. The process of taking the case (which may, according to the circumstances, be obtained in writing, as opposed to face-to-face) and getting a proper description of the problems may also help the patient, in the sense that things which have been buried or forgotten and which are germane to the therapeutic situation may come to light. But the Radionic practitioner is not a psychotherapist or counsellor. We are not delving into the patient's psychological traumas in the hope that revealing them may help the patient release them and overcome them. If the patient chooses to tell me that they were raped, molested, bullied, abused, rejected, victimised, attacked or otherwise brutalised and to reveal the hurt, shame, resentment, denial, remorse, guilt, humiliation, sense of failure, poor self-image, lack of confidence, and so on, then this may be something they feel comfortable in confiding to someone they see as uninvolved and, hopefully, non-judgmental, and who may be able to help. But I rarely press anyone for such information even if I suspect it is there; far better to let it emerge spontaneously, if it must be revealed. Nevertheless, it can of course be cathartic to be able to admit these matters to the practitioner and it is the exercise of this fine line of judgment in how to relate to the patient which, for example, makes Radionics a *healing art*. But there are many different forms of healing art, and it is the method of attempting to deal with such problems in Radionics which is the focus of this book - Radionics as a *therapeutic discipline with its own distinct methodology, the correction of disturbances to the Subtle Anatomy by entraining it with appropriate corrective vibrational patterns*. If Radionics is anything you want it to be - a farrago of healing, counselling, bodywork, herbalism, nutritional therapy, past life interpretation, hypnotism, meditation, visualisation, and so on, with a bit of 'Radionic balancing' thrown in, then it becomes nothing much.[14]

Now 2., *Analysis*, means an understanding of the patient through the filter of an analytical model. Doing so should also bring a level of objectivity. The basic method has been outlined above; the complaints translate into a set of readings for different Locations in the Subtle Anatomy. Then comes the attempt to differentiate the symptoms into what is primary and what is secondary, i.e. those symptoms which are causative and lie behind the whole state of the patient, and those symptoms which are a consequence of the primary problems. To give a simple example, a person may say that they have never been well since a bout of influenza or pneumonia or food poisoning.[15] In such an instance the *chain of causation* may be relatively simple. A patient with a complex chronic illness may present many symptoms, and pinning the causation down to one single or even a few Factors which can be easily or immediately addressed in the hope of a cure or substantial improvement may be difficult, since the chain of causation may be very complex.[16] If it has gone beyond 'very complex' and has degenerated into energetic chaos, then the patient's situation may be irretrievable by any means, conventional or otherwise.

Having completed the analysis, the practitioner will then take up the pendulum and dowse for the most important central symptoms, or for the order in which symptoms must be treated. The intuitive approach notwithstanding, this remains a matter requiring skill, sensitivity,

---

14. But understand that I am not condemning other therapies - far from it. I am not here to make judgements about that. Many may be judiciously used alongside Radionics. However, overloading the patient with too much therapy can also be a problem, and the hypochondriacal patient who runs from therapist to Doctor to therapist is another. In addition there has been, it seems to me, a tendency in some quarters to turn Radionics into a cute and cuddly fuzzball of New Age flummery. This is a denial and betrayal of the efforts of the Radionic pioneers, and misses the point of what it is about.
15. Known informally in homoeopathy as NBWS (Never Been Well Since). The patient has never got his or her health and vitality back to normal because there is some remnant of the illness which results in a quasi-permanent deficit to the system.
16. For example patients being treated with conventional medicine, for example, may end up taking a range of powerful drugs, but the drug interactions themselves may be complex and can produce side effects which entangle with the original illness to produce an extremely difficult situation. You will understand I am not criticising orthodox medicine; I doubt that many Doctors would deny that this problem exists. The analytical problems I am describing here are also well-known in homoeopathy (and no doubt other disciplines); I have heard Jeremy Sherr (1955 -) refer to them as 'the forest of symptoms'.

knowledge and experience. The fact that it can in principal be done also suggests that there may be some innate ordering of causation discernible within the framework of the universal information field. This complex point suggests for example that a *history* of causation is stored within the field, implying that it is multi-layered with respect to the timeline of the physical world, and that past events are somehow stored in it and may possibly be retrieved. Given this, a treatment order may emerge which could, for instance, attempt to neutralise causative Factors in a sequence which corresponds to the reverse order in which they appeared in the patient.[17]

In stage 3. *Treatment*, the practitioner dowses to try and find out the most effective treatments for the patient, using appropriate charts. These charts will display various possible remedies, techniques, and methods of administration and the movement of the pendulum will indicate what is to be done. It should be noted that dowsing in Radionics may also be used as a comparative method; the suitability of Radionic treatment itself may be dowsed in comparison with other possible modalities. The pendulum may indicate that the acupuncturist, the homoeopath or even the allopathic Doctor may be more suitable for patient, or that such-and-such a modality may be used alongside Radionic treatment. In general, however, it is fair to say that the Radionic practitioner is there principally to give Radionic treatment and that within this domain there is a very large palette of possibilities. What must be done is to find the form of treatment which works best to offset the patient's symptom(s), selected in the order of their significance. A certain degree of pre-treatment assessment can of course be attempted; if we find a reading of Respiratory - Infection, 91%, we may dowse to discover by what amount the indicated treatment should, in principle, reduce the reading; preferably - and ideally - to zero.

If the indicated remedy or combination of remedies is judged suitable, the relevant codes are set up on an appropriate Radionic instrument along with the witness. The instrument is then 'tuned', such that a rotation of the pendulum over the witness plate(s) or other

---

17. Homoeopaths will be familiar with Hering's Law of Cure (Constantine Hering, 1800 - 1880) *"From above downwards. From within outwards. From a more important organ to a less important one. In the reverse order of their coming."* In Homoeopathy disease is seen as progressing from the least vulnerable organs to the most vulnerable ones i.e. from the Skin inwards. In an ideal situation of cure, the return of old symptoms in the order in which they occurred would be observed; hence, Hering's Law. This concept is, of course, a matter which should, and no doubt has, provoked volumes of discussion.

appropriate test point indicates that it is in balance. 'Tuning' basically means finding the balance point, which may be set on a dial calibrated 0 - 100%; and, according to the design of the instrument, setting potency (for present purposes, 'power') values for the codes. There are various designs of instruments and each has its own characteristics; this is only a summary description and the intricacies of instrument use must be dealt with elsewhere.

As the treatment proceeds the patient will absorb some of it and the instrument will come out of balance when compared with the initial setting. The 'balance' dial, which initially caused a rotation at 100%, may after some hours cause a rotation when adjusted to 80%; no rotation will be found at 100%. This means that the treatment was 100% needed at the commencement, but, because some of it has been taken up, it is now only needed 80%. Therefore the reading will gradually decrease through intermediate values until such time as a reading of zero may be obtained. This indicates that the treatment has been fully taken up and nothing more is to be gained from applying it. In another instance the treatment may never fall below a level of, say, 27%, which suggests that the treatment selection was not sufficiently suitable and that some additional treatment is needed (or that other Factors have come into play which have changed the patient's situation).

This then brings us to stage 4, *Assessment*. Now bear in mind that many people who seek Radionic treatment have chronic or longstanding conditions which have already been treated using conventional or other complementary methods, and without success - otherwise they would not have arrived at the practitioner's door. Under such circumstances the starting point is already difficult, and the hill to be climbed is potentially very steep. The patient may be incurable, may have *irreversible pathology*, or may only be palliated. If a substantial improvement can be made, it may require a substantial amount of time and considerable persistence. Thus for most patients a gradual improvement is the order of the day, and it can also be observed that a rapid improvement in a chronic case is not a necessarily a good sign because the underlying vitality and fabric of the system has not been restored and the patient is only experiencing a short remission from a longer term trend downwards. Radionics as a *métier* has its rewards but they are usually gained by hard work and focussed application. There can be many dispiriting and disappointing interludes between successes - not a route to instant gratification.

When the patient reports an improvement or change of state (or not, as the case may be), the practitioner may then retake all or a number of readings and compare the new readings with the original ones to see what has improved - or deteriorated. This, then, is one of the basic uses of analysis - to provide a baseline from which an ongoing assessment of the patient's condition can be made. The numerical values obtained for Locations and Factors at various stages in the treatment process can be compared. The patient will provide a subjective report of his or her symptoms, and this might be confirmed by a progressive change in the readings.[18]

REMEDY SYNTHESIS

Finally, it should be repeated that Radionic techniques may also be used to 'program' the energy fields represented by the codes into suitable carrier materials, such as water, *saccharum lacticum* (sugar of milk), and certain types of crystals configured in certain ways. This process is sometimes referred to as *simulation* (by Malcolm Rae) although I prefer the term *synthesis*. By such means any of the entire arcana of Radionic treatments can be encoded into a carrier material and used as an oral treatment, the most common application being the synthesis of homoeopathic remedies. But such synthesis might also include the energy patterns of herbs, flowers, crystals, colours, pathogens, and so on - even emotions and psychological states. The efficiency of this process will vary according to the calibre of the Radionic codes and the vibrational integrity of the instrument being used, but the principle appears to be generally applicable.

CONSCIOUSNESS AND MATTER

The material world is not usually thought of as being influenced by human thoughts and mental projections. It seems to be an article of faith in modern science that the Universe is 'out there' and has an existence completely independent of human consciousness. This type of thinking strongly militates against the concepts of Radionics and appears to be the basis for stating that it is fraud, delusion or magic. The central complaint

---

18. There is also the jolly pleasing instance of where the Radionicist labours for months on a case. In the meantime the patient suddenly decides one morning to take some aspirin and this somehow coincides with the beginning of the hoped-for improvement in the symptoms. 'My God', he says, 'that aspirin worked wonders!' - even when, or if, taken during years of suffering before, it did nothing unusual or noticeable.

seems to be that since there is no known means by which it could work, the obvious conclusion is that it must *not* work.

If the situation is examined more closely, however, there are many examples of anomalies which suggest that the 'hard' materialist certainty of the existence of an independent external reality is nothing more than a very powerful *belief* about the nature of reality. The problem of the interaction of consciousness and matter came to the fore in the development of 20th Century Physics, where it was discovered that consciousness and conscious intent play a controversial role in quantum mechanics - the so-called observer effect in the particle-wave duality problem. The observer or experimenter, through the act of observing, appears to cause a collapse of the probability wave (wave function) and thus enables light to manifest as a particle rather than a wave. Analysis of the experimental process by von Neumann lead to the conclusion that the consciousness of the experimenter was inseparable from the outcome of the experiment. Under these circumstances it may then be asked, to what extent is human consciousness therefore an inextricable part of 'reality'? The question might also be considered as to whether there are other forms of consciousness which are also involved in the creation of reality, and with which human consciousness might interact.

Furthermore, the problem as to where 'deep' reality is, as to how, where, or even if, we might find a permanent and immutable state which constitutes 'absolute' or 'objective' reality, appears to lie at the heart of modern physics. By extension, since physics is thought of as the 'master' science which underpins the rest, this problem underlies all of science. The position is taken by some scientists is that science is a truly rational activity - perhaps the *only* truly rational activity - which allows reality to be understood in absolute, objective, measurable terms. While such measurements seem possible at the material level and within certain limitations, such as those defined by Einstein's Theory of Relativity, a completely different situation is discovered 'inside the box', or, one might say, 'at the boundaries of the box'. I will return to these various points in more detail, particularly in Chapter 7.

Many other experiments, however, have also taken place at the more tangible level of everyday reality. To recount just one example, footnote 3 mentions the experimental work performed over a 30-year period at Princeton University by Jahn and Dunne. Without going into the somewhat lengthy details, the essence of the matter is that over the course of hundreds of thousands of experiments, results showed that the focused human mind could influence the outcome of computer-generated random events by a margin significantly greater than that indicated by chance.[19] This sort of thing is not supposed to happen according to the tenets of 'objective' science. Computers are not considered to be affected by the workings of the human mind. It is not considered possible to change or influence any aspect of physical reality by human thought processes - yet evidence has been provided.

Discussions about consciousness and its relationship to the material world will play a central role in this book. We all experience an external everyday reality, the everyday world of *ordinary objects*, as they are called by physicists but, can we ask to what extent that reality is the way it is *basically because* we think it is that way? This point has been argued over extensively by many in physics, including greats such as Einstein and Bohr. While it is convenient for science to assume that the material world is 'out there' and has an existence completely independent of human perception, it seems that it is very difficult, perhaps impossible, to separate what we perceive to be out there from what *is or may be* out there. Every description of reality is a best estimate based on the available information, or, more cynically, selected from the available information to suit some objective or other.

The intent of modern science is to prove that all phenomena, including life, result from the workings of the laws of physics and chemistry and arise from the action and interaction of matter only. Now the reader may rightly ask, what has this to do with Radionics?; and the answer seems to be that if we are to make any sense of how Radionics might work, it is centrally the question of how, why and to what extent consciousness can act upon 'reality' which may throw some light on the matter. This answer seems to be quite opposed to the materialist trend in scientific thinking.

CLOSING COMMENT

This brief summary of the Radionic method is intended to prepare the reader for the more detailed material which is to follow. Contentious, implausible, ridiculous, fraudulent, deceitful, improbable, risible though Radionics may seem to some - yet utterly believable, convincing, compelling and fascinating to others - this simple overview sets out in basic terms what the contemporary Radionic practitioner attempts to do.

---

19. A good summary account of the Princeton work can be found in Chapter 6 of McTaggart, *op. cit.*

From my own standpoint only I shall conclude this chapter by paraphrasing Freud:

'The purpose of this [brief essay] is to offer as it were a [dogmatic] conspectus of Radionics by bringing together all of its doctrines in the most concentrated and clear-cut form. Obviously, it is not intended to convert or to convince you.

The postulates of Radionics rest on an immeasurable wealth of observations and experiences, and only the person who repeated these observations on himself and others has set about being able to pass his own judgment on them.'[20]

---

20. The parentheses are mine. Freud, *An Outline of Psychoanalysis*, printed in Phillips, 2006, page 1, substituting the word 'Radionics' for 'psychoanalysis'.

2: RADIONICS IN THE CONTEXT OF RADIESTHESIA

If you can use a pendulum, or divining rod, you can demonstrate so many facts to your own satisfaction that you can think things out for yourself.....I did not believe in any of this when I first started the investigation of divining. Each time a new fact comes along I doubt it and often go back to doubting the whole subject; but it will not be denied. If you can find unknown concrete objects again and again when they are completely concealed, it becomes impossible to doubt; and what can be checked for some facts can be checked for others. The result is not faith but conviction. You are convinced by your results.....if you can work the pendulum and are not too lazy to spend considerable time using it, there is nothing to prevent you from finding out all the facts I have mentioned and many more besides. We are just at the start of what appears to be a science embracing all sciences known today. But to be pioneers in this work you need to have a completely open mind; faith is the last thing you want, for it excludes any possibility of using your powers of reasoning from observed fact.

T.C. Lethbridge, *THE POWER OF THE PENDULUM,* p.60 [21]

Just as my paraphrase of Freud at the end of the previous Chapter represents one aspect of my view of Radionics, so the quote from Lethbridge above represents another. This is the ever-present question in the back of my mind as to what on earth I am doing researching Radionics when there are so many more self-indulgent and certainly less arduous opportunities open to the aspiring 21st century hedonist? [22] A goodly number of extraordinary personalities have been involved with Radiesthesia and Radionics, Lethbridge being but one of them. For example, F. A. Archdale, author of the pamphlet *Elementary Radiesthesia and the Use of the Pendulum*:

'Lt-Col. Fulbert Audley Archdale was born August 8th 1890, the son of the late Major M. E. Archdale of the Gloucestershire Regt. After a short time at Malvern College he went to H.M.S. Worcester at Greenhithe. He served before the mast as an apprentice on the three-masted barque

---

21. T.C. Lethbridge (1901 - 1971), the well-known dowser. 'Born in the West Country in 1901, Thomas Charles Lethbridge came from a family that had spawned soldiers, explorers, Members of Parliament and churchmen, many of whom were renowned for their eccentricity. It was in fact Hanning Speke, Lethbridge's great uncle, who had first discovered the source of the Nile....' www.tc-lethbridge.com/anthological_review/
22. Or should it be, '21st Century Schizoid Man'? (*pace* King Crimson).

Inverlyon, travelling three times round the world carrying coal and general cargoes. He served in Survey ships on the coasts of Africa and India, and finally joined the Hoogli Pilot Service in Calcutta. In 1914 he joined the 130th Baluchis and was on active service in German East Africa and Palestine. He was demobilised in 1918 in Karachi and there joined a firm of exchange brokers. He also commanded the Karachi Corps Auxiliary Force for several years. In 1938 as a member of the Reserve of Officers he rejoined the Army in England and worked in the Department for Passive Air Defence, and then in Movement Control. In 1943 he joined the Royal Pioneer Corps with whom he was on active service in Sicily and Italy. He was awarded the M.B.E. (Milty). He was demobilised in 1945.'

I was introduced to dowsing by Rupert Neve, the well-known audio designer, an old friend and former professional colleague, now in his eighties but still very active. I asked Rupert for a few comments on how he had become involved with dowsing, and, being the great *raconteur* that he is, regaled me with these wide-ranging comments in an email (April 2010), which I append here with his permission. I had thought that Rupert had known T.C. Lethbridge, but this turned out to be not true:

'I actually never met Lethbridge. In the early 1980s I became hooked and attended various gatherings of dowsers in the Cambridge [England] area. The name was, of course, well-known but the man himself died in 1971. He was a Cambridge man and left behind quite a cadre of enthusiasts in the area. He was the Curator of Anglo Saxon Antiquities at the Cambridge Archaeological Museum. I was invited to several such gatherings and was able to dowse with the best of them. One man - I wish I could remember names - actually earned his living at commercial dowsing. He recounted how he had been to California at the request of a Mining Co. who, having ceased operations some years before, had "lost" various items of machinery deep underground in a mountain. Subsequently it was thought that there were valuable minerals still to be extracted but how to find the tunnels and the machinery? Our hero dowsed on a set of triangular co-ordinates many thousands of feet up on the surface. He was able to pin-point the machinery and told his clients to "dig here". Not only did they intercept the original main shaft but located the gear with astonishing accuracy. This sort of legacy inspired us, as you can imagine! At one gathering, he challenged those present to find a buried stone in his garden which he had identified by ley lines. I was one of the very few who succeeded in locating the stone! Later I found that I could establish ley lines over large areas of East Anglia. From the rear of my house, I used a

magnetic compass to fix the direction initially of a distant water tower, then, looking along a bamboo stick pointing at the tower, I "willed" a ley line. Taking off in my car, I intercepted my ley line about 70 miles away near to Orford in Suffolk. It was near to Orford Castle which, itself, is rich in ley line emanations. The interesting thing is that I could identify my own "signature" and that of other ley lines, each of which had a personality. I thought they were probably laid down by travellers long years ago to enable them to find their way around. I found that I could follow a ley line and pick it up many miles away. Its signature was as clear as a street name! Was this the way the ancients navigated the country - then covered with dark forests and swamps and with tracks and pathways which varied with the seasons and weather? I still look for ley lines. You might remember the 300 year old Oak in our "yard" [in Texas]. This has five ley lines emanating from it. More than one I have picked up miles away. The US does not have the benefit of easily obtainable Ordinance Survey maps which are invaluable in mapping Ley Lines in the UK. Having wandered a long way from Lethbridge, there's a lot on the Internet about him but, regretfully, it's mostly about what he did, and not how he did it! Take a trip to Orford Castle some day and wander around the perimeter - climbing over the hillocks and hummocks that hide old foundations. The Ley lines will throw you into saturation mode - your detecting device is hardly necessary - they turn you inside out - your arms tingle to such an extent that you wonder sometimes if you are actually communicating with the old timers who are inviting you to follow along "My Way"? There are more things in Heaven and Earth ..... and all that. Digital technology destroys imagination and the latent powers within us!'

As Lethbridge says, 'it will not be denied'. The sceptics may come along and apply their narrow tests of 'reality' to Radionics, e.g. 'can it pass a random, double-blind, placebo-controlled trial' and if it cannot, declare it nonsense, delusional, quackery, etc. There are most certainly uses for this standardised kind of testing but there are also limitations. Many therapeutic situations are not testable by such means; to give a simple example, an event such as a bereavement or a business failure may have triggered certain problems in an individual. Hence, because you treat the person as a whole, it is often difficult to deal with more obvious symptoms in isolation from the patient's psychic state, which may not at all be immediately apparent. The point remains that the more you go into dowsing and Radionics, the more you find that it does appear to be possible to initiate the actions and obtain the responses described in the literature; but you have to do it with a fully open mind which can also accept the possibility that some things which are claimed for it cannot be done, and that there is as yet much misconception in it. Many turn away at the door because they have already concluded that the matter is preposterous and that there is no scientific - or other - basis for Radionics. There is no shortage of box-fresh pre-programmed sceptics, particularly the sort of blowhards who know what they know because some televised Professor-or-other says so and no further discussion necessary. These minds are already closed. A few, however, enter with exactly the same mindset but a greater willingness to experiment, and begin to find to their amazement that perhaps it is the conventionally-accepted version of reality itself which is wanting. Concepts found in science itself suggest to me that there is no reason why this should not be so. Quantum Mechanics has been grappling with the problem of unaccountable phenomena underlying 'reality' for over a century:

'The fact that there are many different ways of looking at the quantum world, and that these interpretations all make the same predictions about the outcomes of experiments, is seen by some people as unreasonable democracy....the one thing you must not do is believe that any quantum interpretation is The Truth. They are all simply crutches for our limited human imaginations, ways to come to grips with the weirdness of the quantum world, which never goes away and is outside the scope of everyday experience.' [23]

This then opens up the matter for a discussion of the ongoing question of how Radionics could possibly work - what needs to be added to our understanding of 'reality' that could help us explain what appears to be happening? One of the methods I use is to *deconstruct* - to ask myself at every stage why I am doing such-and-such a thing and to try and elaborate what each such thing might mean in the context of the overall activity, and the same thing, of course, of the overall activity itself, with respect to what one perceives to be 'reality' or 'happening'. It is the scrutiny of the obvious which can lead to the unveiling of the artfully-concealed secrets of Nature. Since the discussion can start as usefully with

---

23. Gribbin, 2000, p 320. It is actually a bit disappointing to find Radionics upstaged in the weirdness stakes by 'real' science, in this case, Quantum Mechanics one of the great scientific achievements of the 20th Century. But sceptics should take note that the Nature has not conveniently organised itself to support their preconceptions.

dowsing as any other aspect of the art, I shall briefly describe its general aims and methods in this chapter and then explain something about how it is used in Radionics in the next.

DOWSING

Dowsing, sometimes known as Divining, has a substantial exploratory literature behind it stretching back at least some hundreds of years. For example, *The Divining Rod*, by Sir William Barrett F.R.S. and William Besterman, first published in 1926, has a bibliography of approximately 500 books and papers in several languages, some being dated to the 16th Century. *The Divining Hand: The 500-Year Old Mystery of Dowsing*, by Christopher Bird, published in 1993, cites around 470 references. Some are duplicated from *The Divining Rod* but many are not; particularly those papers sourced from the former Soviet Bloc. It is notable that dowsing, and the investigation of certain psychic phenomena, were state-approved research subjects in the former Soviet Union, and it was the publication in 1970 of *Psychic Discoveries Behind The Iron Curtain*, by Sheila Ostrander and Lynn Schroeder, which is said, in due course, to have lead to concern about Soviet activities in this area and eventual CIA funding of the remote viewing project in the USA, the story of which is now pretty well-known.[24] In short, official science in the USA may, broadly speaking, have dismissed research into psychic and paranormal phenomena but those Godless Communists appear to have thought otherwise about it. Such research would not, presumably, have been tolerated in the USSR and its Empire unless it was thought have had

---

24. The Kirlian camera, said to take photographs of the bio-energetic field ('aura') of living organisms, was originally developed in the Soviet Union by Semyon Davidovich Kirlian (1898 - 1978) and his wife Valentina Khrisanovna. From the early 1960s Kirlian photography was recognised and studied by official Soviet science. Radionic photography (photography of living organisms at a distance) was invented in the USA by Ruth Drown (1892 - 1962) and further developed in the UK by George de la Warr (1904 - 1969). The claim is that [X-Ray - like] photographs could be taken of the internal organs etc. of living beings from a considerable distance via the Radionic 'camera', using a witness. Both 'cameras' were granted Patents, which may still be obtained, although at the present time and to the best of my knowledge no-one can get a Radionic camera to work i.e. there is some process involved which is subjective and not presently understood. One of the few remaining de la Warr cameras and the library of approximately 12,000 photographs - we are not talking about a few holiday snaps here - was in the possession of the late Dr Peter Moscow, President of the USPA (United States Psychotronic Association). A DVD of Dr Moscow giving a talk in London about the Radionic camera (shot by the present author with a real video 'non-Radionic' camera) is available from the Radionic Association.

potential uses to the State, and one of them, it was eventually concluded by some in the West, was, in part, a form of psychic spying. In this particular area 'we' were apparently nowhere, since 'our' *official* science denied (and as far I am aware continues to deny) the possibility of such abilities. Various secret research programs into so-called Remote Viewing (RV) began in the USA, running from the mid-1970s into the 1990s, at which time they were discontinued and the information was, it is said, declassified.[25] The late Margaret Belsham, in a talk to the Radionic Association[26], notes that Malcolm Rae was visited by a Soviet delegation in London during the 1960s, asking him for help in tracking 'their' submarines using dowsing techniques. Rae, a former Commander in the Royal Navy, did not assist, presuming that some of the submarines to be tracked were 'ours'. While scientists in the West often like to dismiss and deride dowsing and related phenomena, this attitude is not universal, it seems, throughout all of world science.

One of the most celebrated dowsers of the modern era was the French priest Abbé Alexis Mermet (1866 - 1937) and his testament is the book *Principles and Practice of Radiesthesia*.[27] From a study of this invaluable text we get a good indication of the range of uses to which dowsing may be put, and how dowsing operations may be performed correctly. Space does not permit a complete outline of the book, but a few excerpts should prove to be of interest. The general similarity to what was independently discovered in Radionics will become apparent in due course.

He finds water: '*the local authorities of Oyannax found that their supply of water had dried up. There was no more water. As a result of geological information it was decided to make three or four borings in the neighbourhood of the source of supply at a depth of 30, 50 and 60 metres respectively, but without any success....in despair they contacted*

---

25. The present author has no experience of RV and has no opinion either way as to whether it can be done, but readers may enjoy the film THE MEN WHO STARE AT GOATS (2009).
26. The talk is available on DVD from the Radionic Association.
27. Mermet, 1959, translated by Mark Clement. The original is in French and is entitled *Comment J'opère* (more completely, *Comment J'opère pour découvrir de près ou à distance sources, métaux, corps cachés, maladies*), first published in 1935. My own copy - the English version - was kindly given to me by Antoinette Pernetta. A reprint of the English original can be purchased from Borderland Science Research Foundation (www.borderlands.com).

me....*after an hour's hydrological examination* [i.e. with the pendulum], *I said, 'Here, at a distance of 1.50 metres from the wall of this building, and a depth of between 12 - 15 metres, I can promise you an output of 1,500 litres a minute.' This statement only evoked a smile on the part of those concerned. They would have liked to believe it but it was too good to be true. But a few days later, I received the following message: 'I have the pleasure to inform you that we have found water corresponding exactly with your forecast, that is to say 1,500 litres a minute, at a depth of 12.80 metres and at 1.50 metres from the house where our mechanic lives. (Signed) Lacroix, Directeur.'* (p. 66 - 67)

He finds the source of water contamination: *'One evening, returning from Villers-le-Lac....I was stopped by the local policeman who informed me that the mayor wanted to see me....he told me that in their locality they had had no drinking water for the past five years. I said to him that I could feel quite nearby a powerful spring of water. 'Oh, yes,' he replied, 'but it is contaminated. We have tried everything on the advice of the Government chemists but without the slightest result. Our great fountain is a mockery. It gives us a water with a colour and smell which are repulsive and which bacterial analysis declares to be dangerous.' Holding the pendulum in my hand, and without leaving the mayor's room, I told him that the water was contaminated at a distance of 202 metres from the fountain in a western direction. I detected at a depth of 3.50 metres a streamlet giving 5 litres a minute joining at right angles a stream from a cesspool located 50 metres away. This streamlet was running into a geological fault in the ground connected with the water supplying the fountain...A fortnight later, M. Robbe, an architect who was then mayor of Pontarlier, wrote me as follows: 'We started digging yesterday at the place you had indicated and we duly discovered at a depth of 3.50 metres the streamlet of impure water which was contaminating the public fountain. We diverted it and the water has become once again perfectly drinkable. All our congratulations.'* (p. 81)

He finds oil: *'Boring operation 22, which was in progress while you were on location here and which you said would not yield a sufficient quantity of petroleum* [i.e. pétrole brut in French], *had results in accordance with your forecast, and only insignificant traces were found. I resumed boring operation 21 which you had indicated would give appreciable quantities of petroleum. At depths of 79 metres and 94 metres I found layers giving respectively 600 and 800 kilos a day; and at a depth of 102 metres a layer giving gushings of petroleum was found. Altogether, it* is a success for you. Boring operation 30, which you had forecast would be useless, proved to be so. (Signed) Mena. Engineer-Geologist, Tliouanet (Algeria).' [28] (p. 86 - 87)

He dowses at a distance using maps (Teleradiesthesia): 'The pendulum gives information about what is found on the surface and under the surface of a site 'invisible' to him, provided the radiesthetist is able to see a representation of the area beyond his view (photo, plan, map or drawing)....In the action produced on the radiesthetist and his pendulum, by bodies, distant and invisible, but represented by a photo, map, plan or drawing, distance is of no account; whether such bodies are 10 miles away, 100, 1,000 or 10,000 miles away, they act in the same way. None of the distances measurable on the surface of the ground has any perceptible effect in delaying or weakening transmission.' (p. 126 - 127) and as an example,

'The College of French Marists at Popayan (Colombia, South America) had no water. The director wrote to me begging me to do everything I could to find some water. 'We have 650 students here and we shall be compelled to close the college owing to lack of water. Come and save us from such a dreadful prospect.' I replied that I had neither the inclination nor the time to travel so far but I asked him to send me a plan of the property together with a correct scale. I....returned it with the following comments: There are not several springs on your property but there is one. If your place is in accordance with the scale, you should carry out digging operations at the exact place I have indicated with a cross in red ink, and go down to a depth of 28 metres. You will find the water that you need. The reply to this note ran as follows: 'I have great pleasure to inform you that the water indicated at a depth of 28 metres on a plan of our property at Popayan, which I have been searching for myself for the past five years, has been found exactly at the depth indicated....' (signed) Hermano Anaclet, Rector del collegio di la Immaculate, Pasto, Columbia, 10th August 1927.' (p. 136 - 137)

He traces missing persons: 'The Montbovon Murder Case. In October 1933, at Montbovon (Fribourg, Switzerland), a young man had

---

28. The [ ] brackets are mine. In 2005 or 2006 I read a two-page article in The Daily Mail describing how virtually all major oil companies use dowsers alongside geologists, as they usually proved rapid and cost-effective. Unfortunately I was not able to keep this article and so cannot give an exact citation.

disappeared on returning from a village festivity. Several groups of men, searching thoroughly for nine days, could find no traces of his passage anywhere. In despair, his sister came to see me, with a map of the region and a photograph of the missing young man, together with a tie which he had worn. Immediately I was able to give her the following information: 'First of all, the pendulum swinging over the photograph gives the numerical figure of a dead person; your brother is no longer alive. He followed a certain path (where indeed he had been seen). At that place, I feel the presence of your brother, whose height is 1.55 metres (which was correct) and whose body is carried on the shoulders of another man, about 1.70 metres tall. Your brother seems to have been stabbed in the back and then thrown over a precipice by the roadside. He must be at a certain place in the river of the Hongrin valley where the rocky walls on each side are very close together and where the water is about 4 metres deep. His sister then asked me whether theft might have been the motive for the crime. I replied that it was, in view of the fact that her brother was carrying money at the time and that I could detect no gold or silver on the body now....His sister, on behalf of the family, wrote me the following testimonial:

1. In his rectory at Jussy (Switzerland), after having seen a simple map (scale 1:25,000) of the Hongrin valley, without any information from me, Abbé Mermet told me (a) The path my brother followed on his return from Montbovon (b) The place where he had stopped. These two indications I was able to verify and found them to be quite correct.

2. It was Abbé Mermet who was the first to state that my brother had been murdered, pointing out that he had been carried on the shoulders of a man whose height was about 1.70 metres, while that of my brother was only 1.55 metres, which was quite accurate;

3. He also indicated the place, almost exactly, where my brother's body was to be found, a place where no-one had thought of searching for him, that is to say in the Hongrin river, in a whirlpool more than 4 metres deep;

4. M. Pflug, clerk of the court, confirmed that Abbé Mermet was right when he said the victim no longer had any gold or silver. Indeed, a few days later his empty purse was discovered in the river Sarine.

My family wish to thank you publicly for all the help you have given us. I repeat it is thanks to you that we have recovered the body of my poor brother who had been missing for nine days.

The medical autopsy, made the day after the recovery of the body, showed that my brother had been attacked with a knife, then carried and thrown into the river....with all our gratitude.

(Signed) R. Krummenacher, Allières-sur-Montbobon (Gruyère). 3rd November 1933' (p. 210 - 211)

He uses the pendulum to diagnose disease: '*In 1905 - 6 it occurred to me one day that as it was possible to study the surface of the earth as well as inanimate objects with the pendulum, it should also be possible to study phenomena in living beings.....This idea set me working and observing the radiations of the human body and its organs. I soon found out that organs affected by disease did not give the same figure of radiation as healthy organs....ever since then, in clinics and infirmaries, and chiefly in the course of my ministry to the sick in my parish, I was able to establish certain rules, based on a great number of observations, which laid the foundations for making a radiesthesic diagnosis. I lost no time in communicating my observations to doctors, veterinary surgeons and herbalists, who took up the practice of Radiesthesia with successful results.*' (p. 167 - 168)

Now Mermet has already informed us, in earlier pages, for example 93 *et seq.*, that different materials produce different responses from the pendulum, in terms of number of rotations and direction of rotation, direction of Fundamental Ray etc and that such responses are always typical for that material - as it were, 'standard' responses.[29] Thus he gives (p. 93) 4 rotations for Iron and Steel, 4.4 for Limestone, 5 for Aluminium, 6 for Silver, and so on. Bearing this in mind, and returning to the question of biological Radiesthesia, he states:

A. First of all let us recall that each species of living beings [sic] is characterised by a numerical figure and a direction of rotation which are specific.....

B. Each of the great systems in the human body possesses a special numerical figure: Osseous system, 9; Muscular system, 11; Circulatory system, 15.....the same applies to the principal organs: Brain, 20; Heart, 12; Lung, 10; Stomach, 7; Liver, 12...these figures do not vary, either with the individual or with the state of health and sickness.

---

29. Perhaps even a 'unique identifier' - see Chapter One. Such a number or sequence of rotations maybe referred to as a 'series'. Similarly, Lethbridge, *op. cit.*, describes his own experiences in Chapter 6, 'Pendulum Rates'.

C. Furthermore, each of the systems or organs mentioned above gives another numerical figure which varies from 10 to 0, according to the state of health or the extent of the disease affecting it. For example: Stomach in good health: 10; Stomach affected by disease, 1,2,3,4, etc

D. All microbic diseases have a figure which is the characteristic figure of the causative microbe: Staphylococcus, 24; Pneumococcus, 28; Bacillus of Tuberculosis, 35.5; Streptococcus, 40; Bacillus of Typhoid, 50; Microbe of Syphilis, 55.....

E. There are some diseases which, at the present time, are not regarded as being due to microbes but which, nevertheless, give a special figure. For example, Cancer, 40 - 42; Inflammation of tissues, 60; Paralysis, 19...etc

F. If one has to examine a subject, human or animal, the following questions arise: 1. Is any organ affected by disease? 2. If so, which one? 3. Which part of the organ, and if possible, where is the seat of the trouble? 4. What is the nature of the disease? 5. To what extent has it progressed?

G. We will now proceed to show how these questions should be dealt with..... (p. 168 - 169)....

In later Chapters the Abbé writes about Harmful Radiations (noxious radiations or energies emanating from the subsoil, which we shall later encounter as Geopathic Stress and related phenomena); and Telediagnosis: 'Just as in the prospection for mineral ores it was of little importance whether the area of observation was under our feet, or far distant, but represented by a map, photo, plan or drawing, so the same applies for the indications of the pendulum on a living being, whether present in person or represented by a photo, picture, drawing or object having been used by him and having retained his radiations' [i.e. vibrations] (p. 186).

Then, finally, on p. 172: 'I may be allowed to give an extract from a monograph entitled Pages de Gloire, written by a lawyer, M Dessart, in Liège, in 1926. 'Abbé Mermet holds the pendulum in his right hand and moves it along all over the body, a few inches above it. We have seen him in action at the Institute for Cancer in Louvain, in the presence of three doctors. After having examined ten patients in bed, completely covered up to the chin, and consequently giving no clue as to the localisation of the tumour, and who had been instructed not to say anything to him, he was *able, in eight cases, to indicate exactly the part of the body affected by the dreaded disease. Two other cases remained doubtful for the Abbé indicated the primary focus of the tumour which, according to him, was in the stomach while the doctors only knew the secondary manifestation of it which was in the throat. In any case, it is clear that such experiments give most valuable information to medical men and they may ultimately result in confirming the theories first put forward by the late Dr Abrams in America.'*

Now I do not propose to give much history of Radionics in this book. For example there is an excellent account in *Report on Radionics,* by Edward Russell.[30] *Horizons of Radionics* contains a short but balanced, well-referenced and rather sober assessment by Tony Scofield, entitled *Radionics - the Early Years.*[31] *The Secret Art*, by Duncan Laurie, gives a good deal of useful information, particularly concerning T. Galen Hieronymus.[32] The reader can follow up with these and other books as needed. The basics of Abrams' work can broadly be summarised as follows:

'Radionics was founded by Dr Albert Abrams (1863 - 1924), a native of San Francisco, under the original name of ERA - Electronic Reactions of Abrams. A highly-qualified conventional practitioner with an illustrious career and also the advantage of a substantial private fortune, Abrams was able to pursue his researches without reliance on outside funding. Like Hahnemann (1755 - 1843), the founder of Homoeopathy, Abrams was a master of observation and a tireless experimenter and truth seeker, which attributes eventually led him to make discoveries which brought considerable opprobrium from the medical establishment of the day....he was also capable of making inspired leaps of judgment.

Abrams' fundamental discovery was that under certain conditions the human nervous system will react to the energy field of external elements such as persons with disease conditions, samples of diseased tissue, and so forth. This reaction would manifest by means of a muscle reflex which could be detected by percussing the abdominal wall. Alternatively, Abrams found that drawing a glass rod across the abdomen could also be used to localize the point of response. Different diseases - or

---

30. Russell (1995). This is a detailed and easily-digestible history of Radionics.
31. Scofield, Ed. (2003)
32. Laurie (2009)

as Abrams noted, 'drugs in homoeopathic dilutions can be detected and identified by the stomach reflex' - produced reactions in different parts of the abdomen, which suggested a unique diagnostic method. He then proceeded to develop a technique which placed a person with abdomen bared (known as the Subject) in series with a patient, i.e. linked by a wire which terminated on the Subject's forehead. He could then diagnose by testing on the healthy Subject for response to disease conditions in the patient.

Abrams later discovered that certain diseases produced reactions in the same muscle groups, which neatly threw his method off the rails until he hit upon the idea of placing a variable potentiometer (i.e. a rotary control such as might be used to adjust the volume on a hi-fi) in the middle of the cable linking the Subject to the patient. Settings of the potentiometer would be found which were unique to each disease, thus making it possible to diagnose a wide range of conditions.[33]

Eventually Abrams discovered that he could diagnose just as accurately using a blood sample from the patient, and also found out that he could work at a distance with the patient's sample placed next to the telephone line; such tests were performed over distances of more than 500 miles. He finally discovered that he could work without any form of linking wire between himself and the sample, but not over a distance of more than a mile.

---

33. As I understand it Abrams found that Cancer produced a response when the setting was 50 Ohms, and Syphilis, at 20 Ohms (see for example Abrams (1916) p. 293). From this point other resistance settings could be found for different diseases if required. However Russell, *op. cit.*, page 24 -25, says '....Abrams tried a sample from a patient suffering from syphilis. To his amazement and dismay this evoked a dull note *in exactly the same area as the cancer specimen had done - and nowhere else*....this would be useless for diagnosis unless he could find some way to distinguish one disease from another when two different diseases produced a dull note in the same area....If - he reasoned - the 'radiation' from diseased tissue was electronic in origin, it should be possible to distinguish between one 'radiation' and another by electronic methods; and the simplest and most obvious thing would be to try a variable resistance....an ordinary variable resistance [placed in the circuit] made it possible to distinguish between the reactions of various diseases....though cancer and syphilis produced a reaction in the same *area*, cancer would only do so with 50 Ohms in circuit - neither more nor less - and syphilis would only produce a reaction with 55 Ohms. It was even possible to distinguish between sarcoma and cancer, as sarcoma would only produce a reaction with 58 Ohms.' Those who wish to delve further into Abrams' work can read, for example, *ERA - The Electronic Reactions of Dr. Abrams* and related material, for example available from Borderland Science Research Foundation, web address as cited. Those minded to do so could attempt to replicate Abrams' work and see for themselves how well it holds up, as the circuits are available.

From these basic elements:

- the reflex muscle reaction to the stimulus of an external energy field (i.e. the radiesthesic [dowsing] faculty, from the present-day practitioner's point of view);

- the substitution of a sample from the patient for the patient himself;

- the creation of a unique value representing a disease or other energy factor; and

- the possibility of working at a distance -

are formed Radionics as we know it today.' [34]

Comparing these brief descriptions of the work of two completely different men - Mermet and Abrams - we are pointed to a number of common threads which suggest that in many respects the two approaches are fundamentally but different methods of detecting and interpreting the same underlying phenomena. Mermet uses a map or photograph to work at a distance; Abrams a blood spot. Mermet uses a pendulum; Abrams an abdominal muscle reflex. Mermet counts rotations of the pendulum; Abrams measures a resistance; and so on - other comparative examples can be described. An essential difference, however, is that in most applications of dowsing, once the sought-for object or information has been located, the matter is at an end. In Radionics, however, the detection process is then followed by a correction process - the mobilization of energy patterns identified by unique codes - in the attempt to counteract disturbances in the patient's Subtle Anatomy, the objective being to bring about an improvement in health.

---

34. Franks, 2000, summarised mainly from Russell, *op cit.*, but also other sources. This article can be downloaded from my website www.radionics.co.uk on the Resources page of the Radionics section. It was also published in Nexus magazine, Volume 7, Number 4, June - July 2000, as *Swimming Through The Ether*. In a sense it forms the core from which this book was developed.

3: RADIESTHESIA IN THE CONTEXT OF RADIONICS

PENDULUM MOVEMENTS

To recap, most dowsers use simple equipment such as rods, pendulum, stick pad, bio-tensor, and so on, in order to externalise the dowser's *subconscious* or *subliminal* reaction. By this means the reaction becomes observable to the dowser in his normal conscious state. To give a basic example, the dowser mentally poses a question, such as 'is there water underground within 100 square metres of where I am standing?'; the subconscious reaction follows, and this in turn creates a response in the nervous system which is most typically transmitted to the wrist and hand. These in turn cause a movement of the pendulum or other dowsing equipment, and this, obviously, can be observed and interpreted.

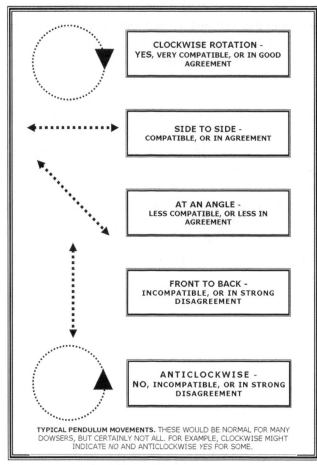

Figure 1 shows a typical range of pendulum movements and we may see that there are basically two different types of test - YES / NO and COMPATIBLE / INCOMPATIBLE. These movements could be in response to any mentally-posed question such as that

Figure 1: Typical Pendulum Movements

21st Century Radionics

described above, or which may occur as a result of holding the pendulum between two objects, or a person and an object such as a foodstuff, and querying the extent to which they are compatible. The dowser will normally have his or her own standard set of movements which allow a consistent interpretation of the pendulum reaction. Here I am only dealing with basic pendulum movements, as opposed to series of rotations such as those described by Mermet in the previous Chapter.

On the question of compatibility testing, we may return to Mermet for a direct example. We read the following:

'The pendulum, which reacts in a certain way to radiations emitted by any given body, reacts differently when placed between two bodies which are not similar in composition. This is a well-established fact and it may be assumed that there is some kind of concordance or discordance between the undulatory periods of these bodies. Observation shows that certain movements are manifested when the two bodies in question are useful, neutral or harmful to the human body....let us take a small quantity of a substance used as a remedy, say for the heart, and place it just in front of that organ while the pendulum is held between the two. If the substance is suitable, the pendulum oscillates more or less markedly, from one to the other. If the substance is a particularly suitable one, the pendulum rotates in a clockwise direction; if it is neutral, the pendulum remains motionless; and if it is unsuitable, the pendulum rotates in an anti-clockwise direction. Anyone can make this experiment by holding, say, a cigar, a flagon of alcohol or tincture of iodine, etc, at the level of the throat, stomach, lungs, heart, etc. The same substance may be good for a certain organ and harmful for another. Such an indication of concordance, or otherwise, may well acquire an important significance in the future from a medical point of view. Up to now such a method of investigation has been confined to cancer. Out of over a hundred plants which I examined I have been able to indicate with the pendulum a certain number which are distinctly suitable for treatment. I know several doctors who use the juice of such plants in the treatment of cancer and who have obtained some remarkable cures.[35]

Note that I am not endorsing or confirming Mermet's comment that cures for cancer were found using dowsing methods. It is Mermet's statement, and his alone; the reader must decide for him or herself as to

---

35. Mermet, op. cit., page 181.

whether there is anything in it. The idea, irrespective of its validity, is that using these and similar radiesthesic methods persons can be tested - or can test themselves - e.g., for their compatibility with various foods; or plants with various fertilisers, and so on. Another and sometimes rather more entertaining usage is to hold the pendulum over a picture of two persons. We often see photographs of two politicians together and we are told just how well they get on and how harmonious and productive is their relationship. The movement of the pendulum may confirm - or refute - the reality of the situation. Many other examples of such tests could be given, limited perhaps only by the imagination of the experimenter.

Tomlinson (1953) in *The Divination of Disease* gives many examples of dowsing in the context of health and begins with various exercises which may help develop the reader's dowsing faculty - the book, unfortunately, appears to be out of print but second-hand copies can be found on the Internet. Maury, in *How To Dowse - Experimental and Practical Radiesthesia* (no publication date but possibly from the 1950s) gives many techniques, examples and exercises. In opposition to my statement that it is the dowser's subconscious reaction which is 'materialised' by the pendulum movement, Maury, a physicist by training, appears to be suggest that the pendulum or other dowsing device is moved by *its* reaction to the waveforms, or radiesthesic fields, emitted by the objects being dowsed over. From this I take it that Maury means that dowsing is an objective exercise which can to an extent be separated from the operation of the dowser's mind. The matter of how dowsing works is not settled. Maury's explanation may be the case in the type of dowsing she describes but this account is not so easy to support in Radionics, where much of the work is, as it were, beyond physics in that it deals with the immaterial nature of the subtle bodies and at a distance not compromised by the normal rules of waveform propagation.

From my experience an extra point needs to be added. You may test a remedy X and find a high level of compatibility with the person being tested; this will be clearly shown by a pendulum YES rotation, as Mermet explains. If the person then takes the remedy and most notably if there is a positive change in the patient's state of health, after a period of time a re-test with the pendulum will have a different type of motion which will generally show a lower level of compatibility. This is because the person then needs the remedy to a lesser extent than when originally tested. If the person has fully recovered from the ailment being treated as a result of taking the indicated remedy, you may eventually see a NO rotation, which indicates incompatibility. Consequently the *context* needs to be borne in mind at all times; what was previously compatible because of its potential curative effect is indicated by the pendulum as incompatible when it is no longer required, because it has done its work. This is a different matter from testing, say, a vial of poison (to give an extreme example, cyanide) which under most imaginable circumstances is not going to be compatible with anyone unless they are after a very prompt exit from this physical world. In the first instance the pendulum eventually shows incompatibility because the remedy is not needed, but in the second, the pendulum shows incompatibility because the remedy is deadly.

Other possible situations of course exist, for instance, such as may be seen when a remedy is only palliating the patient, which is to say, reducing symptoms but not curing the problem. There will be a limited compatibility and because the remedy cannot fully relieve the person, the pendulum will never tend to finally indicate NO - not needed, and will always show some degree of compatibility. By way of example, the diabetic who has got to the state of requiring insulin will probably always require it, but taking it will never solve the actual problem, which is the diabetic illness itself. What you *might* see immediately after the person has taken the needed dose of insulin is a NO reading from the pendulum, but as the insulin is used up so the symptoms of the diabetic state will re-assert themselves and accordingly the pendulum reading for compatibility with insulin should gradually become more apparent as the time for next dose approaches.

CHARACTERISTICS OF PENDULUMS AND MEANS TO ENHANCE TUNING

Now as indicated in Chapter 1, *broadly* speaking, the pendulum is an inert object and does not have any 'power' of its own, as is sometimes believed. Certain forms of dowsing, however, use a specially-designed, or *tuned*, pendulum; for example, when searching for mineral deposits and other forms of prospecting, a small sample of the material (metals, ores, oil, etc) being prospected may be placed in a chamber inside an appropriately-designed pendulum and this may assist the dowser with mental tuning and focus. Certain types of materials may be suited to certain types of dowsing; for example a pendulum made of quartz crystal may be appropriate when dowsing geopathic stress and other earth energy lines and related energetic artefacts. In this regard material, shape, form and design may be combined in ways which can produce an influence on, or focus in, the dowser's mind, in order to increase his sensitivity to certain types of waveforms and radiesthesic fields. This is of course a different matter to attributing some form of innate power to the pendulum, some form of supernatural power or *mana*; what is relevant is that the design (and contents, where applicable) of the pendulum somehow interact with the dowser's energy or personal consciousness field or the radiesthesic fields of the target of the enquiry (or both) to produce an improved, exceptional or unusual degree of accuracy. Analogous to the idea of using samples of materials such as minerals, it is possible to use specimens - for example, tissue samples of healthy and diseased organs, various pathogens, toxins, etc. Wethered describes this method as follows:

'For precision testing I personally prefer the rule method, giving numerical results. For this method of testing we place a specimen [witness] of the patient at 0cm at the left-hand end of a graduated rule (a 100cm. rule is convenient), and the organ sample....at the 100cm. mark at the right-hand end of the rule. The rule should preferably be supported on rubber blocks so as to insulate it from stray vibrations from the table....if the organ in question is healthy, the pendulum will oscillate at right-angles to the rule at a position exactly half-way between specimen and sample, i.e. at 50cm. To find out if it does, hold the pendulum loosely over the half-way point....if the balance point is below 50cm., the pendulum will take up a diagonal oscillation relative to the rule and not at right angles to it, pointing down the rule towards the zero mark on the rule, i.e. towards the patient's specimen. The operator then has to move the pendulum gradually down the rule until the oscillation is at right angles to it. This will indicate the balance point. If the function of the organ is deficient, the balance point will be below 50cm., say at 47cm., or even 45cm. Forty-five centimetres is quite a bad reading and readings below it are comparatively rare. Occasionally a reading above 50cm. will be found, indicating gross inflammation or toxaemia. The rule should be rather longer than 100cm., as it is sometimes desirable to place remedies on the rule together with the specimen. Moreover it is not desirable to place a specimen or witness at the extreme ends of the rule. A good overall length is 106cm., with 3cm. to spare beyond either end of the graduated scale. A satisfactory width for the rule is 3cm.' [36]

---

36. Wethered (1957). Another, similar, device I have seen is the Turenne Board, invented by the French dowser Louis Turenne, possibly in the 1950s. I have been able to find very

Incidentally there are various other approaches to finding the balance point - if your dowsing skills are well-developed, you could try simply holding the pendulum some short distance from and centrally to the rule and 'ask' it to point to the position of balance, instead of moving it slowly up or down the rule (as appropriate) until the balance point is found, as Wethered describes. If the balance point is, say, at 45cm, the pendulum will point straight to it and you can then check for a rotation by placing the pendulum over that position. Alternatively, you can put the index finger of your left hand on the 45cm point and ask 'is this the point of balance (*when testing the condition of organ X in patient Y*) ?', while dowsing with the right hand; or vice-versa, if you are left-handed. The pendulum movement will indicate accordingly. Each pendulist will find his or her preferred techniques.

The idea of adding a remedy to the witness and specimen already sited on the rule is that the presence of the remedy (placed next to the specimen), if suitable for the purpose, will counteract the deficiency in the function of the organ and the pendulum should swing back to, or towards, the 50cm balance point, i.e. according to the curative power of the remedy so will the degree of normalisation of the organ be indicated by the closeness of the pendulum swing to the 50cm point. You will note that this type of test is not *actual* but *predictive*, in the sense that either some conceptual or perhaps 'virtual' process or interaction happens which the dowser detects, and which indicates that the proposed remedy *if given* will produce, all things being equal, a beneficial change in the patient. Feasibly, therefore, one can in principle know beforehand the potential effectiveness of a remedy if taken, but, obviously, verification can only be obtained by giving the treatment and observing the patient's response. This type of experiment can be done not only with so-called 'vibrational' or 'energy' remedies, for example, homoeopathic medicines or gem or flower essences, but also with physical materials, such as medical drugs. I am not suggesting that either Doctors or patients substitute such dowsing tests for the medical procedures which should be used to determine which drugs may be suitable in any particular case, but those researching the matter may be able to judge for themselves by performing the tests as

---

little information about him so I am unable to enlighten the reader further as to his activities.

circumstances allow. Since both medical drugs and vibrational remedies tend to have a wide range of action - in the case of the former, in terms of direct action on the targeted symptom and a range of possible other actions, commonly denoted side-effects; in the case of the latter, a holistic effect on the energy field (denoted the 'Dynamis' in homoeopathy) - such basic investigations are for interest only and need to be put into the wider therapeutic context of investigation of the patient's complete situation. Nothing in Radiesthesia or Radionics is designed or intended to make you abandon common sense or take short-cuts round the acquisition of skills and experience.

The study of the use of special pendulums is more a matter for those interested in Radiesthesia; in my experience special pendulums are not generally required in Radionic practice. The use of specimens may be relevant in certain applications of Radionics, for example, as a means of treatment. But the matter of paramount importance *in Radionics is that the instrument itself, tuned with an appropriate and well-constructed Radionic code, serves the purpose of providing a focus* for the dowser's mind. A well-engineered Radionic instrument should be far more versatile and allow a far greater range of possibilities than a dowsing device such as a pendulum. The instrument provides a means by which the dowser's enquiries can hopefully be accurately interfaced with the information field - or, in Tansley's phrase, *'Radionics, Interface with the Ether Fields'.*[37]

SOURCE OF THE DOWSING INFORMATION

We now come again to the rather complex question of what the dowser is reacting to; to *what* does the dowser have a *subconscious* reaction? If the dowser asks a question in his mind and the response is auto-generated from some other part of his mind, brain or nervous system, then *ipso facto* there is no reason to think that there is any external process or influence in play. Under these circumstances the concept of dowsing considered as a reaction to energetic phenomena *external* to the individual is largely illusory. This would support the contention largely held by contemporary science that consciousness is purely *local* and *arises from material causes*, which is to say, in literal terms, it's all and only in your head; or more completely, consciousness is

---

37. Tansley, 1975. David V. Tansley (1934 - 1988), Radionic practitioner and Doctor of Chiropractic. I use a small brass pendulum for the most part, as the reaction is shown quickly, and since many tests may need to be done during Radionic analytical work, speed is usually of importance.

at most not more than the aggregate effect of the workings of the physical resources and interfaces of the individual's nervous system, and in particular the brain. In short, the nervous system interfaces and interacts with the internal environment of the individual via its various branches, and the external environment through the usual sensory apparatus, and through some means produces what we experience as consciousness. The experience of being conscious - alive, self aware, feeling, thinking - is somehow produced by the activity of the nervous system only; and memory is somehow stored in the brain tissue, somewhere.

Taking materialism to extremes, one could view humans as goal-seeking biomechanoids with an adornment of consciousness, and the primary goal is survival. In this context, humans have no connection to any such universal information field as I describe and, perhaps needless to say, such a field does not exist or, in the event that it does, is unlikely to be accessible to human consciousness in any routine way. In fact the only fields which are considered to exist are those defined by modern physics and all phenomena, including life, arise from those fields - everything is, in principle, explicable from material causes.[38] Thus we are all, as it were, isolated units of consciousness and there is no group or species-wide collectivity or connectivity such as the collective unconscious proposed by Jung, or indeed any other form of shared psychic[39] continuum. In this viewpoint it seems that the only allowable interconnections must have a material basis, such as any commonality resulting from the DNA shared by all life-forms, or the fact that we are made from the same matter, essentially, the complex elements which emerged downstream of the Big Bang.

From this standpoint any experiences which suggest the existence of a reality independent of any physical substrate (e.g. the nervous system) are artefacts produced by the individual's mind. Such artefacts may serve any of a wide number of purposes, for example: hysterical symptoms, visions, hallucinations, out-of-body experiences and so forth, as a way of avoiding extreme neurotic tension; the production of alternative personalities in Multiple Personality Disorder as a means of avoiding situations which awaken unendurable memories, subconsciously-held, of psychological trauma; or the reconciliation of social conflict, in the case of shamans and others who claim to be able to cross the boundaries

---

38. See for example the quote from Pagels at the top of Chapter 7
39. Except where specifically indicated I use the word 'psychic' to indicate the psyche, not some form of mediumistic or supernatural state or experience.

into higher realities and bring back information therefrom, in the case of 'primitive' tribes.[40] If this extreme materialist view is the actual situation then we must be drawn to the conclusion that dowsing is not much other than a self-reflecting or self-absorbed activity in which any results that correspond to any external testable or observable reality are pure chance. The pendulum motions may be real enough but they are simply confirmations of our pre-existing but perhaps hidden or subconscious prejudices, opinions or wishes. The materialist conception does not, however, rule out the idea that pendulum movements are a response to the physical vibrations of the objects being dowsed - the Maury approach; but as noted above I tend to rule physical causation out of most of the explanation for Radionic actions.

Since, however, long years of experience on the part of many suggest that both dowsing and Radionics do produce results which extend well beyond the probability that they are random events (particularly in the areas of animal and agricultural Radionics, where, we will assume, suggestion, transference and placebo effect can be totally ruled out), some informational or energetic medium could be proposed through which the Radionic practitioner acts. This seems to be the most rational explanation for the observed phenomena, or, at minimum, an extremely reasonable line of enquiry. In attempting to understand the mechanics of dowsing itself, it is clear that there were in the past long debates between the 'physical' dowsers, who believed, as did Maury, that emanations from the subject (or object) of dowsing were electromagnetic waveforms and related phenomena within the physical domain (to which humans can be

---

40. And so by creating the impression that they have accessed some higher dimension through arduous ritual, they gain authority from the credulous to make judgments. While I am not some kind of 'back to nature' primitivist we have to accept that human beings managed to survive for hundreds of thousands of years without SUVs, mobile phones, personal computers, refrigerators, oil wells, nuclear weapons, television, SATNAV, the Internet, electricity, sunglasses and all the rest of the cornucopia of desirable objects our civilisation has produced. Life in the past may have been 'nasty, brutish and short' (to quote Thos. Hobbes, see *Leviathan*, 1651) but in spite of our much-vaunted scientific achievements life for the greater part of the world's population still is ('nasty, brutish and short') and given the population growth and resource limitations projected for the 21st century, will remain so. Those cutesy primitives grubbing around in the dirt, living in straw huts and worshipping Strange Gods may be absolutely enchanting to tourists in for the day from passing cruise ships, and pathetic compared to our technological mass civilisation, but it may equally prove entirely hubristic of us to think that we can last longer than they. To quote Einstein 'I do not know with what weapons World War 3 will be fought, but World War 4 will be fought with sticks and stones'. Or they may fight using as clubs electric guitars for which there is no more electricity.

sensitive), and 'mental' dowsers who believed that dowsing was some form of psychic, parapsychological or paranormal process.

In my opinion Radionics is largely a paraphysical (but not supernormal) process which is concerned with forms of energy and information not currently accepted by scientific orthodoxy. As noted this does not rule out the possibility that some forms of dowsing and divination result from the dowser's responses to physical (e.g. electro-magnetic spectrum) waveforms and related fields. It seems however most unlikely when the patient may be several thousand miles away, and even more unlikely when the matter of distant analysis and treatment is considered. There is also the paradox of map dowsing and other forms of dowsing of distant persons or places from images. An inviting possibility is that both explanations of dowsing may be correct in that there is a continuum from which information may be extracted, a part of which is at present unacknowledged by or unknown to science, and a part of which falls within the electro-magnetic spectrum. If this is so then the problem of the paranormal or the occult is largely removed from the equation and the new problem of the nature of the proposed supra-physical reality emerges. In fact the matter goes very deep, in the sense that the obscure healing art of Radionics may in fact throw some light on one of the central arguments of our age, between what might be classed as scientific materialism on the one side and what might be call scientific holism, which attempts to integrate both measurable (objective) and non-measurable (subjective) phenomena. on the other.

DOWSING AS AN INNATE HUMAN ABILITY

In Chapter One I introduce the concept of the universal information field and I consider that:

a) faculties, actual or potential (in that they may be developed through practice) exist within the makeup of the human system through which this field can not only be accessed but also manipulated, to a greater or lesser extent, according to the talent, accomplishment and sensitivities of the individual. This is quite often irrespective of whether they believe in it or know about it or not, because *it is so inextricably bound up with what we are.* Humanity did not need to know of the existence of oxygen in order to breathe and similarly, does not need to know of the existence of a supraordinate realm of consciousness in order to extract ideas or inspiration from it. Here I propose an innate human capability which as such is nevertheless largely unrecognized or dismissed.

Radionics in particular is a therapeutic art which is based on the conscious directed use and development of this ability.

b) the information about the patient obtained by the Radionic dowser is mainly extracted from this all-encompassing information field, and, equally, the patient is emitting data to this field which can be 'read' by the dowser - and, probably, vice-versa to a certain degree within the healing context;

c) this field may be accessed with equal effect from any point within the 3-D Universe but it is also outside the relativistic 3-dimensional Universe (spacetime). This basically means that wherever you might be in the Universe, you can, in principle, access the same information. It could perhaps be thought of as quasi-holographic and non-electromagnetic as well as holographic in the conventional sense, a consequence of the former being that *information can be passed instantaneously*, or at least significantly faster than the speed of light; [41]

d) similarly, the practitioner may act on, or mobilise, an appropriate segment of the field with the objective of bringing about a beneficial change of state in the patient. Within this context, broadly speaking, the healthy individual's subtle energy fields are in a state of dynamic equilibrium and symptoms tend to result from any disturbance to that equilibrium which cannot be rapidly and autonomously reasserted. Furthermore the greater the level of disorganisation in the totality of the patient's fields, the more chronic and complex the physical symptomology. Radionic treatment, therefore, is the attempt to reassert order in, or reorder, the totality of the disturbed fields by evoking energy patterns from the field which may prove corrective to the patient. This re-ordering process is called *normalisation* and it is the presumption of the possibility of normal functioning of the system which sets the essential benchmark against which the objectives of the therapeutic process can be measured. In Radionics this includes not only disorders of the anatomy and physiology but also the psycho-spiritual state and the link between them, i.e., the individual as a totality, holistically speaking.

---

41. I appreciate that holography is an electromagnetic process which is based on the use of interference patterns i.e. interactions between electromagnetic waves. An experimentally-proven theory exist in physics, Bell's Theorem of Non-Locality, which allows information to be passed between connected particles at superluminal (faster-than-light) speeds. The reader will note that Einstein's Theory of Relativity imposes the speed of light c as the speed limit of the Universe, but this only applies to objects (such as particles) which have mass, and information has no mass.

In some respects point d) is not so different from orthodox medicine, which has concepts of normality absolutely central to anatomy and physiology. The internal organs and their substructures and processes are studied and these are set up as standard models against which symptoms and pathology can be measured. However, no sub- or superstructure of Subtle Anatomy is proposed in orthodox medicine and since it does not 'exist', it cannot play any role in illness, and it is therefore not necessary to act on it. Even the purported influence of the individuals' psycho-spiritual state on physiological processes appears to be very strongly disputed in some quarters.

HOMOEOSTASIS AND ARCHETYPES

The idea of homeostasis is a central concept in orthodox medicine, meaning *'The regulation by an organism of the chemical composition of its body fluids and other aspects of its internal environment so that physiological processes can proceed at optimum rates'*.[42] Jung adapted it in his studies of psychology:

'[This fundamental rule is] *the homeostatic rule of self-regulation, which borrowed from biology and human psychology. Homeostasis is the means by which all organic systems keep themselves in a state of balance, despite changes in the environment. In fact homeostatic regulation can be observed at all levels of existence, from molecules to communities, in living as well as non-living systems, and our whole planet is conceivable as one vast homeostatic system. Because the psyche evolved in the context of the world, Jung held that the laws which prevail in the cosmos must also prevail in the psyche. He therefore felt justified in viewing the psyche as a self-regulating system which strives perpetually to maintain a balance between opposing propensities, while at the same time seeking its own growth and development.* "The psyche is a self-regulating system that maintains its equilibrium just as the body does. Every process that goes too far immediately and inevitably calls forth compensations, and without these there would be neither a normal metabolism nor a normal psyche. In this sense we can take the theory of compensation as a basic law of psychic behaviour. Too little on one side results in too much on the other.

---

42. Oxford, 2005, p. 398.

Similarly, the relation between conscious and unconscious is compensatory." (Jung, CW XVI, para. 330)' [43]

As a parallel think of the idea of the interplay between Yin and Yang, constantly seeking balance between the constellation of forces considered to affect this world. One may think that Jung's theory of archetypes suggests there is an ideal realm from which all of reality has been derived. Quoting again from Stevens, we read:

'Essentially, the theory can be stated as a psychological law: whenever a phenomenon is found to be characteristic of all human communities, it is an expression of an archetype of the collective unconscious....the archetype possesses a fundamental duality: it is both a psychic structure and a neurological structure, both 'spirit' and 'matter', and Jung came to see it as the essential pre-condition of all psychophysical events: 'the archetypes are as it were the hidden foundations of the conscious mind, or, to use another comparison, the roots which the psyche has sunk not only in the earth in the narrower sense but in the world in general.' He proposed that archetypal structures are not only fundamental to the existence and survival of all living organisms but that they are continuous with structures controlling the behaviour of inorganic matter as well. The archetype is not to be conceived, therefore, merely as a psychic entity but rather as 'the bridge to matter in general' (Jung, Collected Works VIII, para 420). This purely physical aspect...was an idea that greatly excited the physicist Wolfgang Pauli, who believed it made a major contribution to our ability to comprehend the principles on which the universe has been created. Pauli's enthusiasm encouraged Jung to persevere in his attempts to penetrate that unitary reality which he....believed to underlie all manifest phenomena. To describe this unitary dimension Jung resurrected the ancient term unus mundus, or 'unitary world' - the eternal ground of all empirical being. He conceived archetypes to be the mediators of the unus mundus, responsible for organizing ideas and images in the psyche as well as for governing the fundamental principles of matter and energy in the physical world. Pauli argued that by conceiving archetypes in this way, Jung had discovered the 'missing link' between the physical events (which are the legitimate study of science) and the mind of the scientist who studies them. In other words, the archetypes which order our perceptions and ideas are the product themselves of an objective order which transcends both the human mind and the external world.' [44]

---

43. Stevens, 1994, p. 72. In the less-than-ideal physical realm, generally, speaking, 'normal is not a point, but a range'.

44. Stevens, op. cit. 'Wolfgang Pauli (1900 - 1958), an Austrian-born (later American) physicist who made many contributions to the development of quantum physics in the

Or from Jung himself:

'For him [Gerardus Dorneus], the objective of the alchemical opus is, on the one hand, self-knowledge, which is at the same time knowledge of God, and on the other hand it is the union of the physical body with the so-called unio mentalis, consisting of soul and spirit, which comes about through self-knowledge. From this (third) stage of the opus there emerges, as he states, the Unus Mundus, the one world, a Platonic prior or primeval world that is also the future of the eternal world. We may safely interpret this world as the one which the unconscious sees and seeks to reproduce....' [45]

Jung suggests that there is a supra-physical or proto-physical realm which modulates observable reality and also forms the ground from which not only consciousness but also the physical Universe itself is derived. This realm precedes the emergence of the consciousness and material reality we know. It is at minimum not the exclusive possession of the individual psyche and is not limited by the temporal existence of the individual psyche - the life and death of the individual; it is the possession of humanity, stretching back to the genesis of time, held in common, extending into the future, and, it seems, also coming into manifestation through the efforts of humans to achieve self-realisation. It can be thought of not only as being a part, or even the driver, of the biological evolutionary process but also the organizing principle behind the laws of physics.

Contemporary biologist Rupert Sheldrake also rejects scientific materialism but proposes a dynamic developmental system that does not depend upon some form of absolute or eternal realm:

'My own hypothesis is that the formation of habits depends on a process called morphic resonance. Similar patterns of activity resonate across time and space with subsequent patterns. This hypothesis applies to all self-organising systems, including atoms, molecules, crystals, cells,

---

1920s, notably the exclusion principle, for which he received the Nobel prize for Physics in 1945.' (Gribben, *op. cit.*) Gribben does not mention that Jung and Pauli corresponded from 1932 until Pauli's death. Other examples of the idea of an 'ultimate formative reality' are well-known. For example, Plato's shapes; the Monads of Leibniz; the Five Elements (Wu Xing) of ancient Chinese philosophy; and so on.
45. Jung and Pauli, 2011, p. 128 - 9

plants, animals and animal societies. All draw upon a collective memory and in turn contribute to it.

A growing crystal of copper sulphate, for example, is in resonance with countless previous crystals of copper sulphate, and follows the same habits of crystal organisation, the same lattice structure. A growing oak seedling follows the habits of growth and development of previous oaks. When an orb-web spider starts spinning its web, it follows the habits of countless ancestors, resonating with them directly across space and time. The more people who learn a new skill, such as snowboarding, the easier it will be for others to learn it because of morphic resonance from previous snowboarders.

In summary this hypothesis proposes that:

1. Self-organising systems including molecules, cells, tissues, organs, organisms, societies and minds are made of nested hierarchies or holarchies of holons or morphic units. At each level the whole is more than the sum of the parts, and these parts themselves are wholes made up of parts.

2. The wholeness of each level depends on an organising field, called a morphic field. This field is within and around the system it organises, and is a vibratory pattern of activity that interacts with electromagnetic and quantum fields of the system. The generic name 'morphic field' includes:

(a) Morphogenetic fields that shape the development of plants and animals.

(b) Behavioural and perceptual fields that organise the movements, fixed-action patterns and instincts of animals.

(c) Social fields that link together and co-ordinate the behaviour of social groups.

(d) Mental fields that underlie mental activities and shape the habits of minds.

3. Morphic fields contain attractors (goals), and chreodes (habitual pathways towards those goals) that guide a system towards its end state, and maintain its integrity, stabilising it against disruptions.

4. Morphic fields are shaped by morphic resonance from all similar systems, and thus contain a cumulative collective memory. Morphic resonance depends upon similarity, and is not attenuated by distance in space or time. Morphic fields are local, within and around the systems they organise, but morphic resonance is non-local.

5. Morphic resonance involves a transfer of form or in-form-ation rather than a transfer of energy.

6. Morphic fields are fields of probability, like quantum fields, and they work by imposing patterns on otherwise random events in the systems under their influence.

7. All self-organising system are influenced by self-resonance from their own past, which plays an essential role in maintaining a holon's identity and continuity.

This hypothesis leaves open the question of how morphic resonance actually works. There are several suggestions. One is that the transfer of information occurs through the 'implicate order', as proposed by the physicist David Bohm. The implicate or enfolded order gives rise to the world we can observe, the explicate order, in which things are located in space and time....Or resonance may pass through the quantum-vacuum field, also known as the zero-point energy field, which mediates all quantum and electromagnetic processes. Or similar systems might be connected through hidden extra dimensions, as in string theory and M-theory. Or maybe it depends on new kinds of physics as yet unthought of...this hypothesis is eminently testable.'[46]

Holography gives us an idea of the possible *form* of the universal field and concepts such as that of archetypes and morphic resonance give us an idea of its *function,* simply put, which is *to initiate and reinforce both physical forms and states of consciousness.* Homoeostasis gives us an idea as to how systems might be regulated. The physical world, which includes living beings such as us, is in a constant and immediate interchange with this underlying realm and we have faculties innate to ourselves which allow us to probe this realm and get information from it, and mobilise certain aspects it for our own uses. My position is that ideas and concepts such as these are germane, probably central, to an understanding of Radionics. They will be explored in more detail as the book progresses.

---

46. Sheldrake (2012). (The Science Delusion) For example, Sheldrake does not deny the role of genes in creating biological structures but argues that in themselves they are insufficient to explain how form comes about - *morphogenesis*. This quote comes from Chapter 3. This book was released after I had completed the first draft of *21st Century Radionics*.

RELIGION AND RADIESTHESIA

Again Mermet makes his position crystal clear. The phenomena of dowsing arise from causes recognized by, or potentially recognizable by, science:

'In France, the pioneers in the field of Radiesthesia have been, in the majority of cases, Catholic Priests who invariably have a strong aversion to spiritualism, occultism and all kinds of magic. Is it conceivable that if, in the course of their experiments, they had discovered some suspicious element, they would have continued their researches? The constancy of physical laws, their neutrality in regard to any religious or philosophical question, constitute criteria showing that we are confronted with purely natural forces....In this work, it seems to me that I have written a supplementary chapter to the old textbooks of classical physics....Among radiesthetists, I have observed two tendencies. Some, endowed with a really scientific temperament, seek and see in Radiesthesia a new branch of the physics of waves and radiations. Others, possessing psychic and metaphysical tendencies, attracted by the wonders of occultism, aim at linking up Radiesthesia with phenomena of abnormal hypersensibility or spiritism....I regard Radiesthesia as being purely scientific. If it had not been so, I should have given it up long ago. All the facts I have observed, whether explicable or not, appear to be purely natural and the mystery associated with them is of the same kind as that characteristic of luminous, calorific and Hertzian waves.'

This clearly a very important point for him. A letter of May 1935 from Mgr Eugène Tisserand, Prefect of the Vatican Library, to M. Delattre, Secretary General of the Society, Amis de la Radiesthésie, is printed shortly after the title page of *Principles and Practice of Radiesthesia* and conveys the following:

'I would have written to you much sooner had it not been that I was required to attend an audience of the Sovereign Pontiff for the purpose of explaining to Him personally the nature of the researches to which the members of your Association are dedicated, and to tell His Holiness of your wish to have for the officers of your Association, and for its activities, the Apostolic Blessing. The Holy Father was touched by the sentiments expressed in your letter and has charged me to communicate to you His Paternal Blessing.'

Over the years I have had people telling me that the pendulum is operated by Satan, as a consequence making innocent fellows like me unwitting tools of the Evil One. I have even had Evangelical Christians refuse Radionic treatment on the basis of this objection. They came for help, but as soon as they discovered a pendulum was involved, there was a problem in accepting it, so they did not. Judging from the state of the world, Satan has had far more productive subjects to which to apply his baneful influence than a few obscure researchers on the far edge of Complementary Medicine. However, you never know. It is said that the legions of the Devil are well-organized, and, it would seem, busy. Since there are those who take the religious viewpoint very seriously I append the following, which might be of use to them:

'Catholic priests were responsible for the birth of medical dowsing. In the 7th century, many religious leaders condemned dowsing. However the church from time to time would authorise members of its own priesthood to dowse and divine. In his book of 1693 Jean Nicholas said "My only object is to treat those to whom God, by his influence of the stars, has impressed the faculty of discovering, by the movement of the rod called Jacob's rod, all hidden things, subterranean and others."

Dr Karl Berg, Archbishop of Salzburg, wrote a note "For Christians troubled by the ethics of dowsing" *in which he said that "If a Christian wants to do God's will and protects himself with prayers when doing radiesthesic work and uses his or her instruments only in a helping way, based on love, when examining houses, helping people or finding water, then this work is blessed by the church" (Decree of 26th March, 1942)*

The Catholic priest Abbé Mermet was given the Pope's permission for his extraordinary work with dowsing.

Kathe Bachler, who dowsed over 11,000 cases in 3,000 homes in 14 countries said "I would like to make a comment on the association between science and religion. At the beginning of my research I held the misguided belief that it was important to keep these two separate. Now...in my view, it is only when the scientific dowser feels a responsibility towards God and is humble and full of love towards his fellow man, that dowsing will succeed. Without guidance from above, the dowser will fall into error, and may thus do harm to himself and others. Properly carried out, dowsing is a divine service to one's fellows. This I believe is the answer to the criticism, sometimes voiced, that dowsing is a dark and sinister force. A good dowser is following God's will. This is important for all dowsers to understand, no matter what their religion."

Father Kunibert Reisinger, a South African missionary, was a dowser who helped many people find much-needed water. He said "The work with the dowsing rod and pendulum opens new vistas into God's beautiful world, and into the wonders of creation".

Exodus 4:17 "And then take in thy hand this rod wherewith thou shalt do signs"

Jeremiah 1:11 - "Moreover the word of Jehovah came over me saying 'What seest thou?' And I said 'I see a rod of an almond tree'. Then said Jehovah "Thou hast seen well, for I will hasten my word to perform it".

Michael 7:14 "Feed thy people with thy rod"

Revelations 11:1 "And there was given me a reed like unto a rod and the angel stood, saying, "Rise and measure the temple of God and the altar and them that worship therein".[47]

I did some brief research into the matter myself and find that the Bible also condemns dowsing. Some may choose to follow Deuteronomy 18:9:

'When thou art come into the land, which the Lord thy God giveth thee, thou shalt not learn to do after the abomination of those nations. (10) There shall not be found among you any one that....useth divination....(12) For all that do these things are an abomination unto the Lord....(14) For those nations, which thou shalt posses, hearkened unto observers of times, and unto diviners, but as for thee, the Lord thy God hath not suffered thee so to do.'

From my own point of view dowsing is, in essence, a type of scientific or, at minimum, rational, investigative method. For those of a religious persuasion who need some guidance, the above comments may provide complete, partial, or no, reassurance according to which texts or authorities you decide to accept. I am not qualified to say if the Papal Blessing takes precedence over the predications of Deuteronomy - but, I must presume, the Holy Father is.

---

47. kindly provided by Rebecka Blenntoft.

4: ORGANIZATION OF PERCEPTION AND MENTAL FOCUS IN RADIONICS

MIND AND HABITS OF MIND

From Jung comes the idea that a vast and probably limitless reserve of psychic processes, energies and artefacts exists in the collective unconsciousness of humanity. In addition I propose that there is a universal information field substanding physical reality. In fact the two may simply be aspects of an even greater field which in its totality describes the physical Universe and everything in it. Dowsing may be a means by which the threshold of the unconscious may be breached, or the information field be read.

It may also be that many types of information extending well beyond matters of ill-health and its treatment could be obtained by accessing the universal field. It could however be difficult for the person who gains some level of access to this information to either understand it, interpret it, or use it meaningfully. There may be a colossal gap between perception and comprehension; what may be perceived is one thing, but fitting it into a framework of understanding and relevance may be quite another. Therefore a counterpart to this discussion is some examination of the problem of how perception is conformed to become recognizable as *conscious* process, in other words, the structures of the shared *consciousness* by which we communicate with each other on a daily basis through means such as language. In this context there are also important questions to be considered about the role of habits and customs of mind in the creation and maintenance of a sense of order in the individual and the collective psyche, and how ideas threatening to this sense of order can trigger reaction, sometimes of an extreme nature.

An interesting example may be taken from the development of art. The world becomes comfortable with certain forms of artistic expression but circumstances of history, changes in the *zeitgeist*, the effects of the future coming into manifestation, and the appearance of artists with the talent and sensitivity to respond to this, brings about a change in the mode of expression. The *new* produces discomfort, incomprehension, rejection and a feeling of revolt in some portion of the audience; scandal and outrage ensue; there is something amiss, the secure ground of life has been disturbed, the known certainties have been assaulted. After a while we begin to understand the quality of the new art as the historical and social context becomes apparent to us. What was immediately nonsense may become sense, and sense may become relevance, and relevance may become greatness. But greatness in art can only ensue if the new also reflects some essential facet of the human condition. Some element of what we may consider the eternal moral and ethical truths, what we might call an *archetypal experiential commonality*, must be there to offset the fury of the new. Otherwise, it becomes an art for rage or trivia's sake, disconcerting yet without depth, temporary and disposable. There are of course many examples of which but one is that of Stravinksy's *The Rite of Spring*. It was premiered on May 29th 1913 and caused a riot. The performance was impressively reconstructed by the BBC in a documentary film, *Riot at the Rite*. According to Sarah Shannon in *The Independent*, 9th March 2006, in an article about the production:

'The music assaulted their ears. Stravinsky had experimented with ferocious stamping rhythms and set them against each other so that they clashed unpredictably. The choreography shocked the first-night audience with its daring modernism, ripping up the rulebook of classical ballet with its heavy, savage movements. One of the dancers later commented, "With every leap we landed heavily enough to jar every organ in us." Most shocking of all was the subject matter of pagan rituals and the barbaric sacrifice of a young virgin. The performance split the crowd. Some loved the break from tradition; others were disgusted by this modernist vulgarity. The nay-sayers began to boo. The cat-calling grew until the dancers struggled to hear the music. Scuffles broke out and the theatre's owner flashed the lights on and off to calm the crowd, but to no avail. A near-riot took place in the theatre while the ballet dancers and musicians kept performing.'

Just over a year later World War 1 began, ripping up the classical rulebook of war, and Europe was plunged into a bloodbath the like of which was unknown to history even if there were prototypes of industrial-strength mechanised barbarity such as the American Civil War (1861 - 65). *The Rite of Spring* is now considered one of the incontrovertible masterworks of the 20th Century.

Perception is structured, and necessarily so, is in order to obtain comprehension, in order to manage all the data that the senses produce and reduce it to chunks which can be comprehended, and within this context there must be a degree of functionalism or purposiveness. This is in order to get the basics of everyday life done; there could be no social organisation without group psychological and perceptual organisation. On the other hand perception tends to become habitualised; *'we like what we know and we know what we like'*[48]; habit is the enemy of innovation. There is, in addition, the continual upflow of impressions from the personal and collective unconsciousness, one of the primary forms of its manifestation being via dreams, and these need to be dealt with and will be dealt with according to what might be called the *psychological viability* of the individual. *'The dream is specifically the utterance of the unconscious' 'the dream describes the inner situation of the dreamer, but the conscious mind denies its truth and reality, or admits it only grudgingly.'*[49] Society may demand conformity, but the unconscious does not spare us and recognizes no writ.

All of this incoming 'data' is filtered into the frameset of everyday consciousness, which, one might propose, tends to be quite strictly programmed by what might be called commonality of experience, agreed rules, and thresholds of inadmissibility. A strong example of this is *language*, which is one of the primary means by which the contents of consciousness are represented, described and exteriorised. A language exists because the speakers of that language have explicitly or tacitly agreed as to what the words (i.e. sounds comprised of grouped phonemes) in the language mean; clearly, if there is no such common agreement, verbal and written communication would be impossible. Rules exist to define, for example, how words are spelled and sentences constructed, and this, as a consequence, determines how *meaning* is conveyed. But meaning is not the words themselves; words are *given meaning* by recognition of the relationship between the underlying intellectual and psychological thought forms and emotional artefacts which have been admitted to consciousness, and the sounds and therefore the language chosen to represent them. You can easily test this relationship between words and meaning by attempting to understand a language you do not know - some emotions and basic meaning may be discerned but little else. In short I suggest that language itself is a secondary stage of expression which results from the necessity to express higher level concepts (e.g. such as thought-forms) in a canonical way.

Boundaries (agreed rules) may be flexible but ultimately if they are sufficiently breached, a language will deteriorate into incomprehensibility - James Joyce's *'Finnegan's Wake'* (1939), which is replete with word

---

48. Genesis (1973) 'I like what I know and I know what I like' *I Know What I Like (In Your Wardrobe.*
49. Jung, quoted in Storr (1983) p. 171 (The Essential Jung, Selected Writings).

games and neologisms, is an outstanding example - considered one of the great works of modern literature, but indecipherable to most. Slang, on the other hand, is an example of the continuous re-creation of language in which a subgroup of the population of speakers originate new, or give new meanings to existing, words. Thresholds of inadmissibility govern, for example, how words may be used and therefore what concepts may be allowable; PC (political correctness) is an example of how language has been re-engineered to comply with such thresholds. I would furthermore argue that such rules extend into many or probably most other domains of knowledge and that science itself is not immune to them.[50] Yet in earlier times the Catholic Church persecuted Galileo for heresy (*heliocentrism* - proposing that the earth revolved around the sun, viewed as contrary to scripture); a threshold had been breached which threatened the security delivered by the certainty of a structured consciousness, the comfortable and comforting habits of mind - a fact had intruded on the consensus created by agreed rules about what constituted reality.[51]

Accordingly, if we can accept that consciousness is programmed as to what is allowable, possible and understandable, accessing any information gleaned from the universal field which does not fit with preconceptions or existing knowledge may result in considerable difficulties of interpretation, i.e. because it can only be interpreted in terms of what is already known and accepted, which may be inadequate to describe what is found. This, then, is a problem of which the dowser must be acutely aware; the subconscious may be telling us something via the pendulum movement but our frame of reference may be insufficient to accommodate it, and the result of the inquiry is then dismissed as meaningless. This is yet another reason why dowsing is a matter of great skill and not some form of idiot-simple activity or activity for simpletons; the subtleties of interpretation may require the utmost introspection.

---

50. In terms of science the word paradigm (model) may be used to describe the agreed mind-set governing the knowledge about any particular topic, and any revolutionary moment in science which forces re-organization of the model - such as Einstein's Theory of Relativity - may be considered to be a paradigm-breaker, forcing re-organization of perception. See, for example, *The Structure of Scientific Revolutions* by Thomas S. Kuhn (1962)

51. 'Human kind cannot bear very much reality', T.S. Eliot, *The Four Quartets* (1945). 'Usually with disastrous consequences', appends the present author.

In addition to this very brief exploration of semiotics, we may append similar questions about the nature of external reality, from science:

'*Considered together, Bohm and Pribram's theories provide a profound new way of looking at the world:* Our brains mathematically construct objective reality by interpreting frequencies that are ultimately projections from another dimension, a deeper order of existence that is beyond space and time. The brain is a hologram enfolded in a holographic universe. *For Pribram this made him realise that the objective world does not exist, at least not in the way we are accustomed to believing. What is "out there" is a vast ocean of waves and frequencies, and reality looks concrete to us only because our brains are able to take this holographic blur and convert it into the....familiar objects that make up this world. How is the brain (which itself is composed of frequencies of matter) able to take something as insubstantial as a blur of frequencies and make it seem solid to the touch?*'[52]

And: '*..let us consider as an example the process of observing an atom with the aid of suitable apparatus....the quanta by which the observing apparatus interacts with the atom will change the latter in a way that cannot be predicted, controlled, described or even conceived of. Hence, each different apparatus in a sense creates a different kind of atom. Even this terminology is too picturesque, however, because it implies an atom having definite properties when it is not observed, which are changed by interaction with a measuring apparatus. But in the usual interpretation of the quantum theory, an atom has no properties at all when it is not observed. Indeed, one may say that its only mode of being is to be observed; for the notion of an atom existing with uniquely-definable properties of its own even when it is not interacting with a piece of observing apparatus, is meaningless within the framework of this point of view. If the notion of the objective existence of atoms and other such micro-objects with uniquely-definable properties of their own must be given up, then the question naturally arises, "With what does the quantum mechanics actually deal?"* [53]

---

52. Talbot, 1996, p. 54. David Bohm, 1917 - 1992, physicist; Karl Pribram, 1919 - , Professor of Psychology and Psychiatry (who did not, to the author's knowledge, work together). For another précis of Pribram's work, see McTaggart, *op. cit.*, Chapter 5.
53. Bohm, 1957, p. 92.

Bohm however argues *against* quantum indeterminacy and for an underlying system of order, the 'implicate order'. The point is - as we shall later in more detail - that common agreement as to what constitutes 'reality' has been lost in science:

'Von Neumann then raised the question, "In addition to these 'observables' are there any other at present 'hidden' variables, which would help define the state of the system more precisely than is now possible in terms of the current formulation of the quantum theory? His proof that this is impossible depends, in an essential way, however, on the assumption that at least part of the specification of the state of the system will always be in terms of these observables, while the hidden variables will at most serve to make more precise the specification already given by the observables. Such an assumption evidently severely limits the forms of the theories that may then be taken into consideration. For it leaves out the important possibility that as we go to a sub-quantum mechanical level the entire scheme of observables satisfying certain rules that are appropriate to the quantum-mechanical level will break down, to be replaced by something very different...In this case, the proof of von Neumann's theorem would not be relevant, since the conditions considered here go beyond the implicit assumptions needed to carry out the proof.'[54]

Further evidence appears to come from persons who have taken psychedelic and hallucinatory drugs. Here the normal ordering of perception is broken down, and perhaps the hallucinations are in some part the attempts of the still-functioning rational part of the mind to impose perceptual order on the flood of information overwhelming the nervous system; or perhaps not. Huxley reports:

'Half an hour after swallowing the drug I became aware of the slow dance of golden lights. A little later there were sumptuous red surfaces swelling and expanding from bright nodes of energy that vibrated with a continuously changing, patterned life....at no time were there faces or forms of men or animals. I saw no landscapes, no enormous spaces, no magical growth and metamorphosis of buildings....The other world to which mescalin admitted me was not the world of visions; it existed out

---

54. Bohm, *op. cit,* p. 95 - 96.

21st Century Radionics

there, in what I could see with my eyes open. The great change was in the realm of objective fact.' [55]

So at one minute Huxley sees the usual 'everyday world'; after taking Mescaline, his perception of the everyday world becomes radically transformed and yet he remains convinced that what he is now seeing is what is there - *'objective fact'.* Thus the 'consciousness-set' of the enquirer, which tends to be programmed by accepted or conventional concepts and ideas about the nature of reality, may form a definite limitation to comprehension if, as this example seems to show, perception of the same thing can be so radically modified by some alteration of the state of the observer's perceptual apparatus. In this example the alteration results from ingestion of Mescaline but in the example of Stravinsky's *Rite of Spring*, the alteration comes from some inspirational change in the composer's consciousness, in short - you don't have to take a drug to change the way you see the world. And indeed, Huxley goes on to say,

'Reflecting on my experiences I find myself agreeing with the eminent Cambridge philosopher, Dr. D. C. Broad, 'that we should do well to consider....the type of theory that Bergson put forward in connexion with memory and sense perception. The suggestion is that the function of the brain and nervous system and sense organs is in the main eliminative and not productive. Each person is at each moment capable of remembering all that has ever happened to him and of perceiving everything that is happening everywhere in the universe. The function of the brain and nervous system is to prevent us from being overwhelmed and confused by this mass of useless and largely irrelevant knowledge, by shutting out most of what we should otherwise perceive or remember at any moment, and leaving only that very small and special selection which is likely to be practically useful.[56] *According to such a theory, each one of us is*

---

55. Huxley, 1954 p. 16 (*The Doors Of Perception*).
56. Science states also that the human perceptual range, which might be referred to as the *bandwidth* of human perception, covers but a fragment of what is found in nature. Hearing is said to be limited to the range approximately 20Hz to 20kHz in young people, and this range diminishes with age. Our sight is limited to what is defined as the 'visible spectrum' of electromagnetism (visible light), which is only a fraction of the total electromagnetic frequency range. For example we cannot see X-Rays, Microwaves, and so on. To a certain extent this can be disputed, such as in the case of hypersensitivity to electromagnetic fields (people who cannot bear to be near computers and other electronic devices), and I have

potentially Mind at Large. But in so far as we are animals [I assume he means 'to the extent that we are animals'?], our business is at all costs to survive. To make biological survival possible, Mind at Large has to be funnelled through the reducing valve of the brain and nervous system. What comes out the other end is a measly trickle of the kind of consciousness which will help us to stay alive on the surface of this particular planet. To formulate and express the contents of this reduced awareness, man has invented and endlessly elaborated those symbol-systems and implicit philosophies we call languages. Every individual is at once the beneficiary and the victim of the linguistic tradition into which he or she has been born - the beneficiary inasmuch as language gives access to the accumulated records of other people's experience, the victim in so far as it confirms him in the belief that reduced awareness is the only awareness....so that he is all too apt to take his concepts for data, his words for actual things.' [57]

Neither must we forget the incalculable amounts of time, money and effort which are poured into moulding and programming human consciousness for any number of purposes, most typically for some form of societal control or commercial advantage - religion, advertising, politics, science, business, the media, etc., are all involved in some way or other in the effort, may we say battle, to shape and control consciousness and through that create 'reality'. This is a common characteristic of practically all societies in all times and places and of whatever political character, that someone (usually a relatively small group of the powerful) is trying to convince somebody else (usually the large group of the relatively powerless) that the former are acting, most typically, in the latter's best interests, in short, *'We want your mind and we want it now.'* [58] In this context another side of art is *art as propaganda*, and both the Nazis and the Communists did not fall short in these matters. George Orwell's novel *1984* (published 1949) is perhaps the acme of perfection in the study of

---

seen public tests performed by Rupert Neve which suggest that young people can in fact hear quite far beyond the 20kHz threshold. This is before we even start to consider dowsing, or transcendental states of mind.

57. Huxley, *op. cit.*, p.21.

58. pace The Doors, *When The Music's Over* (1967) 'We want the world and we want it now.'

this question, although his *Animal Farm* (1945) is replete with similar relevance.

From the point of view of psychoanalysis, dreams and symbols act as mediators between regions outside of the everyday consciousness of the individual - such as the *personal* unconscious - and ordinary waking consciousness itself, and the interpretation of these symbolic eruptions may be useful in resolving psychological problems. Symbols, however, may or may not be very helpful in converting ideas and concepts gleaned from the information field into knowledge. For more practical purposes what is observed or experienced has to be modulated into a 'common' symbology, i.e. language or, perhaps, mathematics, before it can become useful; and if appropriate expressions do not exist then they will have to be created and the meanings defined, and to do this some form of contextualisation is required. Thus it may take a long time (if ever) to realise what you have, as it were, 'in your hands' - hence the well-known *'eureka moment'*, when perception crystallizes into comprehension.[59] Bearing this in mind, is it not unreasonable to suggest that in fact all knowledge exists first in a higher-level, superconscious form, perhaps as a *potential*, which is then demodulated into language and other symbolic systems which are the means of expression of mundane consciousness, when circumstances demand, allow or require it?

MENTAL FOCUS AND THE USE OF CHARTS

As stated, *'the dowser poses a question'* and *'specially-tuned pendulums'* etc. suggest that essential to the matter of accurate dowsing is mental attunement and focus, allowing a stronger link to the object of the enquiry. The more precisely the dowser configures the question in his mind, the better he should be able to tune in to the universal information field, and the energetic pattern or imprint of the object of questioning held within it. Dowsing for water, minerals, energy lines and so forth is usually done by holding the idea of the target in the mind; the target is generally local to the dowser and the connection should be easily made. But as we see from Mermet's map dowsing example, when the target is remote to the dowser, some representation of it is needed to assist the process. In Radionics, which queries a wide range of possible targets usually at a considerable distance, similar representations are useful, if not essential. When we come to the matter of the Subtle Anatomy, we enter

---

59. How many people saw apples fall from apple trees prior to Newton and did not make the connections which lead him to formulate his Laws?

into what seems to be a subjective and conjectural realm. We have to conceptualise that which is not visible or measurable; and yet in present-day Radionics the vehicles of consciousness and the life force are considered to be inextricable from the process of physical life. These therefore have to be accounted for in some practical way so that analysis and treatment can include them in the model.

Various strategies have been tried to improve dowsing accuracy and the comprehension of pendulum movements, but here I will describe just one, which is the organising of dowsing investigations through the use of Charts. This method is widely used in Radionics and may, in fact, be a characteristic technique which originated in it. The point is that we wish to impose some form of order or framework on the wide range of responses which might be gained from the field. A Chart, then, is a diagram which facilitates pendulum investigation into a number of different subjects, usually related by feature or function, thereby helping the practitioner organize his enquiries into useable pieces of information. As with other forms of representation of ideas and concepts such as language and symbols, a Chart is an externalisation of a subset of the universal information field and clearly, there *needs to exist a coherent relationship between the chart and what it is supposed to represent*. Note that in Radionic work Charts are typically used in combination with instruments; the Radionic instrument assists the operator in accessing the field, and the Chart and pendulum assist in interpretation of the readings thereby obtained.[60]

As a starting point, in order to have some value the Chart must deal with something which should in principle be knowable or which might be ascertained to be knowable. Obviously this latter is a fine point which could be argued over in some depth, in the sense that we might not know something is knowable until we establish in fact that it *is* knowable [e.g. see comparatively Bohm's comments above], so let me give what I hope should be a simple and clear example. Dowsing over random or basically unknowable events will normally lead to useless results. A typical such instance is dowsing for the outcome of gambling events. While there are, apparently, persons who have been able to consistently dowse winners of horse-races, in practical terms we will assume that gambling is highly probabilistic, in short, chance rules, and the outcome cannot be known as the race has not yet taken place, otherwise the dowser would be reading the future. You could easily construct a Chart of the runners in a race, or

---

60. A discussion of the function of instruments follows in Chapter 14.

to indicate the Lottery numbers, in such a fashion that it is a coherent organisation of the data. In practice the pendulum may indeed point to the name of a horse or certain numbers. Using these indications as a basis for betting, however, tends to be pretty hopeless in terms of getting winning results since, if anything, they simply tend to confirm the probability that a specific horse might win, which is a different matter completely from knowing that a certain horse *will* win, which *will* come second, and so forth. Thus you might get a reading for the horse '*My Favourite Biomechanoid*' as 78%, or '*Huxley's Trip*' as 83%, and these readings could, I assume, be translated into odds.[61] Here one might conclude that in this instance the relationship between the Chart and what it is supposed to be able to reveal, which is to say, the actual winner of a race, is weak. On the other hand enquiry as to whether there is water or oil or any other useful mineral underground in a certain place, or whether a person has a bacterial or viral infection, or whether a certain horse has a particular physical characteristic or weakness, is an entirely different matter in so far as this is, in principle or fact, knowable information and thus a Chart which correlates strongly with the object of enquiry can be devised.

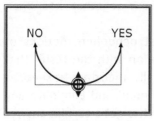

Figure 2: Basic Yes-No Chart

When used with a chart, *the pendulum becomes a pointing device;* it indicates your reaction in terms of one of the possible answers shown on it. Many such charts can be designed and I will give a few illustrations here using some simple examples. A useful basic diagram is the YES - NO CHART. This (Fig. 2) could be printed to any size, but, as should be obvious, the pendulum movement can indicate either YES or NO in response to the question. Any other movement - such as a wavering or

---

61. I have heard a certain amount of tutting (disapproval) at the idea that dowsing could be used for such ignoble purposes as gambling but I think these are perfectly valid experiments. What, then, if you could dowse the racing winners time after time, well beyond the probability that it is pure chance? What would this tell us about the structure of reality? Would this tell us anything about dowsing or it would it suggest that certain persons have a precognitive ability which they trigger using dowsing techniques? Not all agree that 'pure chance' rules; Coyle (2010) suggests that 'luck' is a function of the individual's PK (psycho-kinetic) resonance with the environment and that this can be increased using certain methods, leading to better than average probabilities of winning in gambling and other events. See also Jung (1973) (*Synchronicity: an Acausal Connecting principle*)

uncertain movement, no movement, or a false movement, where the pendulum points to an answer but the dowser can sense that it is not a *real* indication (because it is, for example, a projection of the dowser's desire for a particular answer) - suggests that either the question is ambiguous or equivocal, or cannot be so simply answered.

Clearly, the more comprehensive the knowledge base of the dowser relative to the subject of the enquiry, the better he or she should be able to frame the questions and interpret the answers. The construction and sequence of questions is in itself an important matter. Questions should be unambiguous and to the point, and sequences of questions should preferably follow a logical pattern, as opposed to jumping around wildly from topic to topic. You are trying to order your subconscious responses to get coherent and useable information from them, so working from a degree of disorder is not going to help. Discrimination must be used here. Much time can be wasted going into finer and finer detail which may be irrelevant to a proper understanding of the enquiry. For example, if the patient's symptoms result from some form of systemic energetic disturbance, analysing the many local symptoms which are the visible form of the problem may not assist unless the common underlying thread which ties them together has been identified.

As noted, it is also easy to misinterpret pendulum motions or impose one's own beliefs on the pendulum motion with the result that you go off on the wrong track completely. It is vitally important to keep, as far as is possible, a calm, balanced and neutral mind and eliminate any expectation of any particular answer. If you expect to get a certain answer to your query then your expectation may overrule the information conveyed by the pendulum, giving a false result. Furthermore, the same question should not be repeated over and over again as in general the first pendulum response is accurate and repetition may produce a type of feedback confusion effect in the mind (Fig. 3) that makes subsequent pendulum readings less, and not more, accurate. If necessary stop dowsing for a few seconds and clear the mental process.

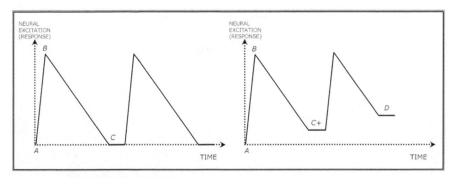

Figure 3: Feedback Confusion Effect

In the graph at the left, the dowser's question is asked at *A* and the mind is in a neutral state; the response peaks at *B* and the mind settles back to the neutral state at *C*. The next question is then asked and the process is repeated, each time with the mind reverting to neutral. In the graph at the right, the dowser does not let his or her mind settle back to the neutral state *C* but creates a new 'floor' at *C+*, which is a level of excitation; with each subsequent question the 'floor' moves away from neutral (which should be at *C*), to, for example *D*, and so on, and this creates a kind of feedback loop which can build energy into the pendulum so that it (for example) seems to rotate more quickly and furiously and - perhaps to the beginner - convincingly than ever. But this works against accurate dowsing since you are not restarting from a neutral, settled state with each new question. While strong - even quite violent - immediate responses can occur in some dowsing operations, such as when using the rods, the dowser must be sure of the situation and know how to distinguish between real and false movements.

Another simple chart – the INTENSITY CHART – allows testing over the range 0 to 100%. In this case, where gradations between NO and YES are in effect provided for, indication of the degree to which something is present, or INTENSITY, is possible (Fig. 4).

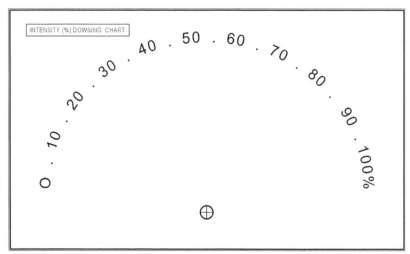

Figure 4: Intensity (%) Chart

Let's say we ask the question *does patient X have a fungal infection*? The basic answer could be either YES or NO, but using the percentage scale, we may get a reading of 90%, which indicates in a general sense not only that a fungal infection is present, but also how strong, or INTENSE, the infection is. We might also ask a question such as, *how intense is the infection at the worst point?* (Peak), or *how intense is the infection on average*? If we were studying a fungal infection in a particular Location such as the Lungs, we could try and pinpoint both the peak and average states and obtain readings such as 90/5, i.e. 90% Peak, 5% Average. This suggests that the infection is strongly localised to a particular place even if the infection is generally present to a certain degree throughout the lung. The higher the average, the stronger the overall presence of the infection may be; so a person giving readings of, say, 90 / 35 could be quite strongly afflicted. Peak /average readings can be particularly useful where there is a systemic problem.

Such semi-circular designs are known as Fan charts, self-evidently because the answers are spread out in a fan shape. The virtue of the design is that a large number of possible answers can be compressed into a fairly small area, and an unequivocal pendulum can be obtained. Nevertheless Charts can be seen which are circular in design. These array the topics around a full 360° circle and the dowser places the pendulum over the centre. The pendulum then swings towards the topic which answers the question, but there is the problem that it is swinging across a 180° range, i.e. seeming to swing between two topics (on opposite sides of the circle) and the question arises as to which one is actually being

21st Century Radionics

indicated. In point of fact it will be found that there is a 'pull' or 'bias' in the pendulum swing towards the answer being designated, but detecting this can be tricky. One way round this problem is to put your finger (as a pointer) on the topic you think is being indicated and ask for a pendulum rotation in confirmation, but this takes more time if there are many topics to work through. Thus I find circular Charts a little difficult to work with because of the sense of ambiguity, and that the Fan design is both easier and more certain.

A SIMPLE EXAMPLE

I shall now describe an extremely simple hypothetical analysis to further show how Charts can be used. We will suppose we are asked to give some treatment to a person. Figure 5 shows a range of primary and basic colours: [62]

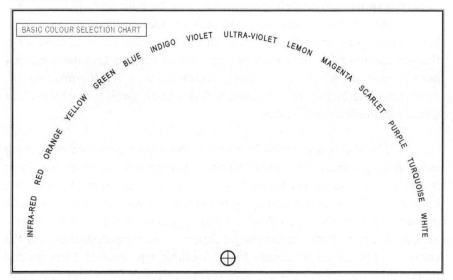

Figure 5: Basic Colour Analysis Chart

The pendulum is placed over the bull's eye at the bottom of the chart and will then swing to indicate the required colour in answer to the question posed by the dowser, for example, *what is the principle colour deficient in the patient's Subtle Anatomy ?* This operation can then be repeated while asking the question *what is the colour next most deficient in the patient's Subtle Anatomy?*, and the enquiry can be repeated until no

---

62. This basically the Spectro-Chrome system. See www.dinshahhealth.org

further response is obtained, meaning that you have completed the enquiry. Or you could ask, *how many colours are deficient in the patient's Subtle Anatomy?* and using a 0 - 10 NUMBER SCALE, (which could be set out similarly to the Intensity Chart, except substituting the numbers 0 to 10 for 0 - 100%), you may get the reading 3, and you can then go on to find out which colours they are.

Clearly, methods can be combined. The pendulum may indicate that Green is the colour most deficient; you can then go to the Intensity Scale and ask *what is the percentage deficiency of the colour Green* (in the Subtle Anatomy of Patient X)? You may get a reading of 80%, in which case you can simply say that the patient is 80% deficient in the colour Green. You can note this down as Green, 80%. Or you may discover several deficiencies - Green, 80%; Blue, 60%; Orange, 50%, and so on. By using this basic method on various Locations in the Subtle Bodies of the patient, a simple colour deficiency analysis can be built up.

The reader should note that colour analysis and therapy are a basic techniques used in Radionics but it has long been applied as a therapeutic modality, one such example being Spectro-Chrome. The first book I read on what is, in effect, Radionics was *Teletherapy*, by Dr. Benoytosh Bhattacharyya. This extraordinary book, given to me by my late friend Pauline Brownell, states:

'The visible and invisible cosmic colours have produced everything tangible by condensation....even the seven Planets are the condensed form of the cosmic colours, according to a statement in the Kurma Purana. *The body of the Universe is made up of the cosmic colours of limitless variety, and among them the seven VIBGYOR (Rays) [Violet - Indigo - Blue - Green - Yellow - Orange - Red] are the chief....Disease means devitalisation and the consequential hunger for cosmic forces for their regeneration. Diseases can be cured by supplying the necessary cosmic forces in the form of rays [i.e. colours] which are wanting in the human system. When the body is sufficiently regenerated and revitalised by the rays, the disease cannot stay longer in the body, and it disappears as a matter of course.'* [63]

---

63. Bhattacharyya (1985) p. 10 and 11. In orthodoxy Light-deficiency disease (SAD - Seasonal Affective Disorder) appears to be a medically-recognized condition, while Spectroscopy, the study of the spectra of light absorbed and emitted by matter, is of course a major scientific analytical technique. Again, McTaggart, *op. cit.*, Chapter 3, writes about the work of Fritz-Albert Popp and his research into biophotons - light produced by living cells (for example, those in your body) and its use in inter-cellular communication.

According to Bhattacharyya, certain types of disease can be associated with certain types of colour deficiency. Respiratory diseases with lack of blue; digestive disorders with lack of yellow; cancers with lack of green; nervous diseases with lack of violet; and so forth. In addition to using pendulum techniques Bhattacharyya explains that the colour makeup of a person can be revealed by examining the face or a photograph using a prism. Fringes will be clearly visible on certain parts of the face (e.g. the eyebrows) and careful observation will show any imbalance in the colour makeup of the fringes, such as deficiency of Green, Yellow, Red, etc. It is certainly true that a prism *does* reveal fringing not only on the human face but upon many objects, and the fringing does appear to have different characteristics for different persons. Whether this indicates the state of health is another matter; those interested could easily perform experiments to verify whether this is the case or not. However, *Teletherapy* should first be studied in detail as there is far more in it than I can possibly recount here, although the reader should note that the techniques Bhattacharyya used are quite different to those which I will describe.

Let us say that you determine that the colour most required by the patient is Green. The question which follows is how best to correct the imbalance, which is to say, how to normalise the absorption of light by the patient so that the required amount is taken up. A variety of treatment options (to be given Radionically) are available to the practitioner and the most suitable method can be determined using an appropriate Chart, such as that shown in Figure 6. Here the movement of the pendulum is indicated by the dotted line, which points to 'Tissue Salt', the 12 Tissue Cell Salts being a group of quasi-homoeopathic remedies which are said to support the basic functions of the cells.[64] Here the idea is that it will be the action of the Tissue Salt - its vibrational pattern applied to the patient - which potentially affords the best available correction of the patient's subtle energy fields, permitting a better balance of light to be taken up.

Note the expression in common parlance, 'off-colour', as in, 'I'm feeling off-colour'. To what colour does this expression refer?

64. Introduced by Doctor Schuessler (1821 - 1898), these are widely available and may be used individually or in various combinations, typically at low potency, to combat various conditions. They are also often used in basic Radionic distant treatments.

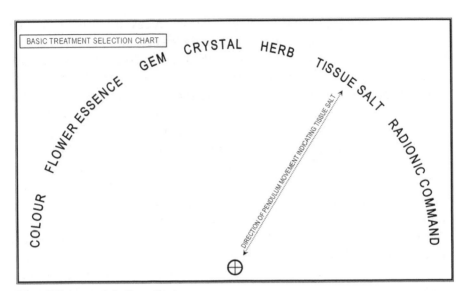

Figure 6:Treatment Options Chart

The practitioner must then determine which Salt is the correct one. Following the usual dowsing enquiry procedures (see Fig. 7), we can discover whether one or several Tissue Salts are required, which ones should be used, whether they should be used sequentially or in combination, for how long (i.e. treatment time), to what extent they will correct the colour deficiency, and so forth. Let us say that only one Salt is required, Ferrum Phosphoricum (Iron Phosphate).

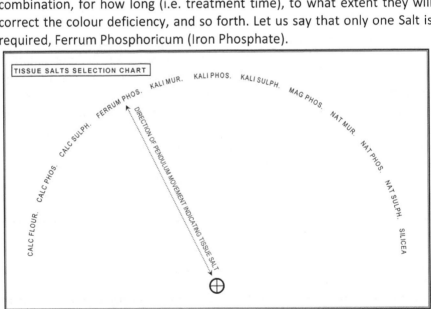

Figure 7:Tissue Salt Selection Chart

The practitioner can then use the code 249977449 for Ferrum Phosphoricum in an appropriate Radionic instrument. This will entrain the patient, via the witness, with the energy pattern of Ferrum Phos., and by this means the treatment is given.[65] To show, basically, how this is done, Fig. 8 below illustrates the control panel of a hypothetical and extremely simple 12-dial, Base 10 Instrument. The 12 rate dials, calibrated 0 to 9, are shown in three blocks of 4 and the top left dial would be the left-most number in the Rate. Since in this case the Rate has a total of 9 numbers, the first three dials are not used and are set to zero; then 2, 4, 9, 9, 7, 7, 4, 4 and 9 are entered in that sequence on the next 9 dials. Note that it is, however, possible to have Rates which incorporate 0, e.g. 301166505334.

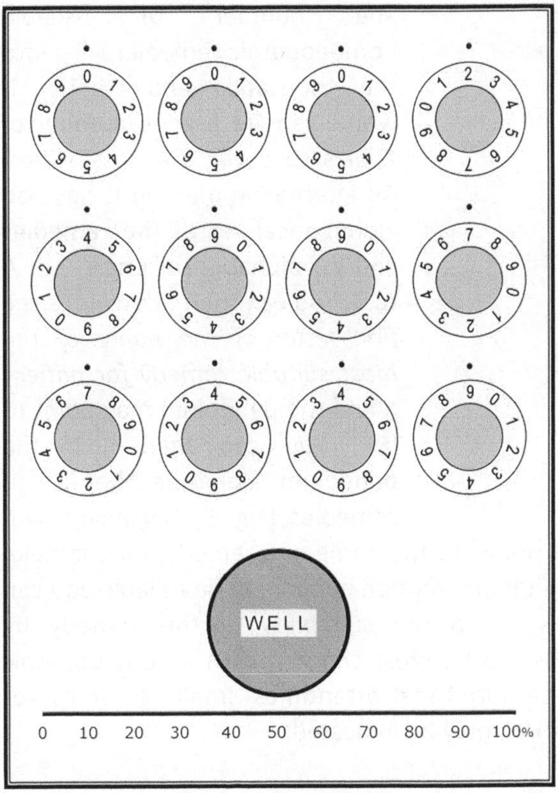

The patient's witness is placed in the well, which is usually a metal dish which may have a depth of 5cm or more. Entrainment of the patient with the instrument will commence as soon as the witness is in place and, using the scale printed beneath the well, the pendulum should indicate that the treatment is needed 100%. After a certain time, for the sake of argument several hours, the percentage by which the patient's need for the treatment may have decreased and this can *be tested again on the* scale and it may

Figure 8: simple 12-dial, Base 10 Radionic instrument

65. Except where indicated the only codes I will give are those developed by myself. 249977449 for Ferrum Phos. is an example of a so-called Base 10 Rate, which means that any one of the numbers 0 - 9 can be found for each position.

now read 70%. The treatment can be continued until the lowest reading is obtained. It should be noted that the amount by which the treatment has been transmitted, say 70%, may not correspond to the amount by which the patient has taken it up, say 40%, i.e. take-up may not be immediate or concurrent with transmission. The patient's reaction to the treatment of course should be noted to see if there is any improvement in the symptoms.

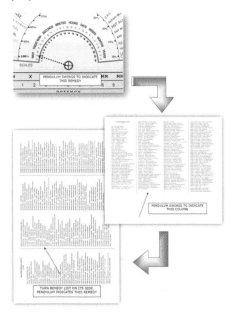

Figure 9:Dowsing in a List

In certain instances there might be a very large number of available options within a particularly category of remedies. The number of useable homoeopathic remedies runs into the thousands and clearly, it would require a good number of Charts to cover the possibilities. An alternative method is have an alphabetical list of the remedies and an alphabetical Chart, i.e. A to Z. You can then ask *what is the first letter of the name of the most suitable remedy for patient X* and the pendulum may point to 'M'. You can then hold the pendulum alongside the list of remedies (Fig. 9) beginning with 'M' and you will find that it points to the name of a remedy, for example, *Mercurius Solubilis*. If the pendulum motion appears to be reliable you can then make further checks as to the suitability of this remedy by Radiesthesic means and this can be cross-checked with a homoeopathic *Materia Medica*. It should be noted that oftentimes 'small' remedies, for which there is little information, may be indicated.

COMPOUND CHARTS

I have given some simple examples of how Charts can be created, but it is also possible to create compound Charts from which much information, potentially, can be obtained. By way of example, the opening analysis chart of the LRI instrument,[66] designed by the author, is shown below (Fig. 10). From even a quick look it should be evident that it is comprised of a central large fan chart linked to a number of sub-charts. Thus, not only can the various sections of the chart be used independently, but they can also be used in combination, to provide, potentially, a large amount of information.

Here we have, in outline, a rather more detailed model of the human Subtle Anatomy showing the main Locations in the outer sector of the Fan, and potential disease-causing impacts to it - the Factors - in the inner sector of the Fan.

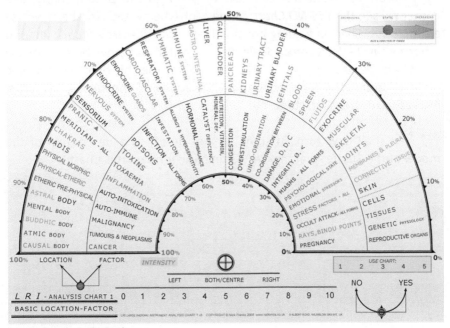

Figure 10:LRI Analysis Chart 1

Directly beneath the left-hand side of the Fan we see a sub-chart indicating Location or Factor, and the pendulum, when placed here, will indicate which of the two sectors should be used. Assume the pendulum indicates Location; this sector of the Fan should be used to make the next reading. You have identified that the outer segment of Locations is the

66. The actual Chart is printed on size A4 paper in colour and housed in a robust Perspex holder. It is one of 5 supplied with the instrument.

one which will provide the immediate answer to the enquiry. The pendulum should then be placed over the crosshairs under the Fan (directly above the words 'Both/Centre') and the practitioner may then ask, for instance, *which Location is most responsible for the patient's current symptoms?*, and the pendulum may indicate 'Liver'.

Using appropriate questions, the pendulum may indicate that the deviation from 0% for the Liver is 90%. You then wish to know what is causing the problem, and will then proceeding to query the Factor sector, which may show that the immediate problem is 'Infection'. Questioning may continue along these lines so that a fuller picture of the situation can be built up.

Various sub-charts can also be seen. In the bottom right-hand corner we see the *YES-NO Chart*; in the centre below the crosshairs we see a simple sub-Chart indicating position (*Left - Both/Centre - Right*); under it a horizontal *0 - 10 Number Scale*. On the outer and inner borders of the Fan Chart we see the *0 - 100% Scale*; and in the top right we a simple graphic intended to indicate *Rate and Direction of Change* e.g. symptom increasing, decreasing, static, etc.

I shall now turn, in some further detail, to a description of the model of the Subtle Anatomy set out in basic form on this Chart.

5: DAVID TANSLEY AND THE DEMATERIALIZATION OF RADIONICS

In 1972 David Tansley published the short book *Radionics & the Subtle Anatomy of Man* and in doing so took Radionics in a new and rather different direction. The situation is summarised in the Introduction:

'If one examines the history and development of Radionics, from the pioneering work of Dr Albert Abrams and Ruth Drown to the latest experimental work at the de la Warr Laboratories, a curious paradox emerges.

Radionics professes to be a method of diagnosis and therapy, which is primarily concerned with the utilization of subtle force fields and energies, for the purpose of investigating and combating the causes of disease which ravage humanity and the other kingdoms of nature. However, in discussions or articles, in the methods of diagnosis or treatment and in the rate books which provide the very core of Radionic therapeutic measures, once finds continual reference to the physical organic systems of man, and precious little of practical value regarding the probability of underlying force fields which might govern and determine the health of the physical form.

It would seem that this unfortunate paradox has emerged because Radionics, which is essentially a paraphysical method of diagnosis and treatment, utilizing the faculty of extra-sensory perception and the concept of 'action at a distance', has predicated its approach to the problems of disease upon a semi-orthodox terminology and rationale....Although both Abrams and Drown treated their patients by means of direct attachment to the instrument....there are references in their writings, even in those early days, which show that diagnosis and treatment at a distance were not only considered, but carried out with effective results....the sequence, if carried to its logical conclusion, leads us ultimately to consider the possibility of utilizing Radionic diagnostic and therapeutic techniques in the light of knowledge derived from the ancient teachings of the East....despite the necessary refinement of techniques and instrumentation over the past twenty-five years, there is a nagging suspicion in my mind that the key implication in the discovery by Abrams and Drown, of diagnosis and treatment at a distance, has been missed.

I believe they pointed the way as far back as 1924, to the concept that man has a body of highly attenuated matter, which he derives from the energy field in the earth, and which links him with all life. This body is referred to in eastern literature as the etheric body.

Today, most if not all radionic practitioners would agree that it is their belief that man does have what is referred to an etheric body. The remarkable thing is that the matter is allowed to rest right there, and the practitioner continues to diagnose and treat in terms of cellular pathology and organic systems....

Man is a series of high frequency energy systems which integrate him into the universal scheme of things. These systems have an anatomy and physiology all of their own, which in the final analysis determine the appearance and activity of the physical form, and diagnosis and treatment can be based on this fact. Abrams and Drown launched this concept, but we have been content to swim along the shoreline ever since, not daring for various reasons to strike out into uncharted waters.

I feel very strongly that the time has come for Radionics to bear witness to the subtle anatomy of man; this I believe to be its innate purpose....'[67]

RUTH DROWN

To illustrate this somewhat further, prior to Tansley, Radionic analysis and treatment was in many respects an analogue of orthodox medicine. Ruth Drown for example, laid great emphasis on treatment of the endocrine glands and system; and she performed blood and urine analysis by Radionic methods. Rates were created for much of the human anatomy, diseases, etc., to be used as required in her H.V.R. (Homo-Vibra Ray) instrument. A series of norms was established and encoded in a set of Rates, and the performance of the body and its systems and structures was tested against these norms. Hence,

'We analyse the normal so that we know the difference between it and the abnormal.'

She sets out what may basically be considered to be an esoteric standpoint quite clearly:

'....the animating Life Force, taken from the ether side....is the energy that creates individuals in all phases of life, and it is the amount of Life Force (which is an invisible light, passing through the brain, the

---

67. David V. Tansley, D.C., (1972). In general Tansley's books are essential reading for the researcher, practitioner and would-be practitioner.

nervous system and the blood vessels) which animates all these bodies, making one human being healthy, and another, through its lack, in a state of dis-ease.'

But then,

'Obviously, a complete and scientifically accurate "blue print" of the condition of a patient's body is of inestimable value to the Doctor. This it is possible to obtain with the H.V.R. instrument, since it may be tuned into any part of the body for measurement of function and for disease....the first step is therefore to register the function of these various organs and glands, and also of the blood vessels and the nervous system. A differential blood count is then made, followed by urinalysis. In addition, the blood pressure, temperature, impinged nerves and diet may be checked on the instrument if desired. This gives a complete ground-work for procedure in diagnosing disease.' [68]

In short (and not at all to denigrate Drown), pretty much what your local polyclinic might do, except that the method is rather different. Following Abrams, Drown considered that all the constituents of the body, disease states, emotional conditions etc have specific vibrational qualities by which they may be identified. She developed a more complex and complete coding system than that used by Abrams, and these codes were collated into an *Atlas of Rates*. Here are a few examples of Drown's Rates:

Anthrax	4019
Anxiety States	90796
Arrhythmias (Cardiac)	
906322810	
Basedow's disease	30665
Bell's Paralysis	5043
Heart	25
Hysteria	70936
Influenza	30822
Liver	48
Lymph Glands	327
Mitral Valve	2567

---

68. Ruth B. Drown, 1982. The first two quotes are from p. 11, Introduction, followed by p. 28, quoting an extract from the H.V.R. Journal, February, 1932.

Pineal Gland	98
Trochlear Nerve	22084
Trigeminal Nerve	22085
Tumors of Spine	508297
Ulcer of Duodenum	30221 [69]

In my understanding a code can only represent one thing, otherwise confusion would certainly occur if it could refer to two or more different things. This unique and exclusive relationship between code and field is, I believe, an essential and axiomatic characteristic of Radionics which underlies all methods used in it. To get things the right way round, it can be proposed that in so far as Radionic codes are a means of representing - or evoking, in appropriate circumstances - the forces and forms of Nature itself, it seems reasonable to suggest that everything in Nature has unique distinguishing characteristics which allow not only the possibility of creating individual codes but also the terms under which they may be created if they are to be of any use. Clearly differences between two similar organisms, let us say two bacteria of the same species, are so small as to be totally insignificant from the point of view of Radionic coding, let alone orthodox microbiology. We may take it that one normally-functioning human pancreas is sufficiently similar to another to allow a standard descriptive code to be established. Thus in such instances it is possible to have a species code (bacterium type x), or an organ code (human pancreas), which is accurate enough, or, effectively, well-enough averaged over all possible specimens, to be usable. However, the more complex an organism the more likely it is to have some degree of individuality and hence the more care is needed when creating a code. One may create a code for 'man' or 'woman' but it will not tell us much about *a* particular man or women, although it is certainly considered possible to create a representative code for *each individual*.

Drown used her Rates as settings on the HVR instrument, the presumption being that when tuned into the patient, any variation from normal functioning in the target organ or process would be detected as there would be a differential between the vibration represented by the Rate and that actually found in the patient, i.e., a disharmony or discordance. Drown's instrument incorporated a stick pad (see Chapter 1); a pendulum was not used. To test the condition of the Lymph Glands the Rate 327 would set on the instrument, and if the 'tuning dial' when set at

---

69. Ruth B. Drown (1951)

'10' produced a 'stick' then the organ being tested was healthy. Any lower reading would progressively indicate reduced vitality or a disease state in the target. Now compare this with Mermet's comments in the opening quote of Chapter 3, *'The pendulum, which reacts in a certain way to radiations emitted by any given body, reacts differently when placed between two bodies which are not similar in composition....it may be assumed that there is some kind or concordance or discordance between.... these bodies....'*. Instead of dowsing between two physical objects, however, the exercise has now moved to a different level, where the *field* of a physical structure (for example the Lymphatic System), represented by a Rate, is compared with that field in the patient, who is represented by his or her witness. Neither system nor patient are physically present. It should also be borne in mind that the patient's Subtle Anatomy is a *totality of fields* of which the Lymphatic System is only part, a sub-field.

TANSLEY AND ALICE BAILEY

Given his conviction as to the real purpose of Radionics, Tansley took it upon himself to change its focus in order to concentrate on the exposition of a method of analysis and treatment based on the presumed non-physical components of the human organism, the so-called Subtle Anatomy. These life-force energies were considered absolutely central to the healthy functioning of the physical body, and the objective of Radionics was now to try and identify and then rectify any disturbances in the life force and thus normalise the flow of energies to the physical system. In so doing, it was hoped, the symptoms or pathology experienced by the patient could be alleviated or removed. Hence I use the term 'dematerialize', because the focus of the therapy was moved away from trying to solve problems by dealing with them on the physical level, to assessing them as disturbances to, or corruptions of, the flow of 'non-physical' energies. The parameters of this system were taken largely from certain esoteric works claiming to expound an occult (hidden) model of the human being. This model had its origins in the philosophy of the Orient and principal among these sources are the writings of Alice A. Bailey, and, most specifically, *Esoteric Healing*.[70]

---

70. Alice A. Bailey (1953). Bailey (1880 - 1949) states that she received her text telepathically from a member of the so-called Hierarchy of Spiritual Masters, D.K. (Djwal Khul, a.k.a. The Tibetan), who during that period was the Abbot of a Lamasery on the borders of Tibet; read the Introduction to *Esoteric Healing* for a little more detail. This

What is immediately relevant are the concepts Tansley took from Bailey and how he incorporated them into the Radionic model. It is clear that Bailey took or developed her ideas, to a greater or lesser extent, from pre-existing Oriental traditions such as Hinduism, Yoga, Ayurveda, and other Asiatic philosophies and disciplines. They are, therefore, an emanation from a much larger, and in many respects earlier, body of thought. These ideas, in my view, can be useably taken apart from certain somewhat political, social, elitist, racist and anti-semitic comments in the Bailey texts which may be disagreeable to the present-day reader.[71]

To give a brief synopsis, Bailey proposed a description of reality as being comprised of seven vast planes of energy, which, viewed from the physical level up, are also finer and finer forms of matter, each with its concomitant forms of consciousness.[72] Each plane is comprised of seven sub-planes, the whole blending into a continuum. Each of these planes (possibly excepting Plane 1) also manifests in each of *us* as a corresponding energy body, e.g. the Etheric Body, Astral Body, and so forth. Simplistically, apart from your physical body, the visible flesh-and-blood construct which enables you to manifest in the physical world, you possess a number of coincident 'higher' bodies which are made up of the material the various higher Planes. The Seven Planes are said to be:

---

series of 24 esoteric books, which took 30 years to write, and of which the centrepiece is *A Treatise on Cosmic Fire*, are considered by some to be a continuation of the works, notably *The Secret Doctrine,* written by Madame Helena Petrovna Blavatsky (1831 - 1891), founder of Theosophy. The present author is not a follower of Bailey, Blavatsky or Theosophy and while there is much of interest in Bailey's work there is a certain amount which, in today's context, may be thought contentious or even offensive.

71. You will judge for yourself. Radionics itself is non-denominational, non-racial and non-sectarian and is open to all. Any attempt to present it as otherwise is a perversion of its aims and ethical position, and is to be rejected.

72. As we know Einstein proposes that matter and energy are interchangeable, and by analogy (e.g. the Hermetic maxim 'as above, so below', implying correspondences at all levels, macrocosm to microcosm) this rule could somehow apply to the proposed higher dimensions, excepting that the conventional limits of physical time and space would be removed or revised. Feasibly Bailey's Planes could be reinterpreted as higher dimensions which are subject to Laws which constitute the 'hidden variables' some seek in Physics, e.g. such as Bohm, or Einstein himself, as suggested by his famous 'God does not play dice' comment. Hence the probabilistic nature of Quantum Mechanics might be viewed as determined by definite Laws when viewed from a higher dimension, and those higher dimensions would, in this model, include consciousness of various forms and degrees of complexity.

1: The Divine Plane
2: The Monadic Plane   (Pure Spirit)
3: The Atmic Plane   (Spiritual Will)
4: The Buddhic Plane   (Higher Intuition)
5: The Manasic Plane   (Mind and qualities of Mind)
6: The Astral Plane   (Emotions and emotional qualities)
7: The Physical Plane [73]

It is important to note that in this schema the Physical Plane is also divided into 7 sub planes, which are denoted, in descending order, the First, Second, Third and Fourth Ethers, sometimes known collectively as the 'Physical-Etheric'; then the 'dense physical' - Gaseous, Liquid, and Solid material. It is these last three which are the visible and measurable constituents of the 'objective' Physical World. It should be noted that the Bailey model appears to pay no attention to the concepts of Quantum Mechanics or that liquid, gas and solid are considered by chemistry to be, basically, different states ('phases') of the same element.

To give the reader a taste of Bailey, we find as follows:

---

73. This is taken from the diagram on p. 117 of *A Treatise on Cosmic Fire* by Bailey (1925), and related text. The diagram is entitled 'The Seven Planes Of Our Solar System' which *in their entirety* are referred to as 'The Cosmic Physical Plane'; of this Bailey states 'the lowest cosmic plane is the cosmic physical, and it is the only one which the finite mind of man can in any way comprehend' (p.116) thus dismissing the attainments and insights of rishis, sages, seers, mystics, philosophers, metaphysicians, scientists, gurus and other investigators throughout the ages. This also directly suggests that there are many more planes above the Cosmic Physical. One may perhaps be forgiven for anticipating that in this model the Cosmic Plenum is a series of Chinese Boxes in gradations of seven, extending incomprehensibly to infinity? I can clearly remember discussing a 'Chinese Box Theory of the Universe' when I was a kid in the playground at school, in fact on the patch of ground where we used to play marbles, and lo and behold, years later one sees the scenario, more or less, animated in the closing sequence of the film *Men In Black* (1997)! Or may we have to agree that Bailey is indeed right? *'A 'true' fundamental theory of the universe may exist but could be just too hard for human brains to grasp'*, said Rees (Lord Rees, former President of the Royal Society and Astronomer Royal) *'just as a fish may be barely aware of the medium in which it lives and swims, so the microstructure of empty space could be far too complex for unaided human brains....there are powerful reasons to suspect that space has a grainy structure but on a scale a trillion trillion times smaller than atoms'*....He adds that there could even be other 3-D universes "embedded alongside ours". *'In theory, there could be another entire universe less than a millimetre away from us, but we are oblivious to it because that millimetre is measured in a fourth spatial dimension and we are imprisoned in just three'*, he said. (Reported in *The Sunday Times*, 13th June 2010, p.11). I am grateful to Charles Bourne for providing me with a copy of this article.

'Man, in essential essence, is the higher triad demonstrating through a gradual evolving form, the egoic or causal body, and utilizing the lower threefold personality as a means to contact the lower three planes. All this has for purpose the development of perfect self-consciousness.'[74]

To expand this slightly, 'the Higher Triad' means the combination of 'Atma-Buddhi-Manas, or spiritual will, intuition and higher mind' which bring into manifestation 'the body egoic or the causal body'. This, in turn, expresses itself in the physical world through the Mental, Astral and (Etheric) Physical bodies.[75] The Causal Body does not originate in any of the Planes but is a construct made by the individual's Higher Self, as is, for example and to a varying degree from person to person, the personality.

Basically, therefore, the human is a combination of spiritual essence, soul's purpose and personality expression. You could consider the Soul as the *quintessence* or *absolute being* of a person, whereas the Higher Ego is the *becoming* of a person, developing through life's experiences. The deeper objective of life is to *align* the Soul's Purpose with that of the Personality via the evolution of the Higher Ego so that the individual, as it were, speaks as one, and, in so doing, becomes *self-realized*. Bailey therefore proposes an esoteric doctrine of self-realization which may, on examination, bear close relation to other Oriental systems. Such a concept is perhaps also somewhat comparable to the psychology of individuation, described by writers such as Jung, Fromm and Maslow as the process by which the individual gradually ceases to become the 'mass man' or 'man in the crowd' and becomes owner of himself. To reiterate, the Soul, or Higher Self (the Higher Triad) is the spiritual essence. This expresses its purpose through the *Higher Ego*, which brings the Causal Body into being as its vehicle. The Personality is the manifestation of the *Lower Ego*. The objective of life is to bring the Lower Ego into a fully harmonious relationship with the Higher Ego.

Personality structure has been studied at length by modern psychology and psychoanalysis, and one depiction is Freud's well-known model, which is centrally comprised of three components, the Ego, the Id, and the Super Ego. These are often in a state of tension with each other as their needs may be in conflict; very approximately, the Id seeks gratification of its demands, which originate in the drives (particularly the

---

74. Bailey (1925) p. 260 - 261
75. Bailey, *op.cit.*, p 261

sex drive); the Ego is the socially-adapted aspect of the personality, which mediates between the demands of the Id and those of the outside world; and the Super Ego is the controlling presence which reins in the other two.[76] Conflicts and tensions between these three foundations of the personality may result in neurosis and other psychological disturbances.

In esoteric psychology, it is considered that the Soul's Purpose and the Personality desires may often be at odds. In addition, therefore, to the ego conflicts described by orthodox psychology, there is a Soul - Personality struggle resulting from efforts of the Higher Self to bring the Lower Self into alignment with its objectives. Orthodox psychology, for all of its complexity, might be viewed as a subsection of a much larger, esoterically-oriented developmental psychology of self-realization.

ESOTERIC AND MATERIALIST VIEWS OF EVOLUTION

The Bailey model is certainly nothing if not evolutionary but it is *consciousness which drives evolution*, and not the reverse, as in, for example, Neo-Darwinism, where consciousness is an end-product, or even by-product, of the evolutionary process and originates only in the material substrate of the physical body. For example,

'One way of dramatizing it is to parody an ancient anti-Darwinian sentiment: the monkey's uncle. Would you want your daughter to marry a robot? Well, if Darwin is right, your great-great-....grandmother was a robot! ....Can it be that if you put enough of these dumb homunculi together you make a real conscious person? The Darwinian says there could be no other way of making one. Now, it certainly does not follow from the fact that you are descended from robots that you are a robot....but unless dualism or vitalism is true (in which case you have some extra, secret ingredient in you) you are made of robots - or what comes to the same thing, a collection of trillions of macromolecular machines [i.e. cells]....So something made of robots can exhibit genuine consciousness, or genuine intentionality, because you do if anything does.' [77]

---

76. See Freud's *An Outline of Psychoanalysis* in Phillips (2006)

77. Dennett (1995) (*Darwin's Dangerous Idea*), p. 206. As the present author understands it neo-Darwinian evolution has no intention, motive, goal or objective; there is just *what happens* as a result of 'natural selection' and 'survival of the fittest', the two motors which drive it along. There it produces dinosaurs; here it produces *homo sapiens*; and presumably somewhere in the Universe (maybe closer than we think) it might produce *homo dinosaurus*!

In Bailey's terms evolution in general, and human evolution in particular, is teleological, in that an ultimate purpose pulls the evolutionary process towards it; part of that purpose is the fully-awakened man, in whom all major Chakras are completely opened and energized. The result is that the individual is fully conscious on all levels of existence, the Chakras being the energy centres in the subtle anatomy through which the human progressively contacts the consciousness typical of the various planes. It should be added that in this esoteric model of the self, the disparity or *friction* between the Soul's Purpose and the Personality's desires is considered to be a possible fundamental cause of illness. Again, in many persons conflict may be experienced between Soul's Purpose and developing Higher Ego on the one hand, and Personality on the other. The triumphs and reverses of life may be thought at least in part to result from attempts to connect with, understand, and act on one's life's purpose and to reconcile it with the (ego-centred) demands of the Personality. If the Bailey model is followed then a fundamental objective of Radionic treatment is, as far as possible, to help align, re-align, or reconcile Soul and Personality - an ambitious task in the context of the dynamic and developing situation of the individual human life.

CHAKRAS

Responding to Bailey's lead, Tansley makes 'centre therapy' the keystone of his new therapeutic approach, i.e. treatment of the Chakras. Tansley quotes Bailey as follows:

'The new medical science will be outstandingly built upon the science of the centres, and upon this knowledge all diagnosis and possible cure will be based.' [78]

Nowadays the concept of Chakras, or energy centres, is quite well-known, although the actual intricate details are not, the subject being extremely complex. One of the earliest introductions in the West to the concept of Chakras came with the publication in 1918 of *The Serpent Power: The Secrets of Tantric and Shaktic Yoga* by Arthur Avalon (Sir John Woodroffe, 1865 - 1936), a British Orientalist. This complex and scholarly work is a translation of, and commentary on, certain ancient Tantric documents describing the Chakras and the raising of Kundalini energy, said

---

78. Tansley, 1972, p. 66. Tansley does not give a page reference for this quote from *Esoteric Healing* and although I searched through the book I was unable to find it.

to lie dormant at the base of the spine. The back cover of my copy states:

'For centuries this material was a closely guarded secret in India; even native scholars were not allowed access to it. In fact, it was so restricted that many Indologists refused to recognize its existence. It took half a lifetime of searching by Sir John Woodroffe to locate the key documents...the result of Woodroffe's work, however, was one of the most important developments in Indian thought, a key to many areas of art and religion that had hitherto been locked. It is also a work that has great interest to Westerners who wish to acquire for themselves the validity of the ultimate experience.' [79]

The idea is that embedded in the subtle bodies are a number of energy transmission and circulation centres known as Chakras; some accounts give the total number as being around 360. Of primary interest in the Bailey model are the 7 Major Chakras, which are located in a series ascending the spinal column and into the head. As the individual develops and his or her awareness reaches a more sophisticated level, so each Chakra 'opens' and becomes receptive to energy flowing from higher and higher sources of consciousness emanating from the different planes. As a consequence there is considered to be a definite direction of progress up the 'ladder' of the Chakras. Although each Chakra is operational to some degree in practically everyone in order to maintain normal life functions, the 'developed' human displays Chakras which are increasingly vivified (energized) and with higher rotational speed. Each Major Chakra is also said to 'externalize' through one of the (physical) endocrine glands and affect a certain region of the body, and the state of the Chakra is considered to condition the functioning of the associated gland and local anatomy, i.e. the quality of health depends upon the quality of the Chakras. This system can be basically set out as in Table 1 (below)

The full table can be seen on p. 45 of *Esoteric Healing*; I have left out some of the more cryptic material in order to simplify matters for the reader's understanding. I have also slightly changed the order, in that Heart and Throat Chakras are switched in the original sequence. This is not to correct the original but because I am trying to explain the sequence in a basic logical manner. The opening of the Heart Chakra would, presumably,

---

[79]. Nowadays there is a plethora of books available on the subject of Chakras - for example, *The Chakra Handbook* by Sharamon and Baginski (1991) - but I think that *The Serpent Power* would be the place to start a study of this arcane subject.

be considered to be of a higher level of attainment than the opening of the Throat Chakra, which is why it is placed higher in the original diagram.

CHAKRA	GLAND	REGION	TYPE OF FORCE (ENERGY)
CROWN (top of head)	PINEAL	UPPER BRAIN, RIGHT EYE	SPIRITUAL WILL, SYNTHETIC, DYNAMIC
AJNA (brow - between eyes)	PITUITARY	LOWER BRAIN, LEFT EYE, NOSE, NERVOUS SYSTEM	SOUL FORCE, LOVE, MAGNETIC, LIGHT, INTUITION, VISION
THROAT	THYROID	RESPIRATORY SYSTEM, DIGESTIVE TRACT	CREATIVE ENERGY, SOUND, SELF-CONSCIOUSNESS
HEART	THYMUS	HEART, BLOOD, CIRCULATORY SYSTEM, VAGUS NERVE	LIFE FORCE, GROUP CONSCIOUSNESS
SOLAR PLEXUS	PANCREAS	STOMACH, LIVER, GALL BLADDER, NERVOUS SYSTEM	EMOTION, DESIRE, TOUCH, ASTRAL FORCE
SACRAL	GONADS	SEX ORGANS	LIFE FORCE, VITAL ENERGY, PHYSICAL PLANE FORCE, ANIMAL LIFE FORCE
BASE OF SPINE	ADRENALS	KIDNEYS, SPINAL COLUMN	WILL ENERGY, UNIVERSAL LIFE, KUNDALINI

Table 1: Basic chakra correspondences

It can be added that the order of development and vitalization of the Chakras, beginning with the Base Chakra and moving upwards, may also be thought to correspond to the expression (and progressive satisfaction) of needs. Some equivalence with the ideas of psychology and psychoanalysis can be suggested. In the Base and Sacral Chakras particularly, we are said to find the energy of drives and instincts - the basic will to exist, to survive, to hold one's own, to prevail over others, to procreate, to protect offspring, and so on - often experienced as barely-controllable forces which are inextricably linked with what some may call the 'animal' in us. The Solar Plexus Chakra is the centre of wants, desires, emotions - in over-excited form, the seat of the endless desires of the often-insatiable, over stimulated and ever-needful personality. Progressing to the higher Chakras, we enter the realm of self-development, artistic and creative expression, individualization, self-sacrifice and spiritual enlightenment.

A well-known example of an 'ideal' progression is Maslow's 'Hierarchy of Needs', according to which human needs can be subdivided into 5 basic groups, these being, in ascending order of satisfaction: Physiological, Security, Social, Esteem and Self-Actualisation. The satisfaction of the lower level of needs enables the human to progress towards the next level; this hierarchy could be correlated with the attributes of the Chakras.[80] It may be thought that certain aspects of action, reaction and dysfunction in the lowest three Chakras mirror, in energetic form, the psychology of Freud, with his emphasis on sex and the origins of neurosis in conflicts affecting the orderly or normal development of the sexual orientation. Jung, focusing on the problem of individuation may be thought by some to be the 'prophet' of the development of the higher Chakras, Heart through Crown.

It should not be thought that the progression through the Chakras is necessarily ordered or smooth; in many people there is a chaotic interplay of conflicting states and imbalanced energy flows between Chakras which are visible in the personality as contradictions, conflicts, neurosis, complexes, inconsistencies and psychological and emotional difficulties of many types.

PRANA

The final point stressed by Tansley is that vitalization of the human system through the correct reception of *prana*, or life-force energy, is essential for the building and maintenance of the Etheric Body and, consequently, the 'dense' Physical Body. Prana is received through certain minor chakras on the upper torso and then is collected into the Spleen Chakra and is distributed through the so-called Pranic Triangle:

---

80. Abraham Maslow (1908 - 1970), founder of humanistic psychology. *'It is as if Freud supplied us with the sick half of psychology and we must now fill it out with the healthy half.'* Maslow (1999) p.7 See also Chapter 8 of this book.

'The spleen chakra which is that centre of force so closely related to vitality, is not a major spinal chakra. Its role is to supply vital energy to all the chakras on all levels of the personality or lower self. It is not directly related to those energies which sweep man into a state of spirituality by way of the major centres....The receptive apparatus for prana consists primarily of three force centres. The best known is the spleen chakra; in addition to this there is another chakra situated just below the diaphragm, and a third lies between the shoulder blades just above the heart chakra....they....are linked by a triple thread of energy to form a triangle of force known as the pranic triangle. Prana enters the etheric body through minor force centres found throughout the upper part of the torso. It is then drawn down to the spleen chakra, and enters to circulate through the triangle formed through the three chakras. Before being discharged from the spleen centre to vitalize the etheric body, the prana is subjected to a process that regulates its potency. If the organism is a healthy one, its vibratory rate will be stepped up. If the health of the individual is poor, then the rate of potency will be stepped down, so that the vitalizing rate of prana will not disrupt the etheric body.'[81]

In fact descriptions of a putative vital force have been made for thousands of years and prana seems to be but one of many names used by many cultures, famously *Qi* (Ch'i) in the Chinese tradition, and the *Orgone* energy of Wilhelm Reich (1897 - 1857). But the question as to what this energy is, and whether there are one, several or *any* such energies outside of those described by physics, needs to be clarified. As an example of the range of possibilities, Dr. Yang, Jwing-Ming, tells us:

'Qi is the energy or natural force that fills the universe. The Chinese have traditionally believed that there are three major powers in the universe. These Three Powers (San Cai) are Heaven (Tian), Earth (Di), and Man (Ren). Heaven (the sky or universe), has Heaven Qi (Tian Qi), the most important of the three, which is made up of the forces the heavenly bodies exert on the earth, such as sunshine, moonlight, the moon's gravity, and the energy from the stars....every energy field strives to stay in balance, so whenever the Heaven Qi loses its balance, it tries to rebalance itself. Then the wind must blow, rain must fall, even tornadoes or hurricanes become necessary in order for Heaven Qi to reach a new energy balance. Under Heaven Qi is Earth Qi....The Chinese believe that Earth Qi is made up of

---

81. Tansley, op. cit., p. 54 - 55.

lines and patterns of energy, as well as the earth's magnetic field and the heat concealed underground. These energies must also balance, otherwise disasters such as earthquakes will occur....Finally, within the Earth Qi, each individual person, animal and plant has its own Qi field, which always seeks to be balanced....Qi can also be defined as any type of energy which is able to demonstrate power and strength. This energy can be electricity, magnetism, heat, or light...Qi is also commonly used to express the energy state of something, especially living things...when something is alive, it has vital Qi (Huo Qi)....the word Qi can represent the energy itself, [but] it can even be used to express the manner or state of the energy...if we think carefully about what we know from science today we can see that (except possibly for gravity) there is actually only one type of energy in this Universe, and that is electromagnetic energy (electromagnetic waves)....this makes it very clear that the Qi circulating in our bodies is actually "bioelectricity" and that our body is a "living electromagnetic field". This field is affected by our thoughts , feelings, activities, the food we eat, the quality of air we breathe, our life-style, the natural energy that surrounds us, and also the unnatural energy which modern science inflicts upon us.' [82]

In this description Qi seems to take a multitude of forms, some of which are covered by modern physics and some of which are not, for example, unless you believe that consciousness in all its aspects is purely a product of the action and interaction of the nervous system i.e. a material phenomenon, then of what types of energy, for example, are *'thoughts'*, *'feelings'* and the *'natural energy that surrounds us'* (in contrast to *'the unnatural energy which modern science inflicts upon us'*) made? The terms Qi and energy are used here interchangeably in a wide range of applications but what we need is something which helps us understand Qi, or prana, as a force in itself. James DeMeo, a long-time student of the work of Wilhelm Reich (1897 - 1957), asserts that Orgone energy has a distinct form with its own characteristics:

'Orgone energy is cosmic life force energy, the fundamental creative force long known to people in touch with nature, and speculated about by natural scientists, but now physically objectified and demonstrated....For instance the orgone energy charges and radiates from all living and non-living substances. It can also readily penetrate all forms

---

82. Dr.Yang, Jwing-Ming (2003), p. 6 - 8

of matter....All materials affect the orgone energy, by attracting and absorbing it, or by repelling and reflecting it. The orgone can be seen, felt, measured and photographed. It is a real physical energy....[it] exists in a free form in the atmosphere, and in the vacuum of space....It is a ubiquitous medium, a cosmic ocean of dynamic, moving energy, which interconnects the whole physical universe; all living creatures, weather systems, and planets respond to its pulsations and movements. The orgone is related to, but quite different from other forms of energy. It can, for instance, impart a magnetic charge to ferromagnetic conductors, but it is not magnetic itself....It reacts with great disturbance to radioactive materials, or to harsh electromagnetism, much in the manner of irritated protoplasm. It can be registered on specially-adapted Geiger counters. The orgone is also the medium through which electromagnetic disturbances are transmitted, much in the manner of the older concept of aether, though it is not in itself electromagnetic in nature. Streams of orgone energy within the Earth's atmosphere affect changes in air circulation patterns; atmospheric orgone functions underlie the build-up of storm potentials, and influence air temperature, pressure, and humidity. Cosmic orgone energy functions also appear to be at work in space, affecting gravitational and solar phenomena. Still, the mass-free orgone energy is not any one of the physico-mechanical factors, or even the sum of them....it is primary, primordial cosmic life energy, while all other forms of energy are secondary in nature. In the living world, orgone energy functions underlie major life processes; pulsation, streaming, and charge of biological orgone determines the movements, actions and behavior of protoplasm and tissues....Both organism and weather respond to the prevailing character and state of the life energy. Orgone energy functions appear across the whole of creation, in microbes, animals, stormclouds, hurricanes and galaxies. Orgone energy not only charges and animates the natural world; we are immersed in a sea of it....it is the medium which communicates emotion and perception, through which we are connected to the cosmos, and made kin to all that is living.' [83]

To this I can add that in my experience an emanation, often rather delicate, sometimes perhaps called the aura, is clearly visible round many people, plants and even objects. It can be seen with the naked eye, varies considerably in size and intensity, its visibility changes considerably according to light conditions, time of day, location, and subject of

---

83. James DeMeo, Ph.D. (1989), p. 11 - 12. Comparatively, see also Wachsmuth (1932).

observation, and generally looks like a featureless transparent halo of shining light with a diffuse boundary. It can sometimes be seen around the whole body as a kind of shimmering ovoid. On occasion colours may also be observed. A vertical 'v' shape is sometimes visible at the top the head, often extending several feet upwards, and as a person walks past the line of sight a 'smearing' of the field may sometimes be seen. Most of these phenomena can also be captured on film and by digital imaging, both still and moving, as they are visible in many photographs and other visual media. This indeed suggests that some part or all of this field is at least partially within the visible light spectrum. Of all the 'subtle energy' phenomena described in this book, this is the one which, in the author's mind, most definitely exists beyond a shadow of doubt - unless, in fact, it is an unnoticed or undiscovered (by science) 'normal' component of 'physical' light.

Assuming therefore that some degree of general correspondence is allowable between these different depictions of the vital force, and if DeMeo is correct that it has a physical presence which at least partially interacts with the forces described by physics, then it is proposed for present purposes that prana is central to energizing those structures in the Subtle Anatomy - the Etheric Body and its various levels, Chakras, Nadis, and Meridians - which are primarily involved in the process of bringing form into manifestation. As a consequence establishment of the correct and balanced flow of prana must be an essential part of the therapeutic effort in Radionics. The feeling of vitality considered a part of 'wellness' comes partially from the optimal functioning of the physical systems proper and partially from the optimal performance of those systems, such as the Chakras and Etheric Body, which allow the physical body proper to come into existence. There are many instances where the patient 'checks out' perfectly according to orthodox medical analysis and yet has no 'energy', an example being various types of fatigue illnesses where no obvious aetiology can be discerned. In such cases one may suggest that a possible causation may be defects in the system of capture and distribution of prana throughout the organism.

THE RESULT: CENTRE THERAPY

Tansley's objective is a much simpler system of analysis and treatment the so-called centre (Chakra) therapy. Instead of a lengthy and laborious investigation of the components and micro-components of the physical system - cells, tissues, organs, fluids, and so on - the Radionic practitioner following this approach analyses the patient's major Chakras and Spleen Chakra and in doing so discovers any Factors considered to be impeding their proper function.[84] The key idea is that by working with the Chakras primarily, the treatment corrects the problems at source, rather than in their manifesting form of the symptoms and pathology experienced and displayed by the patient. These latter are considered to be 'downstream', *effects* resulting from a disturbance higher up the proposed chain of causation, and can be corrected by appropriate adjustments to the Chakras:

'The centre therapist....utilizes the subtle force system of man as his point of departure for analysis and treatment. The physical organic systems are of secondary importance, because they can only respond to and reflect the measure of harmony found in the paraphysical bodies....unless the chakras are functioning in a reasonably balanced and harmonious manner, there never can be an expression of health upon the physical level. Recognizing this, the practitioner aims his treatment specifically at those chakras which exhibit a state of imbalance. By normalizing their action and removing blockages, he enables the energies which are seeking expression through the low self to have free play, thus restoring health to the organism.'* [85]

Tansley's basic therapeutic solution is colour, Radionically given:

'These colours are supplied through the use of cinemoid material which is mounted in 35mm film holders. These fit into the colour slot of the [Tansley's] Mark III instrument, and light is used to carry colour over the resonators and the patient sample located in the centre of the sample chamber. Colour has been found to be the most effective healing agent for this particular form of radionic therapy. Homoeopathic remedies in glass ampoules and radionic healing rates are used to a much lesser degree.'* [86]

Tansley continued to develop his methods and by the time of his last book, *Chakras-Rays and Radionics* (1984) he had described a more complex picture of the human energetic system, problems which can occur in it, and techniques by which it can be treated. The reader should

---

84. Since there will be a lengthy discussion of Factors later in the book, I will not delay the reader with anything on the subject at this point.
85. Tansley, *op.cit.*, p. 76
86. Tansley, *op.cit.*, p.76

21st Century Radionics

peruse this book and Tansley's other later work at leisure; aspects of what are said in it and more will be covered in the following chapters.

THE PRESENT SITUATION

I think it reasonable to say that in spite of the progress of modern medicine the disease challenge has not at all diminished. Some terrifying 'old' diseases, such as smallpox, have indeed disappeared as a result of herculean medical efforts,[87] but there are new problems, such as AIDS and Chronic Fatigue Syndrome, increases in Cancers, Autism, Multiple Sclerosis, Obesity and Diabetes, stress-related psychological disorders, ADHD (Attention Deficit/Hyperactivity Disorder), problems arising from the mass abuse of pleasure drugs, the not-originally anticipated development of antibiotic-resistant bacteria, the possibility of new epidemics developing from organisms such as Ebola or SARS virus, Lyme disease, Morgellon's disease, an anticipated and much-feared new and deadly influenza pandemic, a massive increase in the range and number of allergies, a vicious return of the 'old' venereal diseases, the increase in background radiation and environmental pollution, the development of chronic diseases such as COPD (Chronic Obstructive Pulmonary Disease); and so it goes and on and on. There is no shortage of potential trouble. It must surely ring true that if all the solutions to humanity's ailments were to be found in the Doctor's surgery, no-one would be knocking on the door of the very many therapists offering a non-orthodox approach. The fact remains, and in spite of the often-withering and well-publicized criticism of it from some quarters of orthodoxy, that alternative and complementary medicine is growing in popularity and increasing numbers of people are seeking it out. Part of this also results from a fear of modern medicine and the side effects of its drugs, and suspicion at the motives and methods of some of the large organizations involved in drug sales and development. Perhaps in time orthodox medicine will solve many of the outstanding disease problems via in-depth study of derangements in the genetic structure and gene expression and in doing so render other

---

87. While only an idiot would argue that to rid humanity of a scourge such as smallpox is not a great thing, from a pure Darwinian aspect it seems to me that elimination of a successful species from the 'struggle for existence' automatically creates a very good opportunity for less-successful competitors to rapidly evolve (or adapt?) to the now more-advantageous circumstances. One may be drawn to think that under this schema the appearance of new diseases would be inevitable, the increasingly-sophisticated interventions of man notwithstanding - or even, unfortunately, contributing? See Darwin (1859) (1968), for instance Chapter III, *The Struggle For Existence*.

therapies irrelevant. It is not yet known. I cannot judge which side is correct, cannot say what the future will bring, and in any event the debate - one is almost tempted to say the *struggle* - is already prosecuted furiously enough.

Keeping my attention on my corner of the patch, around the year 2000 I concluded that a revision and recapitulation of the Radionic model was required - not to destroy or denigrate the work of those who have gone before, but to try and build on it as best as possible and bring it to a higher level of coherence and usefulness, the objective being to attempt to meet some of the therapeutic challenges brought by the patients themselves. It seemed clear that centre therapy alone had not met its promise, that the abandonment of attempts to deal with the paraphysical counterpart fields of the body's structures was premature, and that the effects of problems in regions of the Subtle Anatomy other than the Chakras had been somewhat neglected. This is not to say that centre therapy failed; one possibility is that the therapeutic problem posed by Chakra treatment alone is far more complex than realised by Tansley and until this problem is solved we will have to resort to a more varied range of approaches. One may think that the complexity of the Chakra system will not fully yield to relatively simple techniques such as those proposed by him. It is not necessarily true that Radionic practitioners were not aware of the overall situation, but to my knowledge no - as it were - unified and systematic reconceptualization had been proposed and this seems to remain the *status quo*. In the following Chapters I make an approaching to revising the situation.

6: HUMAN SUBTLE ANATOMY

'We must always bear in mind that the planes do not tower up one above another into the empyrean like the storeys of a building, but are conditions of being, states of existence of different types, and though they developed successively in time, they occur simultaneously in space; existence of all types being present in a single being, as we realise when we remember that the being of man is made up of a physical body, emotions, mind, and spirit, all occupying the same space at the same time.'

Dion Fortune, *The Mystical Qabalah*, p. 38[88]

As a direct consequence of Tansley's work Radionics appears to have accepted the proposition that the human originates in higher consciousness as a soul or spirit energy. Through evolutionary processes in evolutionary time this manifests in a physical form, that of the human being. In order to do so it employs a number of 'bodies' of manifestation which, as briefly described above, perform various functions necessary to the expression of that which is us. To repeat, Tansley states:

I feel very strongly that the time has come for Radionics to bear witness to the subtle anatomy of man; this I believe to be its innate purpose....[89]

Now I happen to disagree with this, in the sense that I consider that Radionics is first and foremost a therapeutic discipline which aims to reduce the burden of disease and suffering in humans (and other organisms, such as animals) and *this* is its innate purpose. Radionics works by entraining defined and specific energy fields, or, perhaps more accurately, code-identified vibrational patterns (waveforms), which are used to counter vibrational disturbances in the subtle anatomy. These corrective waveforms, I propose, find their origins in a putative 'universal information field' and can be described and evoked *more*, or *less,* accurately according to the calibre of the codes made to represent them.

---

88. Dion Fortune (1987) (first published 1935). Although I am not a Qabalist (Kabbalist) I like Dion Fortune's work; she appears to start from the position of being *one of us*, with no claims to special insider knowledge. *The Mystical Qabalah* is the only book I have read about this subject and it may, or may not, agree with the interpretations of the Jewish sages and mystics.
89. Tansley (1977)

Radionics then, is not here to bear witness to anything except that which it can demonstrate, and, if it *can* demonstrate that the proposed model of the subtle anatomy of man, or something like it, is a viable approximation of reality, then well and good; but if we commence with the presupposition that it is some form of exercise in demonstrating the validity of a particular metaphysical construct or esoteric doctrine, then we face the possibility of painting ourselves into a corner with our preconceptions. Under such circumstances we are not doing therapy but an experiment in metaphysics, and this is not what the patient usually comes to Radionics for. Granted that we have incorporated the general idea of the Subtle Anatomy into Radionic thinking and that therefore a model of this is required for analytical and treatment purposes, but like any other model, be it in science or any other discipline, it is only as good as the results it produces and if found deficient, it should be modified accordingly. In this regard it is, however, worth noting Tansley's comments in Chapter 2 of *Dimensions of Radionics*. Briefly,

'*We must look for the "commonality of factors" and seek where there is agreement, learning in this process to determine the "idiosyncratic factors" which have been built in by this guru or that guru or 'because my master says this or that'. There are authorities in the basic spiritual teachings of the world, the Bible, the Vedas, the Upanishads, and the Tao to name a few which are superior to any latter-day promoters of truth....I have found that the model put forward by Theosophy, and presented later in much greater detail by Alice A. Bailey in her writings, carries within it many 'commonality factors' and can be seen to agree with most other systems.'* [90]

If we purport to be able to treat some form of ill-health then the objective, whether achievable or not, must be the removal of clinically-

---

90. *Dimensions*, page 18. So far and so good, but, '*cuius est solum eius est usque ad coelum et ad inferos*' (for whoever owns the soil, it is theirs up to Heaven and down to Hell). There are those, for example in the Evangelical Christian movement, who regard the New Age (and certainly Alice Bailey as progenitrix) as the spawn of Satan and part of a supposed Luciferian-Illuminati world-domination conspiracy. See for example Cumbey (1985) 'It is the contention of this writer that for the first time in history there is a viable movement - the New Age Movement - that truly meets all the scriptural requirements for the antichrist and the political movement that will bring him on the world scene.'; or from an Orthodox Jewish point of view, see the website http://philologos.org/__eb-trs/naF.htm (*The Rainbow Swastika*). Bailey's work may have much to offer, and for the time being we will follow Tansley's lead to a certain degree, but irrespective of this Radionics is not some kind of fifth column for the New Age.

discernible ('real') symptoms and pathology. An infection or some other form of pathology can in principal be measured by standard medical techniques and its removal could be confirmed by those same methods, if the creation of such forms of evidence was thought desirable or relevant. To measure the reduction or change in a psychological or emotional state is rather more subjective, although in general freedom from adverse reaction to a previously-provocative stimulus might be considered to be a good start. Take for example a phobia; if the patient had a fear of spiders but after treatment no longer has that fear then there is a clear change in the psychological position. Similarly if the patient has an allergy and treatment reduces or removes the allergic response, demonstrably when exposure to the allergen takes place, then it is reasonable to presume that there has been an effect. In short, it is feasible that a range of possible tests could indicate that such non-material techniques as are used in Radionics actually do produce effects in the physical world. Such results would tend to support the proposition that there are supra-physical levels of reality, and these levels may indeed be shown to correspond to some significant extent to those proposed by Tansley. This in turn could be used to justify his integration of Bailey's work into Radionics, but this is a different matter entirely from an *a priori* acceptance of Bailey's ideas. Nevertheless, my conclusion is that the basic conceptual leap which Tansley took into a dematerialised version of Radionics opens the door to a very wide range of treatment and investigative possibilities, as I hope becomes clear from this book.

MODELLING THE SUBTLE ANATOMY

In order to give the practitioner a coherent framework in which to perform analysis and treatment , we need to define the parameters, the 'chunks' into which we can subdivide the subtle energy fields of man. Because these are neither static nor isolated but active and interactive, both with each other and, to a greater or lesser extent, the external environment the reader should not understand them as if they are rigid structures or separate 'boxes' without interaction - a trap it would be all too easy to fall into. What follows is an attempt at a useable description, the objective being to set out a general framework in which a) the supra-physical forces and energies of consciousness and b) the paraphysical, morphogenetic energies underlying form can be correlated c) with the structures and pathways through which they are thought to flow. These, it is proposed, are the means by which the self-conscious being, the human, manifests in, and experiences, the physical world.

Effectively, from the Radionic point of view, human existence and evolution is, ultimately, consciousness-driven. In practical terms, and although the matter is exceedingly complex, it is the quality of these forces and energies which determines the calibre of the physical body; and it is deficiencies in, or insults to these energies which are involved in the type of illness which the individual may have or to which he or she may be susceptible.

Some of the basic energies to be considered as essential to the functioning of the human system are:

1. Soul Energy, manifesting through the Subtle Bodies;
2. Ray Energy, co-opted by the Soul;[91]
3. Vital Force (Prana), vitalising the paraphysical structures;
4. Magnetic Radiant Energy, vitalising the Aura;
5. the forces and fields described by science, particularly physics;
6. the energy systems described by orthodox medicine, e.g. bio-electric and bio-chemical energy - such as the Krebs (Citric Acid) Cycle - and so forth.

Item 6. in particular will not be dealt with to any extent as these systems and processes are described in detail in the medical textbooks. It should be borne in mind, however, that the calibre of functioning of the biological systems of the body may be much qualified by the flow of subtle energies.

It should also be re-emphasised that the Planes as depicted by Bailey and outlined here are said to have a reality in much the same way as the physical plane. They are considered to be made of 'finer' matter than physical matter and are much more plastic to the related forces of consciousness. Thus emotional states have an immediate effect on the astral material and will rapidly 'colour' it with positive or negative emotions. That these other planes should have a real existence or even *any* existence may seem far-fetched but the reader should absolutely bear in mind that some modern theoretical physicists propose, with the utmost seriousness, the existence of multiple parallel universes and, in the case of

---

91. I will deal with the concept of the Rays in due course but basically, the Rays may be thought of as absolutely fundamental qualities or characteristics which permeate everything in manifestation. For immediate purposes a parallel of sorts might be found in the 5-Element (*Wu Xing*) Theory of Traditional Chinese Medicine (Fire - Earth - Metal - Water - Wood).

string theory, an extra number of dimensions (possibly as many as 26). Although the existence of additional universes and dimensions has yet to be demonstrated, it is fair to say that we all know very well what emotions (Astral Plane), states of mind (Mental Plane) and 'Soul' Music are.

Figure 11 (below) depicts this extended model of the human energy system in the form of a flow chart. Although this simplified presentation is for explanatory purposes only, nevertheless, the divisions shown here can be used as Locations in Radionic analysis (see Appendix 1 for a listing).

SOUL ENERGY
Broadly based on Tansley but with some extensions, Soul Energy can be considered as taking the following route on its path into manifestation through the human form:

Soul, Spiritual Will, manifesting through the ATMIC BODY;
Higher Intuition, manifesting through the BUDDHIC BODY;
Egoic Lotus (Higher Ego), manifesting through the means of the CAUSAL BODY;
Mind, manifesting through the MENTAL BODY, particularly as psychology and intellect;
Emotions and the Emotional Self, manifesting through the ASTRAL BODY;
The underlying template of the physical form, the ETHERIC BODY, subdivided into
PHYSICAL-MORPHIC FIELDS, and
MERIDIANS and related structures, such as acupuncture points.
The Etheric Body and related fields will be discussed in the following Chapter.

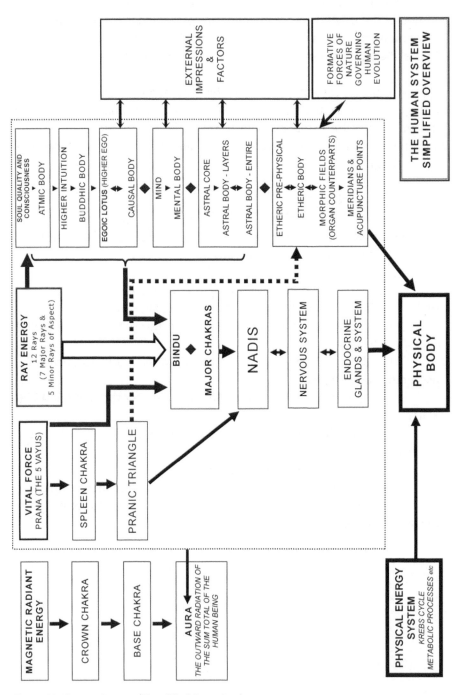

Figure 11: Human System (Simplified Overview)

ATMIC BODY

The idea of the Soul has existed in various conceptualizations for thousands of years, probably since time immemorial. Some interpretations view the Soul and the Body as inimical, the body with its instincts and drives being the enemy of the spiritual part of the human, hence, for example, mortification; denial of the needs and desires of the flesh; philosophies, dogmas and doctrines of oppression using guilt, fear and shame, etc., in certain religions and philosophies. In the system proposed by Bailey the developing self awareness of the Soul struggles with the Personality in order to overcome the Personality's egocentric tendencies, culminating in complete identification or unification of the individual with their Soul and in doing so entirely overcoming the self-centred traits of the Personality - the *development of perfect self-consciousness* mentioned in the previous Chapter.[92] Bailey supports the doctrine of reincarnation, and within this context, the process of harmonization of Soul's Purpose with the Personality can take many lifetimes.

The Radionic practitioner, however, working at a more mundane level, has to deal with the patient as he or she *is*. We are not here to either impose or suggest a route to self-realisation; we are not here to make you a superman. Although Radionic treatment may be used, potentially, to reinforce positive traits, the more general objective of the therapy is to attempt to remove blockages and disturbances in the subtle bodies which inhibit the person's inner life or physical health; the two are often closely intertwined. Each patient *is where he or she is at*. The argument, for instance, as to whether there is some kind of route map of progress towards divine self-realisation or whether there is only absolute death, the obliteration of any sense of personal consciousness, life ends and that is that - this is a secondary matter. What the person chooses to believe or follow is a matter for them; from the practitioner's point of view the disruptions of the flow of energy in the subtle anatomy, and manifesting symptoms and diseases which may be linked to them, can be thought of to a goodly extent as *objective* phenomena. For example I find so far no indication in psychology that neurosis is limited to any particular type of person, societal structure or religious creed. Different religions, social structures or persons may produce a different *character* of neurosis according, on the one hand, as to how the religion or the society prescribes the negative or the prohibition, the boundaries which must not

---

92. See for example Bailey (1953) p. 506 - 7.

be transgressed, and, on the other, how the individual incorporates the rules into his psyche such that a psychological conflict might result.

Hence the person's *soul quality*, if such an expression may be used, is found such as it is in the patient's present state; as opposed to their soul *potential,* the expression of which lies in the future. Treatment may facilitate development of such potential, but cannot make more of the patient than he himself is capable. The process of life may also bring him to a much enriched soul quality as a result of experience and as a result of how he uses that experience to reach a deeper state of self-understanding. But in order to get to *there*, he may need help getting beyond *here,* where he may be stuck. The Soul, *ultimately*, may be considered to have both personal and transpersonal aspects and to be the highest aspect of the self as a totality, and its purpose is to express its divine prerogative through creative work of the highest order in the lower manifested (physical) worlds; but for present purposes, it is the highest sense of self you can experience as far as you are capable at the present time. There might be limitless possibilities for development inherent in a human life, but the practitioner does not say to the patient 'then go away and come back in twenty years when you have processed this illness and I will think about treating you.'

The Atmic Plane proper may be defined as the fundamental existential and vibrational layer in which the individuated Soul finds itself when it comes into manifestation as a result of the exercise of the will-to-be and at the point where it achieves some measure of self-reflecting consciousness. Soul Energy, or Soul Consciousness, manifests initially through the Atmic Body[93], and this informs the Egoic Lotus - the Higher Ego or Higher Self, which can be considered in the present context to be one's deepest sense of higher purpose, calling or vocation.

CAUSAL BODY

The Causal Body, is, therefore, the vehicle of manifestation of the Higher Self or Higher Ego, i.e. the 'materialised' form of the Soul and the

---

93. Atman. (Sanskrit: "breath" or "self") Comparatively, 'Basic concept in Hindu philosophy, describing that eternal core of the personality that survives death and transmigrates to a new life or is released from the bonds of existence....It underlies all aspects of personality, as Brahman underlies the working of the universe.' (*Encyclopaedia Britannica*) The *ultimate* expression of the individual is said by Bailey to be the Divine Spark, or Monad, but at this point in time we are not concerned with it since it has no role, from the therapeutic point of view, being, one might say 'that which it is'. But I mention this for the sake of completion, and completism as an obsessive activity is no small matter.

embodiment of the Soul's Purpose in so far as the individual's development may allow it to act in the lower planes. The Causal Body may be more or less developed according to the extent to which a person is 'in touch' with their soul's purpose, or, in the broadest sense, their existential nature, their *raison d'être*. As noted in the previous Chapter, the Causal Body is a construct made by the Higher Self and is built steadily over time as a vehicle of expression, as experience and the situation of life allows.[94] There are many forces which play upon human lives which may be favourable or inimical to self-development. Many lives are cut short because of circumstances such as war; some say 'you chose that experience'; others may counter 'you had no choice.' On the other hand there are many stories of people who say they were living empty, stupid, meaningless and purposeless lives and through some dramatic circumstances such as war, suffering, severe illness, reaching the bottom of some personal abyss, the destruction of some deluded belief, and so on, found or renewed their direction in this world. This experience *could* result from some contact between the Personality and the Higher Self or Soul's Purpose, a degree of renaissance of the life coming about as a result. There are other persons in this world who in the same space of a lifetime rise to great prominence and achieve much and thus might be thought to be strongly connected to their Higher Self. But this cannot automatically be assumed to be correct as many who are successful are driven by ego, under which may lie a sense of insecurity, of being an underdog, second-best, resulting in a driving need to prove to the world *who they are*.

It also must not be forgotten that many people have been cruelly deluded by some kind of apparent salvation or purposive experience, or convinced by persuasive conditions that they have progressed beyond the problems of the present life, only to find themselves trapped by a revised version of the old difficulties - back in the same trap but the problems look different. As another example, there are many convincing purveyors of self-improvement programs, but not everything that looks like a revelation *is* a revelation. It should also be added that, as it were, reaching a 'higher turn of the spiral' does not mean that new adversities may not arise.

The practitioner may read disturbances in the Causal Body of the patient during an analysis but as the above indicates, it should not therefore be automatically interpreted as meaning that the inhibition

---

94. Says Maimiti to Fletcher Christian in *The Mutiny on The Bounty* (1962) 'Either you eat life or life eats you'.

originates in it. The problems may be a reflection in the Causal Body of stresses at the personality level, some of which may have a very powerful negative effect on the individual's 'higher' or more altruistic psychology and motivation.

BUDDHIC BODY

In this context the calibre of the Causal Body in turn conditions the Buddhic Body, or Higher Intuition, that which allows us to feel that we are *guided* by our inner Self - that sense that we are being 'true' to ourselves, and our essential purpose.

In the broader sense the Buddhic Plane stands prior to the Plane of Mind (Mental Plane) and may be defined as the fundamental existential and vibrational level from which comes higher knowledge, consciousness, awareness and understanding of the transcendental and highest aspects of Truth *beyond all duality* and thus is *immanence* personified. Understanding at this level may be gleaned via the faculty of Higher Intuition, which uses the personal *Buddhic Body* as its vehicle of connection or manifestation. Development of faculties upon the Buddhic Plane is said to allow immediate perceptions of the inner nature of reality without the filter of preconceptions or processes of intellectualization. Things are seen as they are.[95] But a person with such rarified faculties and insight is unlikely to be the *typical* Radionic patient. It is the patient who feels, perhaps, that he or she has lost his way who comes for help in untangling their knots. The practitioner may be able to identify disturbances in these higher bodies which inhibit the individual's purposive expression, and by counteracting them, reduce the difficulties.

The functioning of the Higher Intuition, however, should not be confused with what might be termed 'Instinct', for example the feelings or forebodings of imminent danger that people sometimes experience, or other similar perceptions which are often bound up with self-preservation. These may be felt through the outer layers of the *Astral* Body, which connect us to a certain type of commonality of human shared emotional experience and related sensations and phenomena.

---

95. Some may say for instance that the *Tao Te Ching*, by Lao Tzu, or the music of Bach, are examples of inspired insight unimpeded by intellectual process. This is not saying that there was no intellectual process involved, but that it becomes a tool by which the end is achieved, and not the end in itself.

MENTAL BODY

This totality of the Higher Self then expresses through the Personality, which is a construct of Mind and Emotions; roughly speaking, Mind being the thinking process and Emotions being the feeling process. This is not the same as identifying Mind or Emotion as actual and primary psychological or philosophical concepts. For example the range of feelings an individual typically experiences may be considered to be part of their personality, but absolutely does not exhaust or comprise the total feeling-range available to humanity as whole, which must for all practical purposes be considered to be illimitable, in the same sense that Jung, for example, considers the unconscious illimitable and inexhaustible.

The Mental Plane itself may be defined as the plane in which the sum total of the process of intellectual and rational enquiry into all aspects of the manifested Universe - including Nature and the human organism - coalesce into thought and knowledge fields. To a certain extent, therefore, the combined mental efforts of humanity create the content of the Mental Plane.

The vehicle of Mind, which is to say the body of manifestation through which the individual's mental processes express themselves, is known as the *Mental Body*. This, for present purposes, can be divided into two subsections, the Intellect, and the Psychological character, although the latter is a plexus which combines both mental and emotional aspects. Psychological states are often typically key to the emotions felt or expressed. Response to the same stimulus via a process of conditioning may produce completely different reactions in different people. To give a simple example, one person as a result of experience dislikes dogs, and the sight of one may produce an adverse psychological reaction with accompanying emotions of fear, revulsion, etc; the sight of the same dog by another results in feelings of pleasure, joy, delight and so on.

Intellect may be thought of as the thinking, reasoning, rational functions of mind which are governed by logical and analytical processes, and of course the intellectual process can be disturbed in many types of illness. Many types of intellectual delusions have also developed in humans, and the conflicts produced by 'reality testing' - an expression from Freud - have resulted in many forms of denial, dishonesty and sophism. The Psychological character contains the behavioural and cognitive characteristics of the individual through which he or she builds up a sense of self and identity. Such constructs can be described in part as *thought-forms*, habitual conceptualisations which through social programming, repetition and the underscoring of experience are beliefs or belief systems which tend to become accepted as objective facts, as realities, and which in a sense develop an objective presence, 'a life of their own'. Some may be useful, positive, helpful and life-affirming; others negative, destructive and undermining and may become vested with enormous power in determining the fate of individuals, whole societies or nations, especially when manipulated by those with appropriate skills and motives.

To give an example, great efforts have been made in some societies to improve the self image of minorities, the group self-image of being inferior or 'second-best' being a commonly-held thought-form usually reinforced by any amount of actual negative experiences visited upon them by the dominant society. This negative self-image may even be reinforced by ignoring behaviour in the dominant group which favours the minority, in order to cling on to the thought form. What if your identity revolves round being an underdog? Who now are you and how do you then know how to relate to society - or yourself? To quote Jung, '*Everyone knows nowadays that people "have complexes". What is not so well-known, though far more important theoretically, is that complexes can have us.*' [96] Or people harbour beliefs such as 'I am a failure...' 'I lack self-confidence...' 'I'll never get anywhere...' 'I'm not good enough...' 'I'm a loser...' 'I have an addictive personality...' 'I am not lovable...' and so on to the point where the person comes to identify totally with the thought-form into which they have invested themselves and, as it were, succeeds in manufacturing their own self-fulfilling catastrophe. They become what they believe themselves to be.

Certainly a focus of Radionic treatment may be to attempt to relieve or counteract negative mental and psychological states. If the problem is of somatic origin, arising perhaps as a result of disturbance to the processes of the nervous system, treatment of the paraphysical aspects of the illness may relieve the symptoms in the mind. If, however, the problem is of psychic or psycho-spiritual origin, then it may need to be treated as a matter in itself. In any event, in spite of the differentiation between Mental and Astral bodies for present purposes, in many individuals the psychological and emotional state is inextricably bound up. The rational part of the mind may see the personal dilemma as illogical and ridiculous, but no amount of logic can, in general, defeat the power of the emotional impulse or instinctual demand, especially where it is grounded in, or conflicted by, the drives.

---

96. Storr, *op. cit.*, p. 38 Thus, perhaps, the origin of 'victim mentality', for example.

ASTRAL BODY

The Astral Plane is the vibrational field from and through which all emotional activity, feeling and experience emanates and is propagated. Beyond the emotional experiences of humanity it has aspects which imbue the natural world with feeling-toned[97] qualities, recognised and described by humans since the beginning of recorded time. Human emotional and psychological activity and responses had their very ancient origin in responses to fundamental seed-forms, or resonances. Jung refers to these as the *archetypes*:

'....a kind of fluid interpenetration belongs to the very nature of all archetypes. They can only be roughly circumscribed at best. Their living meaning comes out more from their presentation as a whole than from a single formulation. Every attempt to focus them more sharply is immediately punished by the intangible core of meaning losing its luminosity. No archetype can be reduced to a simple formula. It is a vessel which we can never empty, and never fill. It has a potential existence only, and when it takes shape in matter it no longer is what it was. It persists throughout the ages and requires interpreting ever anew. The archetypes are the imperishable elements of the unconscious, but they change their shape continually. It is a well-nigh hopeless undertaking to tear a single archetype out of the living tissue of the psyche; but despite their interwovenness they do form units of meaning that can be apprehended intuitively.'[98]

---

97. An expression used by Jung.
98. Jung (1959) paragraphs 301 - 302.

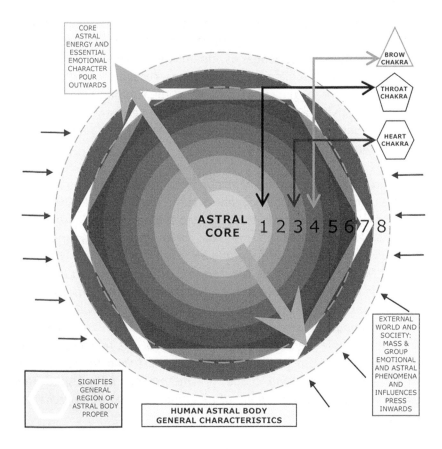

Figure 12: Human Astral Body (basic concept)

In Tansley the Astral Body is presented as an undifferentiated unity, but here a rather more complex picture, different to the Bailey model, is proposed. In this model the Astral Body is comprised of layers, the inmost and most personal layer being denoted the core, which itself is the *essential* or *personal* emotional character, or *emotional self-identity*. This is the 'unprogrammed' or 'natural' inner emotional self, an integral part of the personality, which seeks self-expression through life's activities. In many people expression of the core emotional character may be greatly qualified, suppressed or inhibited by the group and social context - for example, the need or pressure to conform to the expectations of others. The core is surrounded by 8 Layers of emotional response and expression.

Figure 12 illustrates the idea of the general structure of the Astral Body; note the specific connections between Layer 1 and the Throat

Chakra; Layer 3 and the Heart Chakra; and Layer 4 and the Brow Chakra. These proposed connections between Astral Body Layers and Chakras requires much more research before the role of disturbances to them in the development of illness can be fully assessed.

To aid understanding the *Astral Body* may be pictured as a *graded continuum* of layers which has at its centre the personal emotional self and at its periphery, a connection to the group Astral field which can bind masses of people together in common emotional and psychological responses. This group field may, for instance, be powerfully affected and activated by appropriate manipulation, e.g. advertising, propaganda, news and other media, disinformation, mass-marketing, mass psychological programming, and so forth - more specifically, it is group interaction between, and group entrainment of, the outer layers of the Astral Body of individuals which creates the crowd phenomenon. Mass hysteria or group spirit ('morale' *'gestalt'* *'zeitgeist'* *'esprit de corps'* 'peer pressure' etc) and other collective phenomena come into existence or can be propagated and directed to many ends - and perhaps not all are to be taken as negative, by any means.

People with a strong sense of personal identity may, amongst other factors, be those who are strongly aware of their core feeling-state and who tend to resist submersion into the group. Those who feel lost and sheep-like or who are easily manipulated and follow mass trends and have no 'centre' are those more likely to live in a delusional state resulting from the overpowering influence of group emotional phenomena. It may be proposed that various forms of somatic illness have their origin in these emotional fantasias and the anxiety, insecurity and sense of frustration which tends to result when reality testing, typically the irruption of unexpected, ignored or discounted external forces, takes place. Maslow describes the loss of self dramatically:

'How is it possible to lose a self? The treachery, unknown and unthinkable, begins with our secret psychic death in childhood - if and when we are not loved and cut off from our spontaneous wishes. But wait - it is not just this simple murder of a psyche. This might be written off, the tiny victim might even "outgrow" it - but it is a perfect double crime in which he himself gradually and unwittingly takes part. He has not been accepted for himself, as he is. Oh, they 'love' him, but they want him or force him or expect him to be different! Therefore he must be unacceptable. He himself learns to believe it and at last even takes it for granted. He has truly given himself up. No matter now whether he obeys

them, whether he clings, rebels, or withdraws - his behavior, his performance is all that matters. His center of gravity is in 'them', not himself....what has happened? He has been rejected, not only by them, but himself. (He is actually without a self. What has he lost? Just the one true and vital part of himself: his own yes-feeling, which is his very capacity for growth, his root-system....From the moment he gives himself up, and to the extent that he does so, all unknowingly he sets about to create and maintain a pseudo-self....This necessity is not life - not his life - it is a defence mechanism against death....from now on he will be torn apart by compulsive (unconscious) needs or ground by (unconscious) conflicts into paralysis....and all the while he is disguised as a normal being and expected to behave like one! In a word....we are neurotic to the extent that we are self-less.'[99]

As we progress out through the layers the *acquired* emotional character is perceived, which may often be a mask or persona which conceals the inner nature. Comparatively,

'The persona is a complicated system of relations between individual consciousness and society, fittingly enough a kind of mask, designed, on the one hand, to make a definite impression on others, and, on the other, to conceal the true nature of the individual....Society expects, and indeed must expect, every individual to play the part assigned to him as perfectly as possible....what goes on behind the mask is then called "private life." This painfully familiar division of consciousness into two figures, often preposterously different, is an incisive psychological operation that is bound to have repercussions on the unconscious....people really do exist who believe they are what they pretend to be.'[100]

The combination of psychological and emotional aspects which typify much of modern man is designated *kama-manas*, or desire-mind,[101]

---

99. Maslow (1968)
100. Jung, from *The Relations between the Ego and Unconscious*, quoted in Storr, *op. cit.*, p. 94 - 95. And of course we have a whole industry of gossip- and scandal-sheets which makes vast amounts of money out of this 'painfully familiar division' as we read of one public figure after another who is exposed 'for what they really are' 'career in ruins' 'promoted family values but had a secret blah blah...' 'double standards' (etc *ad nauseam*).
101. The concept of kama-manas is described in greater, and more esoteric, detail in Bailey (1925) page 486 et. seq. Kama-Manas (Sanskrit) [from *kama* desire + *manas* mind]. I am not entirely happy with the use of some of these expressions, particularly 'Astral', but I find

that combination of mind and emotions which is the totality of desires and ambitions (and conflicts and complexes) of the personality. These may be formed very strongly in successful and prominent people and may have startling combinations of both negative and positive aspects - the ruthless entrepreneur who gives millions to charity, the self-serving, shamelessly greedy politician who brokers a peace deal, and so on.

Many people experience conflict between what they believe they would like out of life and what they feel society demands of them and to which they feel obliged to conform to some degree. This can be a great source of stress and unhappiness, or, alternatively, a challenge which tests and motivates. In the therapeutic context one may find the admixture of emotions and reactions - the psychodrama - which drives many modern humans. In particular, the city dweller - the alienated, anomie-struck individual, workaholic, perhaps suppressing sociopathic feelings, rootlessness, existential anxiety, insecurity, fear of failure, stressed out, worried, seeking social validation, the trend-hopping follower of fashion grabbing every passing meme, the secret addict, the social climber, the failed marriages, the string of unhappy affairs, the alienated children, the deep financial worries, the sense of irresponsible entitlement, the member of the chattering classes, probably aspiring to do 'something good' in the world but knowing where to start, the *'what's it all about?'* kinda guy - they are everywhere and nowhere at the same time.

For the Radionic therapist disturbances, particularly in the Astral Body and psychological elements of the Mental Body, may be of paramount importance as these can affect the functioning of the paraphysical bodies, leading to increased susceptibility to illness by weakening the vitality and the channels through which the vital force flows. In these disturbed functions we may see a kind of esoteric prototype of the bodymind relationship, of how the condition and conditioning of the psyche affects the state of health in the physical.

---

myself somehow stuck with this mélange of English, Sanskrit, Hindu, Theosophical and other terms. However there is only so much of the wheel you can judiciously re-invent before you end up with something that resembles a flat tyre. I am trying to progress from the basis that Tansley and his predecessors laid down, rather than write Radionics anew.

7: THE ETHERIC BODY

'With this background we can now list the central dogmas of relativistic quantum field theory:

1. The essential material reality is a set of fields.

2. The fields obey the principles of special relativity and quantum theory.

3. The intensity of a field at a point gives the probability for finding its associated quanta - the fundamental particles that are observed by experimentalists.

4. The fields interact and imply interactions of their associated quanta. These interactions are mediated by quanta themselves.

5. There isn't anything else.

These points make up the conceptual framework of modern relativistic quantum physics. They give us the basic picture of reality. Within this framework physicists must try to account for all of physics....People are always interested by the question of whether physicists invent these theories or discover them as Columbus discovered America. Are theories "out there" in the world waiting for some bold and clever person to find them? I don't think so - theories are inventions.'

Heinz Pagels, The Cosmic Code[102]

ETHERIC BODY - THE TEMPLATE

The forces and energies of consciousness described in the previous Chapter interact with the fields and forces which substand the objective Physical Body, the flesh and blood being. The presumption is that there is a complex organizing field, the Etheric Body, which is the basic paraphysical template for the Physical Body in its entirety:

'The etheric body is the inner "substantial" form upon which the physical body is built or constructed. It is the inner scaffolding which underlies every part of the whole outer man; it is the framework which sustains the whole; it is that upon which the outer form is patterned; and it is the network of nadis (infinitely intricate) which constitutes the counterpart or duplicate aspect of the entire nervous system which forms such an important part of the entire human mechanism. It is thus definitely, with the blood stream, the instrument of the life force.'[103]

---

102. Pagels (1983) p. 271 - 272

103. Bailey, *Esoteric Healing* p. 79. In Radionics the Etheric Body is sometimes referred to as the Physical-Etheric Body. This 'Ether' is possibly not to be confused with the 'Luminiferous Aether' of classical physics. The existence of this prototypical medium, on

'The etheric body has three basic functions, all closely interrelated. It acts as receiver of energies, an assimilator of energies and as a transmitter of energies. If each of these functions is maintained in a state of balance, then the physical body reflects this interchange of energies as a state of good health. The key to health lies in the correct reception, assimilation and distribution of energies.'[104]

In short, here are three central ideas about the Etheric Body:

First, that it has a vitalization function, concerned with the correct provision of vital energy (life force energy); this will be discussed in more detail in the following Chapter, particularly in conjunction with the functions of the Spleen Chakra and related structures.

Second, that it has a morphogenetic function, concerned with the generation and maintenance of form; and

Third, that the calibre of the higher Subtle Bodies and Chakras conditions the Etheric Body and its subsystems, which in turn determine the health of the Physical Body proper. Disease and illness may be considered to be a mirror of conditions in the Etheric Body, but a further point is that the quality of health or type of disease process may be thought to be at least in part triggered, or even determined, by the individual's spiritual, psychological and emotional state.

As stated previously, the Etheric Body can be subdivided into regions, which for descriptive purposes may be denoted:

1. Etheric Pre-Physical, from which are drawn the
2. Etheric Body proper, with its subdivisions, the
3. Physical-Morphic Body;
4. Physical-Morphic Fields;
5. Meridians and related structures, such as acupuncture points.

It should be noted that these subdivisions are a somewhat new conceptualisation proposed by the author. In Tansley, the Etheric Body is

---

which electromagnetic radiation was supposed to be propagated, was said to be disproved by the Michelson-Morley experiment (1887).
104. Tansley (1972) p. 18 - 20

seen, effectively, as an undifferentiated whole; there is no mention, for example, of the Meridians. This new level of differentiation provides an extended range of interpretation and therapeutic possibilities.

ETHERIC PRE-PHYSICAL

The Etheric Body itself is said by Bailey to be constructed from the 'material' of the etheric field of the planet as a whole, called *Prana*. For present purposes, however, Prana is considered to be a separate energy, different from the consciousness-driven primary force-energies from which the Etheric Body is built. The present view is that there are seven such primary energies. Considered from the esoteric standpoint, these combine together in the Etheric Body in different ratios according to various personal qualities, such as the constitution (Rays etc), karma, and soul's objectives (or soul's purpose) of the individual. There may also be other influences such as group characteristics, typical of the human group or race one is born into, influences of the age in which one lives,[105] and so on. The result is a certain degree of individualisation of the Etheric Body. In so far as all humans have certain characteristics in common - such as the general structure and morphology of the physical form - the Etheric Body of all will be similar. However, humans also differ widely within the general range and this must also be reflected in the characteristics of the Etheric Body.

These seven primary energies must be drawn in to create the matrix of the Etheric Body; the in-drawing process may be described as the Etheric Pre-Physical conformation. Certain disturbances may take place which result in a corruption of this energy as it is acquired. These are discussed in more detail in Chapter 11. If the Etheric Body is in good enough condition then some of the potential problems with this incoming energy might be auto-compensated. In other instances, however, one therapeutic task may be to attempt to eliminate or reduce such disturbances, i.e. remove blocks to the correct acquisition of the incoming primary energy. Accordingly conformation is the first stage in the manifestation (and maintenance) of the Etheric body and a point where

---

105. Bailey states that we are currently leaving the Piscean age (dominated by the 6th Ray) and entering the Aquarian age (dominated by the 7th Ray) and the qualities of these epochs produce different characteristics in the Subtle Anatomy. More routinely, different diseases have characterised different historical periods, Tuberculosis being typical of the age of industrialisation and urbanisation. These diseases, over many generations, also leave their marks on Etheric Body.

the disease process might begin. However, the question remains as to why the Etheric Body takes the form it does and this inevitably leads back to a discussion of the nature of the evolutionary process.

ETHERIC BODY AND THE ARCHETYPES

The Etheric Body is a totality which for analytical and treatment purposes in Radionics can be subdivided into several regions as the formative forces condense into physical form. Broadly speaking the Physical-Morphic Body, Physical-Morphic fields and Meridians may be considered to be substructures of the Etheric Body, i.e. 'components' of a complex integrated field which becomes progressively more specialised as it comes to correspond to the well-defined individual structures of the Physical Body proper.

The Etheric Body is tightly and intricately bound to the material of the Physical Body in a reciprocal process. The Physical Body is the mirror of the Etheric, with the Etheric being the progenitor of the Physical; but there is also a continuous two-way exchange of 'data' between them. Impacts to the Physical may bring about disturbances to the Etheric, for example, a break in a bone would immediately be reflected as a discontinuity in the Etheric field, because the energy being transferred to the Physical Body is reflected back (i.e. involving a reflexive feedback-type process) into the Etheric Body imperfectly. At this point the Etheric field would attempt to adjust its energy flow into the Physical to compensate for the problem, which is to say in more familiar terms, a healing process would begin. This is of course in addition to any of the better-understood normal physiological healing processes which are considered (by medical science) to run autonomously.

On the other hand resilience and clarity in the Etheric Body may limit the possibility of catching or developing diseases of whatever type, or help determine how quickly the break in the bone might heal - hence, the well-known concept of 'vis medicatrix naturae' - the healing power of nature. The main point, however, is that 'the etheric body forms the archetypal plane in relation to the dense physical body' [106] and therefore is prior to the Physical Body proper in the sequence of manifestation. Bailey's use of the word 'archetype' is indicative. I have noted the Jung-Pauli correspondence in Chapter 3, and have given an idea above of how Jung defines the archetype. Taking the idea further it might be proposed

---

106. Bailey (1925) p.80 There is a fairly lengthy discussion of the Etheric Body and Prana on pages 77 - 128.

that the human form in general is the result of an evolutionary process which has unrolled from archetypal forms, *urformen*,[107] all of which in total are the *potentials* for *all* forms, animate or inanimate, which are found, have been found, or are yet to be found in the physical universe. But do not get the idea that, for example, 'somewhere' there is a little archetypal 'doll' or homunculus which serves as a model for a human form - the same concept of 'miniatures' applying to all the other forms of nature, for that matter. Neither may there be some perfect archetypal world of which the physical Universe is an imperfect reflection. According to Jung and as quoted in the previous Chapter, an archetype *'has a potential existence only, and when it takes shape in matter it no longer is what it was.'*

This, then, suggests a view of evolution which proposes a different solution to the problem of the origins of both life and morphogenesis to that put forward either by Divine fiat (Creationism, and, presumably, Intelligent Design) or accidental self-assembly from primitive chemicals, driven by randomness (i.e. natural selection), genetic determinism, and survival of the fittest (Neo-Darwinism). In the former view it seems that the rational, analytical faculty of the mind is supposed to be suspended in favour of uncritical belief in what might be called Divine Magic. In the latter view we are asked to believe that the physical Universe from its own simplest components, or even *from nothing*, can become more complex, which clearly suggests that one of its integral and essential characteristics is *negentropy* (negative entropy) - meaning, that it can auto-create order out of chaos, or, to put it another way, more complexity out of less complexity, and, even more relevant from the human point of view, living matter out of dead matter. This appears to be in strong contrast to the standard view in Physics that the general trend of physical systems is *entropic*, which is to say, tending towards chaos (disorder), stabilizing at the lowest level of energetic excitation inherent in a system (Second Law of Thermodynamics). In fact Dennett argues fiercely and at length[108] in favour of this exact view, that *more* complexity *can* emerge from less complexity autonomously, i.e. without *any* overarching, underlying, or external triggering or guiding process, or even without an autonomous but progressive process such as that proposed by Sheldrake - in fact as a result of no other 'process' than the randomness of natural selection.

---

107. German for archetype or prototype. This is my usage of the word, not Jung's.
108. Dennett, *op. cit.*, e.g. in Chapter 3.

Pagels[109] argues that randomness has not yet been defined. *'Mathematicians have never succeeded in giving a precise definition of randomness or the associated task of defining probability.'* Is part of the problem an inherent paradox, in that if you can define what is random, then it is not, by definition, random? Common sense gives us the idea that things happen 'at random', or 'by chance' but Pagels explains that a probability distribution often underlies such phenomena. For every time something happens 'by chance', there are in fact many more times when it didn't happen at all; but sooner or later, however, the event is going to coincide with the statistical probability of it happening. Someone calls up, and you say 'that's amazing, I was just thinking of you.' But how many times did you think of them and they didn't call up? Conversely, perhaps you *increase the probability* of them calling up by repeatedly thinking of them and therefore create the possibility of a *synchronicity*? From such arguments and no doubt many others related, can we truly confirm, in an absolute sense, that natural selection is driven by 'randomness' or is it, perhaps, that evolutionary development is subject to a probability distribution which determines the outcome of mutations? If so, what is the probable 'event' and from where does it originate? Jung states:

'Although common prejudice still believes that the sole essential basis of our knowledge is given exclusively from outside....it nevertheless remains true that the thoroughly respectable atomic theory of Leucippus and Democritus was not based on any observations of atomic fission, but on a "mythological" conception of smallest particles....where did Democritus, or whoever spoke of minimal constitutive elements, hear of atoms? This notion had its origins in archetypal ideas, that is, in primordial images which were never reflections of physical events but are spontaneous products of the psychic factor. Despite the materialistic tendency to understand the psyche as a mere reflection or imprint of physical and chemical processes, there is not a single proof of this hypothesis. Quite the contrary, innumerable facts prove that the psyche translates physical processes into sequences of images which have hardly any recognizable connection with the objective process.[110] The materialistic hypothesis is much too bold and flies in the face of experience with almost metaphysical presumption. The only thing which can be established with certainty, in the present state of our knowledge, is our ignorance of the

---

109. Pagels (1983), p. 105
110. And see, comparatively, comments in Chapter 4 about Bohm and Pribram.

nature of the psyche. There is thus no ground at all for regarding the psyche as something secondary or as an epiphenomenon; on the contrary there is every reason to regard it, at least hypothetically, as a factor sui generis, and to go on doing so until it has been sufficiently proved that psychic processes can be fabricated in a retort....Hence the psychic factor must, ex hypothesi, *be regarded for the present as an autonomous reality of enigmatic character, primarily because, judging from all we know, it appears to be essentially different from physicochemical processes....if we regard the psyche as an independent factor, we must logically conclude there is a psychic life which is not subject to the caprices of our will....From the unconscious there emanate determining influences which, independently of tradition, guarantee in every single individual a similarity and even a sameness of experience, and also of the way it is presented imaginatively. One of the main proofs of this is the almost universal parallelism between mythological motifs, which, on account of their quality as primordial images, I have called* archetypes.'[111]

PHYSICAL-MORPHIC BODY AND PHYSICAL MORPHIC COUNTERPART FIELDS

The Etheric Body is also considered as an overall structure which devolves into an ensemble of more specialised sub-fields, i.e., there is a cascade of functions from the general to the particular. Thus the Physical-Morphic counterpart fields are the fields which exactly substand each organ and defined structure in the physical body, to the minutest detail, also including the genetic structure i.e. DNA, Chromosomes, etc. It is convenient to use the standard nomenclature to identify these Morphic fields, so for example the terms Liver, Kidneys, Colon, Heart, Aorta, Eye, Cell, Thymus, Spinal Cord, Skeleton, Synapse, Ganglion, Blood, Nucleus, Lung, DNA etc (in no particular order) will serve perfectly well. *In Radionics, all of these terms refer only to the underlying fields and not to the directly-observable physical material*. A listing of the basic Locations in the paraphysical body is given in Appendix 2.

The morphic fields, then, are the counterpart fields of the well-known structures of the physical anatomy, i.e. they may be denoted the *paraphysical* anatomy. From the analytical and therapeutic point of view, the morphic fields can be considered, and also as noted above, to be nested in a hierarchical structure. Taking, for example, any organ or

---

111. Jung (1959) op. cit., paragraphs 116 - 118

system, its component parts are substructures of the field which governs that organ. The Respiratory tract can be anatomised into substructures such as lungs, bronchi, etc and these in turn can be sub-anatomized into alveoli, cartilage, smooth muscle, mucous membranes, and so forth. This vertical or hierarchical organisation also has a degree of parallel horizontal organisation, since it may be considered that there are substructures in common to many organs, or the whole body, the cell and its genetic material being preeminent; muscle tissue of several types, bone, cartilage, etc being others.

In certain instances it is also necessary to analyse and treat the Physical-Morphic Body as a whole. Certain problems - typically denoted chronic or systemic diseases - may affect its general functioning. This impairment of the general function may affect many substructures in the counterpart fields, creating an overall deterioration in the patient's health.

Analysis and treatment needs to be focused on the most appropriate point. One may think, following Tansley, that treatment of the relevant Chakras or perhaps the Etheric Body only will serve to bring all of the sub-fields of the subtle anatomy back into line. Experience, however, shows that this is perhaps a necessary but not sufficient part of the required approach, especially where there is advanced physical pathology. In all circumstances the depth of penetration and degree of localisation and generalisation of the disturbance needs to be considered. It may be necessary to attempt to remove or neutralize pathological disturbances to energy and fields at many levels. To give a complex example, what we will call for now 'cancer' energy may have to be removed not only locally - from the fields of the afflicted organ and its cells and tissues (primary site), but also from the fields of any secondary sites; from the Chromosomes, if involved, and also generally, from the Physical-Morphic Body as a whole, from the Etheric Body, the Astral Body, perhaps even as far into the organism as the Causal and Atmic Bodies.

Excessive 'anatomization' of the health problem - i.e. focus on the paraphysical level with disregard for the higher levels of the Subtle Anatomy attempts to force Radionics to behave as if it was an analogue of orthodox medicine, which it is not. Orthodox medical treatment is subject to a different set of laws and rules (those governing physics and chemistry), being based, largely, on study of the interactions of physical matter only. Radionics is concerned with formative forces and energies, the fields of consciousness and morphogenesis, the principles behind which are much less well-known, and which may also include the driving forces behind the external laws studied by science.

MERIDIANS & ACUPUNCTURE POINTS

When localised as organs and their substructures, the Physical-Morphic fields in turn are interconnected and to some great extent integrated by the systems of Meridians (energy lines and points) first described by Traditional Chinese Medicine. In fact to a certain degree the Meridians may be thought to precede the Physical-Morphic fields in order of manifestation, and to a certain degree they are parallel to them in function. The principle action of the Meridians is to allow a balancing and regulation of energy flows (i.e. Qi) between organs. As is well-known the Meridians are interactive and closely synchronised to the circadian and biorhythmic processes which link the human organism to the time sequences and energy flows of the environment.

For the general purposes the Meridians may be split into 4 groups, although a more detailed classification is of course possible:

EXTERNAL MERIDIANS (14) ;
COLLATERAL MERIDIANS;
INTERIOR MERIDIANS (39); and
INTERIOR COLLATERAL MERIDIANS

where Collateral Meridians are considered to be secondary pathways linking the main External and Internal Meridians. Although some have created Radionic codes for treatment of individual acupuncture points, of which there may be around 400, in general, from the point of view of Radionic treatment, it may not be necessary to go into such localised detail, i.e. a Meridian or group of Meridians may be treated as whole. TCM (Traditional Chinese Medicine) classifies disturbances into categories denoted Wind, Heat, Damp etc but these characterisations appear to be vivid descriptions of different forms of toxic (i.e. polluted or distorted) Qi and related energies.

ETHERIC BODY AND QUANTUM MECHANICS

It is possible to suggest a more specific idea as to how the Etheric Body may be involved in the morphic - structure-organising - process. Modern physics, principally via Quantum Mechanics, teaches an unusual and disconcerting view of the world we experience. So far as can be discerned, and according to the experimental evidence, there is no 'solid', and no 'ultimate', physical reality. Atoms, we now know, are composed mostly of empty space; and therefore what we perceive to be impenetrable physical matter, e.g. objects in the physical world, are, in turn, mostly 'empty' space. The particles of which atoms are constituted are not made of some kind of 'hard' material; the orbiting electrons are not little billiard balls flying like tiny planets round the nucleus, which is comprised of protons and neutrons. Neither is there a fixed, unchanging and permanent continuum - an absolute reality - underlying the world. All that which seems so real to us is, feasibly, nothing more than particles produced by fluctuations in the quantum vacuum - the zero point field. A very short way of looking at it is that 'everything' originates in 'nothing'.

At the beginning of the 20th Century Einstein showed that matter and energy are interchangeable; they are not two things but different forms of the same thing. Quantum Mechanics explored the problem that light could function either as a wave[112] or as a particle (photon), depending upon the experimental context. *'In his 1924 dissertation Recherches sur la théorie des quanta (Research on Quantum Theory), French physicist Louis de Broglie hypothesized that all matter possesses a De Broglie wave similar to light. That is, under the appropriate conditions, electrons and other matter would show properties of either particles or waves.'*[113]

How, then, is this wave/particle duality detected? In his description of the prototypical double-slit experiment, in which particles of light are fired through two apertures (slits in some type of opaque material) onto a phosphor detection screen, Gribben writes:

'....the central mystery of quantum mechanics is revealed in all its glory when single quantum entities (either photons or electrons) are fired one at a time through the experiment, and the pattern on the detector screen is allowed to build up gradually.

We stress that this has really been done, both for photons and electrons, with the pattern they make being allowed to build up on a TV-type screen (or photographic film) as the spots made by each arriving

---

112. All vibrations, such as sound, or, in the electromagnetic domain, light, radio waves, microwaves, etc are waveforms ('waves') which can be described precisely by mathematics. Frequency is a function of the rate of vibration. Thus your favourite piece of Mozart, can, in principle, be described accurately in terms of various mathematical co-ordinates. Your emotional reaction to the music, however, cannot.

113. en.wikipedia.org/wiki/Electron#Quantum_mechanics. Furthermore, *'In the* standard interpretation of quantum mechanics, *the quantum state, also called a* wavefunction *or state vector, is the most complete description that can be given to a physical system. Solutions to Schrödinger's equation describe not only* molecular, atomic, *and* subatomic systems, *but also* macroscopic systems, *possibly even the whole* universe.' Wikipedia, entry for 'Schrödinger equation'.

electron or photon accumulate. Now, single particles are travelling one at time through the experiment, and each makes a single spot on the screen. You might think that each particle must go through only one or the other of the two holes. But as more and more spots build up on the screen, the pattern that emerges is the classic interference pattern for waves passing through both holes at once. The quantum entities not only seem to be able to pass through both holes at once, but to have an awareness of past and future, so that each can 'choose' to make its own contribution to the interference pattern, in just the right place to build the pattern up, without destroying it....if you think this is fishy, and set up a detector to tell you which hole each particle is passing through, all of this mysterious behaviour disappears. Now you do indeed see each particle (photon or electron) going through just one hole, and you get two blobs of light on the detector screen, without interference. The quantum entities seem to know when you are watching them, and adjust their behaviour accordingly (again, we emphasize that this version of the experiment really has been carried out). Each single quantum entity seems to know about the whole experimental set-up, including when and where the observer is choosing to monitor it, and about the past and future of the experiment. And this just doesn't apply to electrons and photons, although they are relatively easy to work with...it applies to all quantum 'particles', and similar experiments (with similar results) have been carried out with neutrons, protons, and even whole atoms. Hold on to these ideas....'[114]

A key problem which emerged was that the presence, i.e. the consciousness, of the observer could not be separated from the result of the experiment. To give an idea of the situation, Herbert describes von Neumann's attempts to discover where the wave function collapses (i.e. at which exact point light, behaving as wave, begins to behave as if it were a particle)[115]:

'Von Neumann was understandably anxious to find a natural location for the wave function collapse, which is essential for his interpretation of quantum theory. He systematically examined the measurement process for clues for a special feature of measurement which

---

114. Gribben, op. cit., p. 112 - 113. The complete entry (p. 109 - 113) describes the experiment in detail and begins *'The experiment which, in the words of Richard Feynmann, encapsulates the 'central mystery' of quantum mechanics.'*
115. The *'collapse of the wave function'* i.e. the point at which waves transform into a fixed point - a particle - is part of the 'Copenhagen interpretation' (of reality) developed by Nils Bohr (1885 - 1962).

might give rise to a Type II process [collapse of the wave function]. He visualized the measurement act as broken into small steps, stretching from the quon [particle] gun to the observer's consciousness where the measurement result is ultimately registered....A solution to the measurement problem....would consist of "severing von Neumann's chain at the first true measuring act." In other words, where in fact is a quantum measurement actually accomplished?

While searching for a natural place to break his chain, von Neumann proved an important mathematical fact that deepens the mystery of measurement. Von Neumann showed that as far as results are concerned, you can cut the chain and insert a collapse anywhere you please. This means that the results themselves can offer no clues as to where to locate the division between system and measuring device....On each side of the wave function collapse, von Neumann erects impeccable mathematical structures familiar to quantum physicists - the world expressed as proxy waves. However, separating these two sides of the argument - the world unmeasured and the measured world - is a logic gap in which von Neumann effectively writes, "And then a miracle occurs."

Von Neumann could not find a natural place to locate his "miracle". Everything, after all, is made of atoms; there's nothing holy about a measuring instrument....driven by his own logic, in desperation von Neumann seized on its only peculiar link: the process by which a physical signal in the brain becomes an experience in the human mind. This is the only process in the whole von Neumann chain which is not mere molecules in motion. Von Neumann reluctantly came to the conclusion that human consciousness is the site of the wave function collapse....In von Neumann's consciousness-created world, things (or at least their dynamic attributes) do not exist until some mind actually perceives them, a rather drastic conclusion but one to which this great mathematician was forced by sheer logic....' [116]

Thus human consciousness seemed to be somehow inextricably involved in the creation of reality. The larger problem, according to Herbert, is that Quantum Mechanics (QM) has not been able to provide a single, unitary, coherent and universally-accepted concept of an ultimate underlying reality. The certainties of the 'classical' age of Newtonian

---

116. Herbert, Nick (1985) p. 147 - 8. John Von Neumann (1903 - 1957). Herbert defines a quon as 'any entity, no matter how immense, that exhibits both wave and particle aspects in the peculiar quantum manner.'

physics have been swept away - *'Classical physics in a nutshell: the universe consists of nothing but matter and fields - and we know the laws of both.'* [117] To Newton, God was the source of everything, the Universe was knowable and predictable down to the last detail, and the nature of reality was clear. Things have now changed as a result of developments in physics; no-one now knows if there is an absolute reality underlying Nature, or even if one can be found. We are lost in space with no way home.

Herbert lists 8 different, and presumably equally valid or useful, interpretations of what reality might or might not be. These interpretations arise from QM, and include:

1) Copenhagen - *there is no deep (underlying) reality behind the phenomena observed in quantum mechanics*

2) Copenhagen 2 - *reality* (i.e. attributes of observed phenomena) *is created by observation*

3) Bohm and others - *Reality is an undivided wholeness*

4) Everett's Many Worlds interpretation - *reality consists of a steadily increasing number of parallel universes*

5) Quantum logic - *the world obeys a non-human kind of reasoning*

6) Neorealism - *the world is made of ordinary objects* (the universe exists independently of the existence of observers such as us)

7) Consciousness creates reality

8) the duplex world of Werner Heisenberg - *the world is twofold, consisting of potentials and actualities.*[118]

As can be seen from this list, these competing ideas are also contradictory; for example, compare 6) and 7). From some study of the situation of modern physics I come to a slightly unusual proposition which differs from those above and which may help us understand Radionic actions, this being my central concern. What is axiomatic is that the world today looks and behaves in the same way as it did yesterday, and will tomorrow. Whatever incomprehensible forces may be in play at the quantum level, experience tells us that the everyday world we live in is knowable and predictable.

---

117. Herbert, *op.cit.,* p 33 - 34. Isaac Newton (1642 - 1727). Contrast with the description by Pagels at the top of this Chapter, where matter is described as emerging *from* fields.
118. Herbert, *op. cit.,* summarized from p. 16 - 27. There is of course a wide range of books on QM and the problems of modern physics.

Physical matter is composed of particles, not waves; but looking at the wave/particle duality central to Quantum Mechanics one may propose that the manifest physical world, or, for that matter, the entire universe, is the result of an absolutely incredibly complex process in which the vast number of waveforms which comprise matter in prospect become interrupted to produce matter in experienced reality At every moment each particle from which the atoms, molecules, compounds, etc, of the physical world are composed exists as a potential - as a set or series of waveforms - and at every moment something functions as a 'consciousness' which causes matter to come into existence by collapsing the waveform.

The analogy I am proposing is that the human consciousness which brings about a collapse of the waveform in the laboratory experiment serves as a miniature of the gigantic scale on which this happens in Nature. It is the 'consciousness' of Nature which causes the physical Universe to come into existence. As a result of complex dynamic, developmental, interactive, evolutionary and evolving processes - which may also incorporate necessary quantum 'randomness'[119] - this consciousness comes to act as a *function* (i.e. in the sense of being mathematically-definable) which as a result of iteration develops enough power to collapse the waveforms in such a way that recognisable forms and structures appear and are maintained in form. This, somehow, could be the morphogenetic field proposed by Sheldrake and the iteration process is what he characterises as the 'habits' of Nature. At the beginning of the Universe[120] this starts with an undifferentiated and highly-energised field from which primary particles emerge, and, as time progresses, more complex materials such as the elements, and structures such as the galaxies, come into being.[121]

---

119. It can be argued that what are perceived as random quantum fluctuations are actually a necessary flexibility in nature. Rigid structures may break when flexed, so randomness gives Nature a certain latitude of action when under stress. As far as I recall Pagels, *op. cit.*, also suggests something like this but I could not find the passage to reference it.

120. By 'beginning' I infer the Big Bang, which is the current accepted science - the 'Standard Model'. Even if there was no Big Bang but some other origin of the universe, the argument is not weakened because we see the same forms and structures - such as Hydrogen atoms and galaxies - occurring time after time and also back into primordial time.

121. The materialist may well object. 'Consciousness of Nature? Ugh! Ecch! Anthropomorphism!' (the attribution of human characteristics to non-human organisms, such as animals, or objects, such as the Universe). But materialism considers that human consciousness arises from 'dead' matter - such as the material from which the human

Nature, metaphorically speaking, acts as the ultimate 'observer' and holds the material from which the living body is made to a constant pattern. This may be to some as yet undetermined extent through the medium of what is here denoted the Etheric Body and its paraphysical substructures in the Physical-Morphic field - the energetic counterparts of the body, including genetic material such as DNA, cells, tissues, organs and general morphology. In short, part of the function of the Etheric Body may be to act as an information field. It enables the components and structures of the physical body in every detail to emerge from the ocean of waveforms. These are organised in levels of complexity, equivalent to Sheldrake's 'nested holons'; a set exists for the cell; the cell is part of an organ, for which a higher set exists; and so on. Such a process, then, would be central to a possible understanding of how manifestation of the physical out of the etheric and higher fields takes place.

At the more directly-observable level, subordinate laws of Nature come into play such as govern the many bio-chemical and bio-electrical phenomena which maintain the functioning of the physical system. It is these which are studied by orthodox medical science and are used as the rationale for its method of therapeutic intervention.

EVIDENCE?

We may look for something which supports these general ideas. Dr. Harold Saxton Burr (1889 - 1973) describes decades of experimentation in his book *Blueprint For Immortality*. Using relatively simple equipment, nowadays easily and cheaply obtainable, Burr measured the electrical fields of many organisms, from humans and animals to simple life forms such as slime mould. Results of his work, for example, enabled correlation of changes in the electrical fields of trees to

---

nervous system is made. Yet that same dead matter is part of all the matter in the Universe, so how comes it that the only form of consciousness that can arise from dead matter is human consciousness? Is the organic matter of planet Earth the only substrate from which consciousness can arise? If we make a machine with AI (Artificial Intelligence) using silicon-based microchips, what then is the substrate on which a form or simulacrum of consciousness is arising - certainly not carbon-based organic material! Or to put it another way round, if we assume, as we must, that the Universe came before man, then what *we* call anthropomorphism may actually be *cosmomorphism*, i.e. our attribution of aspects of the cosmos to human and other living organisms. So which did come first - the chicken, or the egg?

changes in the electrical potential of the environment, and changes in the field of the human female to indicate ovulation - or, to a high degree of accuracy, cancer and other malignancies. Burr's basic conclusion, stated in his Foreword, is that

'The Universe in which we find ourselves and from which we can not be separated is a place of Law and Order. It is not an accident, nor chaos. It is organized and maintained by an Electro-dynamic Field capable of determining the position and movement of all charged particles. For nearly half a century the logical consequences of this theory have been subjected to rigorously controlled experimental conditions and met with no contradictions.' [122]

He continues:

'When [the necessary electronic instruments and techniques] *became available, however, an entirely new approach to the nature of man and his place in the Universe became possible. For these instruments revealed that man - and, in fact, all forms - are ordered and controlled by electro-dynamic fields which can be measured and mapped with precision. Though almost inconceivably complicated, the 'fields of life' are of the same nature as the simpler fields known to modern physics and obedient to the same laws. Like the fields of physics, they are part of the organization of the Universe and are influenced by the vast forces of space. Like the fields of physics, too, they have organizing and directing qualities...organization and direction, the direct opposite of chance, implying purpose. So the fields of life offer purely electronic, instrumental evidence that man is no accident. On the contrary, he is an integral part of the Cosmos, embedded in its all-powerful fields, subject to its inflexible laws and a participant in the destiny and purpose of the Universe....until modern instruments revealed the existence of the controlling L-fields [the fields of life], biologists were at a loss to explain how our bodies 'keep in shape' through ceaseless metabolism and change of material....the electro-dynamic field of the body serves as a matrix or mould, which*

---

122. Burr (1972). Burr's work seems to have been ignored by mainstream science, even though it is entirely objective, resting on measurements made with standard electronic test instruments using a strict methodology which is described in detail in the text. I did a few casual experiments looking for an electrical field around tomato plants. Using a £14 multimeter attached to the plant with standard probes and set to the 0 - 200 mV DC range, varying readings were always present, typically between 40 and 180 mV.

preserves the 'shape' or arrangement of any material poured into it....When the L-field in a frog's egg, for instance, is examined electrically it is possible to show the future location of the frog's nervous system because the frog's L-field is the matrix which will determine the form which will develop from the egg....a 'battered' L-field - that is, one with abnormal voltage patterns - can give warning of something 'out of shape' in the body, sometimes in advance of actual symptoms....malignancy in the ovary has been revealed by L-field measurements before any clinical sign could be observed....abnormalities in L-field voltages can give advance warning of future symptoms before they are evident. This does not apply only to the early detection of cancer....it is probable that they will be used to give early warning of a variety of physical problems in time to tackle these effectively. And they have already been used to forecast certain psychological and psychiatric troubles.'[123]

From the above we understand that Burr's claim is that an electro-dynamic field is responsible for morphogenesis, and also appears *prior* to the manifestation of the corresponding physical structures, and in illness becomes disturbed or distorted *prior* to the manifestation of symptoms. In a footnote in *A New Science of Life* Sheldrake, however, states that Burr's electrodynamic fields are not the same as his morphogenetic fields,:

'The identification of morphogenetic fields with electromagnetic fields is responsible for much of the confusion inherent in H.S. Burr's theory of electrodynamic 'Life Fields'. Burr (1972) cites indisputable evidence that living organisms are associated with electromagnetic fields, which change as the organisms change, but then goes on to argue that these fields control morphogenesis by acting as 'blueprints' for development, which is a very different matter.'[124]

Since an electro-dynamic field would be comprised of charged particles (most typically, electrons, i.e. electricity) and since electrons are subject to the wave/particle duality rule described above, this suggests that the appearance of a measurable field would have to occur *after* the 'collapse' of the underlying waveforms. This latter, according to the present proposal, results from the action of the 'consciousness' of Nature; and I propose that the 'consciousness' of Nature is, in at least one of its

---

123. Burr, *op. cit.*, p. 11 - 16. Oschmann (2000) comments on Burr's work.
124. Sheldrake (2009) p. 323 Chapter 4 note 1.

central aspects, an information field - in fact, the *universal information field*. According to Burr, abnormalities in the L-field indicate or predict the onset of symptoms or pathology in the body. From the Radionic standpoint, it may be suggested that disturbances to the relationship between information field and physical form are *an aspect of the pathology* and amongst other things it is these which need to be corrected for any chance of amelioration of symptoms to occur.

To summarise, Burr shows that disturbances, or potential disturbances, to the organism are indicated by abnormalities in the organising field; quantum mechanics suggests that the interaction of consciousness with matter may be central to the manifestation of objective reality; Radionics maintains that (at minimum) should the normal relationship between the Subtle Anatomy and Physical Bodies be thrown out for some reason, disturbances to the physical organism will result. Consequently, and simply put, a central part of the therapeutic objective in Radionics to normalise, as far as possible, not only disturbances *to* the organizing fields and disturbances *between* different regions of the organizing fields, but also disturbances *in their relationship with* the physical form, and axiomatically, this must be done in the correct manner and in the correct sequence.

It should be obvious that these relationships are extremely complex and not easily subject to effective intervention. But the proposal remains in place that such interventions as are proposed by the Radionic method are not only possible but are an integral part of the possibilities allowed by Nature or perhaps, Nature in its 'higher orders' of reality. This means, for example, that it is not - or seems not right now - possible to affect physical matter directly as if by direct 'magical' action but only indirectly, and within certain limitations, using the appropriate forms of *information*. What is proposed here is that Radionic methods can provide a precisely-tuned interaction with the 'consciousness' or formative forces of Nature in order to steer them in various ways so that remedial effects on the health of the patient may be brought about; furthermore, that a framework explanation as to how this can be achieved may be inferred from science itself.

NATURE OF RADIONIC CODES

Jung asserts that the unconscious, mediated by the archetypes, is the wellspring of consciousness and that symbols are the means by which the unconscious makes itself manifest to us. Many forms of symbol have emerged and amongst these one may include both language and mathematics. Some symbols are more powerful than others and some allow more 'work' to be performed than others; the results of Einstein's formula $e = mc^2$ became quite clear with the explosion of the first nuclear weapons:

'Physics...is in the position to detonate mathematical formulas - the product of pure psychic activity - and kill seventy-eight thousand persons at one blow. This literally "devastating" argument is calculated to reduce psychology to silence. But we can, in all modesty, point out that mathematical thinking is also a psychic function, thanks to which matter can be organized in such a way as to burst asunder the mighty forces that bind the atoms together - which it would never occur to them to do in the natural order of things, at least not upon this earth. The psyche is a disturber of the natural laws of the cosmos, and should we ever succeed in doing something to Mars with the aid of atomic fission, this too will have been brought to pass by the psyche. The psyche is the world's pivot; not only is it the one great condition for the existence of a world at all, it is also an intervention in the existing natural order, and no one can say with certainty where this intervention will finally end. It is hardly necessary to stress the dignity of the psyche as an object of natural science. With all the more urgency then, we must emphasize that the smallest alteration in the psychic factor, if it be an alteration of principle, is of the utmost significance as regards our knowledge of the world and the picture we make of it.'[125]

Therefore Radionic codes are, in principle, the means by which the therapeutic objectives and intentions of the practitioner may be harnessed in such a way that they have the potential to interact in an efficient and effective manner with the organizing forces of Nature; potentially, a strong mode of interaction between consciousness and the forces substanding living matter is herein described. The practitioner's intention, necessarily reinforced by appropriately-constructed Codes and amplified and fixed in its action by appropriately-constructed instruments, causes or allows Nature to reassert its hold on the parts of the organism which are malfunctioning or dysfunctional and by this means attempts to restore order - to help them function correctly. Radionic codes may, therefore, be described as a form of psychoactivated symbology.

---

125. Jung (2010) p. 150 - 151

As a result, if the relationship between the organizational pattern or information and the form it generates has been properly reasserted, the possibility then exists that symptomatic and pathological conditions can be corrected. Intermediate stages might involve the removal or neutralisation of the energetic presences of inimical Factors, such as pathogens, or poisons and toxins, but this also would be attempted at the energetic, and not the physical, level. The hoped-for result should be the removal or reduction of the disease or disease process - in point of fact, *normalisation* of the relationship between consciousness, field and form. It therefore appears to be possible for human consciousness, within limits, to initiate and complete actions which may be construed as emanating from conscious activity alone yet which manifest on the quantum mechanical and related levels of physical reality. The basic limit is the pattern evolved by Nature.

To illustrate this, referring back to the wave/particle duality problem, we note for instance that when a human observer causes a collapse of the wave function, the result is constrained by the more powerful force of Nature - light as a waveform becomes light as a particle (photon). Through conscious intervention we may influence the process decisively but we do not cause it to mutate so that it gives some other or exceptional result. There is no transmutation - light as a waveform does not become a neutron, an atom of gold or silver, or other particle or force beyond the usually-observed object, which is a photon. The world tomorrow remains the same as the world today. Thus what a practitioner can reassert is normal functioning, or perhaps even enhanced functioning, but only within the possibilities provided by Nature. By this means supernaturalism can be excluded from Radionic methods, but only by showing that what appears to be supernatural is part of Nature itself.[126] Artefacts from consciousness, appropriately described by symbols, propelled by intent, may be used to interact with the forces of Nature to redetermine the health condition of a human or other organism.

There is of course a range of Radionic therapeutic actions and above I only describe the most fundamental possibilities. Chapter 13 deals with treatments in more detail.

---

126. Notwithstanding, I have noted above that the limits of Radionics are not yet apparent to us, just as the limits to the manipulation of matter through scientific techniques have hardly been fully defined. If there is an endgame, it is not in sight.

8: RAYS, CHAKRAS AND THE AURA

The development of the Chakras is said to be the means through which humans evolve at the level of spiritual, or higher, consciousness. Rays are said to be the fundamental qualities from which the many forms of consciousness emerge. Within the general parameters of each Ray - since each is considered to have both positive and negative aspects - can be found the basis for the characteristics of all creative and destructive states in the broadest sense conceivable, from the largest scale to the smallest. The concern of Radionics is with disturbances to the functioning of the Chakras, and to the quality of relationship between the individual, his or her Chakras, and the Rays upon which he or she works (consciously), or Ray qualities to which he or she is attuned (unconsciously).

RAYS

The role of the Rays and the Chakras - the energy centres - is to impart qualities and characteristics to form, emotions, and mind. This comes about as a result of the interplay between the Rays, the Subtle Bodies, and the Chakras. The Rays are certain unmodified and unqualified vibrational quintessences which in the relevant esoteric literature are stated to be absolutely fundamental to all existence and to its manifestation. The word Ray itself is somewhat misleading as it implies a directional beam of light, i.e. a vector, but in fact Ray energy is, as it were, *scalar*, which is to say that it is available everywhere equally, to be used or acquired according to need. Ray energy cannot however be described using terms such as form, formalisation, direction, point or mathematical function. The above mentioned 'need' is not in the sense of everyday needs but in the rather more esoteric sense of characteristics to be acquired and used in order to accomplish some objective.

A detailed study of the Rays was set out in the work of Bailey[127] but earlier literature shows the idea to have been known since ancient times. From physics comes Newton's well-known experiment in which passing sunlight through a prism enables white light to be split into its seven constituent colours. If the physical Universe (i.e. the manifest Cosmos) is considered to be consistent and a unity then all white light can be shown to be made up of these same constituent colours; all matter can be shown to have a definite spectral character according to its atomic and

---

127. For example Bailey (1936), Esoteric Psychology - five volumes in all.

chemical makeup; light (red shift etc.) can be used to indicate velocity on a Cosmic scale, and so on. From an esoteric point of view if the *Un*manifest is taken to be an Absolute Unity (for example the *Ain Soph Aur* - Endless Light - of Kabbalah) then as a primary step into manifestation it can be considered to differentiate itself first into the entire frequency range of the electromagnetic spectrum, of which the 7 visible Rays of light have the most obvious significance for humanity. The 7 Rays therefore are the occult correspondences of the 7 physical Rays of visible light and can also be defined as having fundamental colours, and, more particularly, fundamental creative qualities.

In recent decades the 7 Rays have been augmented to 12 as the expanding consciousness of humanity - particularly in response to scientific discoveries and attempts to understand the structure of the material Universe - has enabled a refinement of the concept to be made. The 5 'new' Rays are actually distinct colour and character blends emerging from the original 7 but as a result of present conditions have acquired a permanent quality of their own. Thus from the fundamentals 'need' can be shown to elicit a response according to the requirements of the moment. Rays 8 through 12 are now, as it were, materialising through human conscious awareness as a result of the endeavour of those attempting to penetrate to a higher level of understanding of reality and this may come from those involved in many areas, including science, whether the individuals realise it or not. Rays 8 through 12 may, however, be considered as secondary to the 7 primary Rays first described by Bailey.

RAYS 1 - 7

The Rays and their qualities underlie and condition the whole manifest Cosmos from the atom to the galaxy, including all living beings. They are also in a constant state of flux and interplay over time cycles varying from millennia to moments. As may be imagined, the Rays constitute a vast area for study in themselves and this is only the barest outline of the subject.

Bailey describes 7 Rays, grouped as Rays of Aspect and Rays of Attribute. Their characteristics can be described as follows, giving a basic description:

RAYS OF ASPECT

RAY 1	Will (will-to-be, to exist, to come into manifestation, the existential urge, the urge to power); also enforced and directed Unity; Destruction, Severity, Justice not tempered by Mercy, Law - notably, the Laws formulated by Science; singular Purpose, and so on.
RAY 2	Love (in the highest sense, expression of communal concern encompassing all orders of existence; its by-product or end result is said to be wisdom, hence more commonly, Love-Wisdom); also, Expansion, Compassion, Mercy, Co-operation, Tolerance, Inclusiveness, Brotherhood, Charity, Justice tempered by Mercy, and so forth.
RAY 3	Active Intelligence (focused desire mitigated by reason, intelligence and rational functions); also Contraction, Reduction, Organisation, organised Creativity, Structure, Form and Definition, etc.

The Rays of Aspect underlie the fundamental characteristics of everything in manifestation and are the three irreducible primaries from which all else is derived. The three Rays of Aspect may also be associated with the 3 *Gunas,* or fundamental operating principles of Nature in Hindu *Samkhya* philosophy, these being Creation (*Sattva*) - Ray 1; Preservation (*Rajas*) - Ray 2; Destruction (*Tamas*) - Ray 3. These qualities describe the basic dynamic of all processes in the Universe, for instance, childhood and youth are *sattvic*; middle age is *rajasic*; old age tends towards death and is therefore *tamasic*. Comparatively, Avalon states:

'....the gist of the matter is simple and in accordance with other systems. There is first the unmanifested Point (Bindu)....the state of primordial unity. There is one Spirit, which appears three-fold as a Trinity of Manifested Power (Śakti). As so manifesting, the one (Śiva - Śakti) becomes twofold, *Śiva and Śakti, and the relation (Nāda) of these two (Tayor mithah samavāyah) makes the threefold Trinity common to so many religions. The One first moves as the Great Will (Icchā), then acts as knowledge or wisdom (Jnāna) according to which Will acts, and then as action (Kriyā).*' [128]

Lao-Tzu writes:

'*The way begets one; one begets two; two begets three; three begets the myriad creatures. The myriad creatures carry on their backs the* yin *and embrace in their arms the* yang *and are the blending of the generative forces of the two.*' [129]

These fundamental processes are considered to be in continual interplay, with the overall idea of beginning, middle, and end; but the end of one thing is often be the beginning of another, and so forth. Therefore we describe not only process, but also the stages and contours of process, which may be involved and interrelated in many complex ways with results which are often not clearly discernible at the time.

RAYS OF ATTRIBUTE
These Rays develop from the interaction and interplay of the 3 main Rays of Aspect and may be described as follows:

RAY 4	Synthesis & Reconciliation (i.e. synthesis resulting from the reconciliation of conflicting forces; unity from opposites); Art, Beauty and Harmony; Inspiration, Creativity.
RAY 5	Intellectual Process (Scientific and Concrete Knowledge gained through intellectual ordering of process via rational understanding and logical

---

128. Avalon, *op. cit.*, page 175. Compare also this concept of the primordial Bindu with the idea of the Singularity in which all the primordial material of the Universe (spacetime) is concentrated prior to the Big Bang, which, according to modern Physics, is the origin of the Universe.

129. Lao-Tzu, *Tao Te Ching* (1963), stanzas 93 and 94.

methodology; perception of linear and absolute causality within the manifest physical realm); manipulation of matter using the Laws of Physics and Chemistry.

RAY 6   Idealism, Devotion and Self-Sacrifice; Mass or Group emotional character; organized Religion; politically, Absolutism and Totalitarianism; also Being, Fixed Process, Rigidity, Inflexibility.

RAY 7   Order, Routine, Organisation, Ceremony and Ritual, especially Rhythmic and Repetitive. Manipulation of Forces into Form wielding energetic processes via consciousness and ritual; materialisation appearing to have a quasi-magical character; also Becoming, Dynamic Process.

Some preliminary indications as to the nature of the 5 additional Rays are:

RAY 8   Action on the Plane of Mind; Manifestation through the specific focus of thought energy;

RAY 9   Art & Creativity derived from the Unconscious Images of Noble & Transcendent Human Archetypes; inspiration and aspiration drawn from values which are centrally and essentially human (as opposed to illusions and desires promoted by or originating in mass social control methods and mechanisms);

RAY 10   Material Science and Knowledge transformed for Humanitarian purposes;

| RAY 11 | Fusion of Soul Ray, Causal Body and Personality; unison, unity of life purpose and personal desire; |
| RAY 12 | Mystical Transformative Aspects of Love and Sexuality |

Bearing the above in mind we may begin to see a close involvement between the Rays, the Subtle Bodies, and the Chakras. It is proposed that each Ray works through all the forms and phenomena of nature to a varying degree and has both *positive and negative* aspects, particularly where these are employed by consciousness in its various manifestations.

THE RAYS IN MAN AND NATURE

An example from Nature would be the Darwinian and neo-Darwinian ideas of survival of the fittest, and the Selfish Gene. These are First Ray characteristics, manifesting as the competitive system which is said to drive evolution. Viruses and other pathogens inimical to humanity also operate on the 1st Ray; their will-to-be (survival instinct)[130] is integral to their continued existence, but may be destructive or deadly to the human victim. Hence the First Ray can at the same time be the Destroyer, breaking down Form (erosion, disease and decay) and the Builder, bringing new forms into existence (e.g. from earth sciences, through tectonic forces, raising up mountains, lifting the sea bed to become land, and so forth). Some bacteria, however, have positive benefits to the host, such as the bowel flora of the human, which are essential to the functioning of the digestive and eliminative process. This, then, is an example of the 2nd Ray aspect of Nature, *co-operation*, and it might be said that Nature is essentially 2nd Ray (dynamic equilibrium) working through the 1st Ray (natural selection) to build (3rd Ray) a natural order - the ecosphere. Tansley tells us:

'Each aspect of the esoteric constitution of man is qualified by a ray energy. So there is the ray of the monad or spirit, the ray of the soul,

---

130. If DNA, which is basically and to put it crudely, an *organized* chain of chemicals, can be ascribed a characteristic or motive (selfishness) then I see no reason why Viruses and other micro-organisms cannot, equally, also be ascribed with characteristics. The point we argue is which came first, the evolutionary urge or the physical means by which it is brought into manifestation? The chicken, the egg, or the *will-to-be*?

the ray of the mental body, the ray of the emotional body and those of the etheric body and personality. The personality ray comes into being when the individual has brought about a degree of integration between the various bodies of the lower-self....these rays then form the life-pattern of the individual and confer upon him his strengths and weaknesses, his potential and limitations.'[131]

Bailey suggests that for practical purposes a primary Ray may be deduced for the Causal, Mental, Astral, and Etheric Bodies and the Personality. Hence each individual may be thought to work with the qualities of certain Rays and where the Ray characteristics are over- or under-emphasized there may be various personality, psychological and nervous problems. It is possible to analyse the individual in terms of his or her Ray makeup; an approach to this was proposed by Tansley in *CHAKRAS-RAYS AND RADIONICS*, where he gives a useful outline of the characteristics of the Seven Rays as manifesting in humans. For example,

'Each Ray has its virtues, vices and glamours. Virtues and vices are straightforward enough but glamours are the insidious, illusory qualities of a ray which can deflect us from the truth - glamours are like a mist that veils and distorts reality.[Of the 1st Ray]:

Special Virtues: Strength, courage, steadfastness, truthfulness arising from absolute fearlessness, power to rule, capacity to grasp great questions and measures in a large minded way, and to handle men and measures.

Vices: Pride, ambition, wilfulness, hardness, arrogance, desire to control others, anger and obstinacy.

Glamours: Love of power and authority. Pride and selfish ambition. Impatience and irritation, separativeness, coldness, aloofness and self-centred.

Virtues to be acquired: Tenderness, sympathy, humility, tolerance, patience. A sense of caring for others.

Michael Eastcott points out that history is rich with 1st Ray personalities and lists...Roosevelt, Churchill, Napoleon, Genghis Khan, Alexander the Great, Hitler and Mussolini....'[132]

---

131. Tansley (1984), p. 20
132 . I have slightly changed the order of this paragraph. Tansley (1984) p. 26.

This is well and good, but obviously it must be borne in mind that there are many other factors and circumstances - such as the historical, social, economic and religious context - influencing how any individual uses their Ray characteristics. Clearly Hitler is a 1st Ray personality working through the 6th Ray (mass control) using 7th Ray methods (mass manipulation through ritual and symbolism, propaganda, mind control etc), but had the outcome of the First World War been significantly different, circumstances would have been such that it is probable he would have remained the nonentity that he was and would be unknown to us now.

Ray changes may sometimes occur in any of the Subtle Bodies or major Chakras as new or different activities or lines of endeavour are undertaken, or the possibilities inherent in a Ray are exhausted for the individual.

CHAKRAS

As noted in Chapter 5, embedded in the subtle bodies are a number of energy transmission and circulation centres commonly known as Chakras. Various depictions of the structure and nature of the Chakras may be found, but typically each of the major Chakras is considered to have a number of petals, varying from 4 in the case of the Base Chakra to 1000 in the case of the Crown Chakra. The petals are described (for example by Avalon) as having various Sanskrit characters marked on them; various 'seed sounds' (Bijas) can be intoned to energise each petal in turn. In esoteric literature it is proposed that as the individual develops and consciousness evolves, so each Chakra 'opens' in turn and becomes receptive to energy flowing from increasingly complex sources, i.e. the various higher planes of consciousness. Bailey states:

'In the case of individual man, development proceeds through his seven centres, which are the key to his psychic evolution.' [133]

The objective in this approach to what might be described as self-realization is the *ordered and progressive* opening of the seven Chakras, proceeding from the Base Chakra upwards. Even the most primitive or undeveloped human would be considered to have at minimum a functioning Base Chakra. To put this in a psychological context we may

---

[133] . Bailey (1925), p. 60

return to Maslow's concept of the hierarchy of needs, mentioned in Chapter 5. This we might correlate as follows:

MASLOW'S HEIRARCHY OF NEEDS	CORRESPONDING CHAKRAS
PHYSIOLOGICAL	BASE, SACRAL, SOLAR PLEXUS, HEART, THROAT
SECURITY	BASE, THROAT, SOLAR PLEXUS
SOCIAL	BASE, SOLAR PLEXUS, BROW
ESTEEM	SOLAR PLEXUS, BASE, THROAT, BROW
SELF-REALISATION	THROAT, BASE, CROWN

Table 2: Maslow's Hierarchy of Needs

Physiological needs are for those things which form the basics of physical life such as food, water, oxygen, warmth, etc.

Security needs are those which are satisfied by feeling safe, free from physical and psychological danger.

Social needs are satisfied by conditions of love, belonging, acceptance and approval of peers.

Esteem needs are met by feelings of self-respect and respect from others; and

Self-Realisation needs begin to be met when a person initiates those activities which they feel are their life's work, their central purpose or vocation.

Maslow's hierarchy of needs would appear to be a potent description of various aspects of human motivation. Although Maslow was looking for the *'healthy half of psychology'*, prolonged frustration of these needs could lead to any number of problems; for example, hungry people can initiate war and revolution, and socially- and esteem-deprived people can feel the full forces of alienation, isolation and despair which thread through modern society. Under more normal conditions, as each basic need is fulfilled, so the individual turns his or her attention to the next. From the esoteric standpoint, in doing so, responses occur in, and interactions occur between, the equivalent chakras. Broadly speaking the progression approximates the order in which the Chakras are said to be arranged, which is to say, satisfying primary needs generally corresponds to the activity of the lower Chakras and meeting higher-order needs generally corresponds to the activation of the higher Chakras.

The esoteric concept of the opening and development of the Chakras goes much further, extending into higher reaches of spiritual aspiration and inspiration to include *practical* idealism, selfless service, compassion, higher creativity, wisdom and many other attributes considered typical of spiritually-developed persons. In all these aspects it is the Ray energy used by the individual in various ways which determines the sphere of activity. The successful businessman who becomes a great philanthropist should not be considered less than the impoverished artist who paints great masterpieces - the actions of either may reverberate down the centuries.

In all this we see that the contents of consciousness have their equivalent in vibrations - fields of energy. It does not necessarily matter if we do not understand or do not perceive that we have chakras and subtle bodies, Rays and many other complexes of forces acting upon us and with which we interact. By way of analogy, for most of its existence humanity was unaware of the nature of the forces described by Physics. Ignorance of the Laws of Gravity did not prevent men falling out of trees and in equal measure, the force of Gravity was not suddenly felt when the Laws governing it were defined. We are, nevertheless, often acutely aware of the actions of these forces and in no different way have we been unaware of our needs, emotions and thoughts.

From the standpoint of the present study it is how Radionics can correlate what we *feel* or *sense* is wrong with us with the various Locations in the Subtle Bodies; in short, how the symptoms experienced can be correlated with which energy structures are distressed. In Radionics we attempt to describe and understand these fields and their relationship to the living conscious organism. When things go wrong, we attempt to discover where the energetic disturbance lies and to reassert the primacy of normal function as far as is possible. It is this correction that the patient may feel and experience as a change in the mind, emotions and physical body towards a more positive state.

CHAKRAS AND NADIS
Hence Chakras are, in principle, force centres in the Subtle Anatomy which integrate the states of consciousness linked to the various subtle bodies with the physical anatomy. In Chapter 5 we have seen a basic description of the Chakras and the type of energy which generally infuses each of them. In the human system, the Chakras are considered to be integrally linked with both the (physical) Nervous and Endocrine systems; as noted, each of the major Chakras is said to externalise through

a related Endocrine Gland. Each of the major Chakras is also innervated by the Nadis, a complex network of energy channels considered to be the counterpart of the Nervous system:

'The conduits of Prānik or vital force are the nerves called Nādi, which are reckoned to exist in the thousands in the body....The Bhūta-śuddhi Tantra speaks of 72,000, the Prapancasāra-Tantra speaks of 300,000, and the Śiva-Samhitā of 350,000....'[134]

It is arguable that for the purposes of Radionic treatment the Nadis may generally be considered as a complete system. Consequently Chakras, Nadis, Nervous and Endocrine Systems form an integral and in this regard, Bailey writes:

'The nadis, therefore, determine the nature and the quality of the nervous system with its extensive network of nerves and plexi covering the entire physical body. The nadis, and consequently the network of nerves, are related primarily to two aspects of man's physical equipment - the seven major centres [chakras] in the etheric body, and the spinal column with the head....The nadis in the physical body correspond to the life or spirit aspect; the nerves are the correspondence to the soul or quality aspect. That which demonstrates as their united externalisation is the endocrine system which corresponds to the form or matter aspect. These three - the nadis, nervous system and the glands - are the material correspondences to the three divine aspects; they are esoterically responsive to these three aspects and they make the man upon the physical plane what he is. These three groups are themselves conditioned (via the seven centres....) by the astral or mental vehicles, or by the integrated personality, or by the soul which begins to use the personality as a transmitting and transmuting agency....these three major systems within the human being express through the medium of the physical body the condition or the state of development of the centres....When the centres are awakened throughout the body....the result of this will be a well-balanced endocrine system....the vitality and life pouring through the entire body will then be of such potency that automatically the physical body will be resistant to disease, either innate, hereditary, or of group

---

134. Avalon, *op. cit.,* 109 - 110; in general Chapter 5 contains a detailed commentary on the Nadi, Chakras and Nervous System.

origin....I express for you a future probability but not an immediate possibility.' [135]

Part of the problem of disease results from imbalances in energy flows through the chakras. Again:

'Today as there is uneven development, with some centres unawakened, others overstimulated, and with the centres below the diagram overactive, you have consequently, whole areas of the body where the nadis are in an embryonic state, other areas where they are highly energised but with their flow arrested because some centre [chakra] *along the path of their activity is unawakened....these uneven conditions produce potent effects upon the nervous system and the glands, leading to overstimulation in some cases, subnormal conditions in others, lack of vitality, overactivity, and other undesirable reactions which inevitably produce disease.'* [136]

It is the calibre of these energies, and the quality of their transmission into the Nervous and Endocrine systems, transfused via the Chakras and Nadis, which does much to determine their functioning. In short the constitution and character of each individual is determined to some considerable degree by the calibre and condition of the Chakras and Nadis. Consequently ongoing worry, hidden anxieties, self-destructive feelings, toxic beliefs, poisonous attitudes towards others, disproportionate and continued emotionalism, stress, anger, rage, fear, excessive sympathy, over-identification with others, idealism, mysticism, one-sided materialism, greed, hypocrisy, repression of the personal unconscious, subconsciously-held negative beliefs, denial and self-denial, oppression of or domination by others, feelings of powerlessness, helplessness, guilt, religious zeal, obsession, violence, tragedy, trauma and a whole vast other range of psychological and emotional states - which are so very human and which so much make us *the humans that we are* - can disturb or even destroy the balance between chakras and other elements of the subtle anatomy. The resulting uneven and imbalanced energy flows may form fertile ground for the development of many forms of disease, and again we can come to a further definition of Radionics - the science of *alignment, co-ordination* and *normalisation* of the human subtle energy

---

135. Bailey, (1953), p. 196 - 198.
136. Bailey, *op. cit.*, p. 198

fields. Equally, because such flows can be grossly disturbed, it follows that the system can, to a presently-unknown degree,[137] be returned to balanced and even functioning.

For the purposes of Radionic treatment the following 9 Chakras could be analysed to determine their condition, this including the 7 major Chakras and two others:

CHAKRA	APPROXIMATION LOCATION
CROWN	apex of the skull.
BRAIN (also known as Pineal or Soul Seat):	more-or-less midway between the Crown Chakra and Brow Chakra.
BROW	above the forehead and slightly above the centre point of the eyebrows. The Brow Chakra is often confused with the Third Eye; in fact the Third Eye manifests as a result of the development of certain abilities in the individual.
ALTA MAJOR	base of the skull.
THROAT	slightly below ALTA MAJOR, effectively, in the middle of the neck.
HEART	above the spinal column at the same level as the entry point to the right Atrium.
SOLAR PLEXUS	typically at the same level as the fundus of the stomach.
SACRAL	between 4th and 5th vertebrae of the Spine.
BASE	at the base of spine, immediately beneath the Coccyx. Not to be confused with a related chakra located between anus and genitals (known as the Hui Yin point in acupuncture).

Table 3: Chakra positions

---

137. In the sense that we have not yet found the limits to the potential of Radionics, although there certainly will be some. Of course, Radionics is not the only approach to this problem, and practices such as meditation, Qi Gong, Yoga, Pranayama, etc etc all may have a similar objective and various levels of effectiveness.

The 'spinal' chakras - i.e. Alta Major to Base - are principally located slightly above the spinal column at the position described in the Table above. However the Chakras are often imaged as if located on the front of the body, and there may be a 'mirror' manifestation of certain major Chakras on the anterior aspect. [138]

CHAKRAS AND MANIFESTATION OF THE PHYSICAL BODY

Each Chakra is said to have at its centre, or deepest level, a focal point known as the Bindu, this meaning *dot, point*, or *drop* in Sanskrit. The Bindu point is the central or essential necessity which brings the Chakra into manifestation, and therefore functions as the principle gateway which enables consciousness and its formative forces to interface with the Physical form via the intermediate fields:

'The Cakras are the bodily centres of the world of differentiated manifestation, with its gross and subtle bodies arising from their causal body, and its threefold planes of consciousness in waking, sleeping, and dreamless slumber.'[139]

The genetic code is the means by which DNA controls the manufacture of specific proteins and is considered by biological science to be the ultimate determinant of life.[140] But the underlying idea in Radionics is that evolutionary processes and development may be conditioned by *at least* two forces - or, to put it another away, there are two forces in particular which interest us. As proposed in the previous Chapter, the *stronger* by far are the impersonal forces of Nature, the formative forces or *consciousness* of Nature, which, compounding as a result of repetition through evolutionary time and perhaps originating in archetypes, determine form itself by *very strongly affecting the probability*, at the quantum level, that certain forms will come into and continue in manifestation. On this basis, since I offer a 'deep' theory about reality DNA itself is not simply a product of chance but would have evolved as a result of archetypal and resonant processes and could be subject to changes in

---

138 . The locations relative to the spine are given to assist those practitioners who may seek to relate disturbances of the spine to dysfunctions of the chakras.
139. Avalon, *op.cit.,* p. 127
140. Oxford (2005), p.354

them.[141] The *weaker* are the forces generated by the individual in response to his situation in the physical world, his responses - his *state of consciousness* - which, if negatively conditioned, may inhibit the performance and functioning of the physical body in any number of ways. The Subtle Bodies, which are the non-physical vehicles of manifestation of the individual, connect to the Physical body through various routes and may condition its functioning from the genetic level upwards.[142]

The Bindu point at the heart of the Chakra is the focal point through which conditioned Etheric force and prana, distributed via the Nadis, emerges into the Physical realm. Thus the Bindu points are nodes around which Chakras coalesce and develop. As noted the Chakra Bindu points may also be considered to be the transition points between the deeper levels of consciousness, the probabilistically-defined quantum-mechanical field and the actual living physical human body - the point, perhaps, although hardly in actual physical space, at which the putative 'collapse of the waveform' occurs i.e. the nexus between consciousness and matter. These, then, comprise the vitalization and morphogenetic functions of the Chakras noted at the beginning of the previous Chapter. We may correlate the waveforms described by physics with esoteric concepts. Avalon states:

---

141. For e.g. 'The sameness of all atoms with a common wavefunction influences the way our world works....MIT physicist Victor Weisskopf points out an important biological consequence of atomic identity: No two classical systems are really identical. But in quantum theory it makes sense to say that two iron atoms are 'exactly' alike because of the quantized orbits. So an iron atom here and an iron atom in the Soviet Union are exactly alike. Our hereditary properties are nothing else than the quantum states of parts of DNA. In some way the reoccurrence every spring of a flower of a certain shape is an indirect expression of the identity and uniqueness of quantum orbits.' Herbert, *op. cit.*, p. 122

142. Thus, for example, although genetic structure (DNA) might be more or less predetermined (fixed by evolutionary processes), the new science of Epigenetics studies the way in which physiology, cell functioning and therefore gene *expression* can be conditioned by the environment, including, in short, how beliefs, psychological states, emotions, reactions and so forth can promote or inhibit health and well-being. See for example, Lipton (2005) (*The Biology of Belief*). Bruce Lipton Ph.D. is a cell biologist who shows, in a direct challenge to hard line genetic determinism, how environmental conditions affect the functioning of cells. In the widest sense he rejects the central dogma of genetics, which is, that genes control all aspects of our lives and are impervious to any external force or influence. Lipton explains how the environment impacts upon the membrane of the cell, and how this, in turn, via signals generated by the membrane, can strongly determine how the genes express themselves.

'The whole human body is in fact a Mantra, and is composed of Mantras. These sound powers vitalize, regulate, and control, the corresponding gross manifestations [i.e. cells, tissues, physical organs and related structures] in the regions surrounding them.'[143]

As Bailey puts it:

'A mantram is a combination of sounds, of words, and of phrases that, through virtue of certain rhythmic effects achieve results that would not be possible apart from them. The most sacred of all the Eastern mantrams....is the one embodied in the words 'Om mani padme hum'. Every syllable of this phrase has a secret potency, and its totality has seven meanings and can bring about seven different results. There are various mantric forms, based upon this formula and upon the Sacred Word [Aum], which, sounded rhythmically and in different keys, accomplish certain desired ends, such as....definite work, either constructive or destructive, upon the planes. The potency of a mantram depends upon the point in evolution of the man who employs it. Uttered by an ordinary man it serves to stimulate the good within his bodies, to protect him, and will also prove of beneficent influence on his environment. Uttered by an adept or initiate its possibilities for good are infinite and far-reaching....All these mantrams depend for their potency upon the sound and rhythm and upon the syllable emphasis imparted to them when enunciating and intoning. They depend too upon the capacity of the man who uses them to visualise and to will the desired effect.'[144]

In short, the correct sounding and *repetition* of a Mantra can produce definite effects or changes in the individual, and even the physical world. Looked at scientifically, the sound of a Mantra would produce a waveform in the air and even the slightest variation in pronunciation would result in an equivalent change in that waveform. This waveform can of course be heard; it can also be analysed, electronically, into absolutely specific parameters, the most basic ones of which are frequency and amplitude, to which can be added, for example, waveshape (envelope),

---

143. Avalon, *op. cit.,* p. 166. Mantras, when sounded, themselves being waveforms and see n. 18 below.
144. Bailey (1925) p. 926 n.

harmonics, and propagation over time.[145] It is certainly a medical fact that the body itself generates electrical waveforms, such as those created by the brain, and that different states of consciousness such as meditation or deep sleep produce waves of different frequencies.

A Mantra, however, is also an *externalization in sound of a process in consciousness*, which will perhaps produce a different type of waveform internally. Many people, and often without realising it, repeat a different kind of Mantra, which could go something like this: *'I'm no good' 'I'm a failure' 'I'm ugly' 'Nobody loves me' 'There's no hope for me'* - and so on and so forth. What kind of effects, then, could this produce upon the individual or upon others? There is no use pretending that only positive thoughts can produce results - although it must be borne in mind that the correlation between thoughts and results is not simple. It is often much more difficult to discern our *real* beliefs about ourselves, as opposed to those which are more temporary and circumstantial, such as socially-conditioned, *acquired*, attitudes and behaviour. Many people have, superficially, a negative self-image which ought to be destructive, but they achieve great things in life regardless, and we may therefore assume that a completely different deeper or more powerful core belief exists, less obvious or apparent, which in the final analysis drives them along, overruling many or all of their self-doubts. The opposite may also be true. The successful person riddled with self-doubt is also well known. There are many instances of successful people who conceal a mass of negative feelings beneath the confident image they project. In this regard I refer back, to some extent, to my discussion of the Astral Body and its layers. In the centre or 'core' lies the emotional idea or expression of the *'real me'* and at the periphery lies the idea of the group, of the tides of emotion which sweep through *us*. We all know of these tides and we continually read about or describe them, in such terms as *'mass hysteria' 'a great atmosphere' 'herd mentality' 'peer pressure' 'irrational fears' 'fashion' 'memes' 'brainwashing'* etc. Hence,

'Because receptors [in the cell wall] can read energy fields, the notion that only physical molecules can impact cell physiology is outmoded. *Biological behaviour can be controlled by invisible forces, including thought, as well as it can be controlled by physical molecules like*

---

145. In general all forms of electromagnetic waves, sound waves, pressure waves through materials, etc, can be described by certain similar basic parameters.

penicillin, a fact that provides the scientific underpinning for pharmaceutical-free energy medicine.'[146]

Some have proposed a simple linkage between Rays and Chakras, such that Ray 1 links to the Base Chakra, Ray 2 to the Sacral Chakra, and so on. Such notions need to be treated with great caution, since energies from various different levels in the Subtle Body may flow into each Chakra. A wide variety of combinations of Rays may flow into the Chakra system of any individual. It is, as a consequence, difficult to fix a standardised relationship between Rays and Chakras. In Chapter 7 I suggest a means by which Nature determines material form and here I also suggest, amongst other things, how the human psychological state may affect the condition of the body, this process taking place principally through the Chakras and their related structures.

THE AURA

The sum total of the energy state of the various Subtle Bodies and Chakras is said to be reflected in the condition of the Aura. This field is said to emanate from living beings and is said to contain 'information' about the state of health of the individual; various persons consider that they can 'read' the Aura and perform acts of healing on it. The healthy Aura is said emanate bright colours and the Aura of a sick person is said to emanate dark or muddy colours - hence, for example, the idea behind the expression *'I'm feeling off-colour'*; and changes in the Aura may well precede changes in the individual's health.

The Aura, furthermore, is considered to be magnetised by excess prana; whatever is taken up but cannot be used by the system is thrown off through it, and here we get the idea of *'a healthy aura'* or *'animal magnetism'* or *'an aura of confidence'* or *'in rude health'*; or in the case of other persons *'an aura of evil' 'an aura of menace'* - something which can be instinctively felt before it is experienced. Famous and prominent persons such as film and rock stars, politicians, television personalities and religious leaders are sometimes said to have a tremendous 'aura' or tremendous 'magnetism' - 'charisma' - and this Aura has, in some cases, been described as extending many feet or even hundreds of feet beyond the physical body. Some of this magnetism will obviously be a

---

146. Lipton, op. cit. , p. 54 -55, my emphasis. 'At the atomic level, matter does not even exist with certainty; it only exists as a tendency to exist. All my certitudes about biology and physics were shattered!' (p.68 - Lipton discovers Quantum Mechanics)

psychological effect - as we might term it, a group Astral effect - produced in the minds of onlookers by expectations, by continuous image-building and publicity exercises, by mass projection. Certain persons, however, really do appear to emanate a large amount of vital energy which is almost tangible in its presence and may have a real effect on the onlooker. A classic work on the Aura is by Walter Kilner:

'In 1908 Kilner conceived the idea that the human aura might be made visible if viewed through a suitable substance, and he experimented with dicyanin, a remarkable coal-tar dye. This dye appeared to have a definite affect upon eyesight, making the observer temporarily....more readily able to perceive radiation in the ultra-violet band....Kilner described techniques for viewing the human aura, which he claimed had inner and outer components. The inner aura followed the body outlines, while the outer aura was more nebulous. Kilner said that there were marked changes in the appearance of the aura in states of health and sickness, and that his viewing screen could be used for diagnosis.'[147]

According to Kilner the Aura has a definite structure and can be subdivided into 3 main regions, denoted the Etheric Double, the Inner Aura, the Outer Aura, although he also proposes the existence of an 'Ultra-Outer' Aura which becomes visible in certain circumstances. Various phenomena may be observed in the Aura and disturbances to it such as distortion, discolouration, damage and so forth may be noted; these reflect the condition of the patient's health. He also describes how, as health returns, the condition of the aura normalises and signs of disturbance disappear. Here we get the idea that each person has an energetic presence which in a certain sense precedes their physical presence as a phenomenon. This can be sensed or 'read' to reveal various aspects of their inner state, which may not be apparent to the ordinary observer:

'The common size and shape of the outer aura has been fully described....it consists of a faint amorphous cloud and appears entirely structureless, capable of being illuminated, but not, in the ordinary acceptation of the word, auto-luminous. During a prolonged inspection it

---

147. Dr. Walter Kilner (1847 - 1920), *The Human Aura* (1965). Except from the Foreword. Kilner had a distinguished career at St Thomas' Hospital in London, although his researches into the Aura were not so well looked-upon.

will be evident that the aura is not absolutely stable, as it constantly undergoes changes in various parts. A portion may become much more brilliant, and, after a few seconds or minutes, fade back to its original state while some other area commences the same cycle of changes....Rays, the most frequent of temporary changes, may for practical purposes be divided into three groups: - 1. Rays which proceed from one part to another part of the body, or from one person to another. 2. Streams which issue straight from the body into space. 3. Brighter patches entirely surrounded by the aura, which, as they seem to arise in the same manner as a ray of the other two groups, have been termed pseudo-rays.'[148]

Kilner recounts some 88 descriptions of the Aura from his case histories and it can be seen that the Aura is strongly conditioned by the state of health of the patient. Thus, for example:

'Case 62. F.F., a shoemaker, twenty-two years of age. When a boy of seven he had hip disease, and for years suffered from abscesses due to sequestra. He had undergone several operations, but for the last five years had enjoyed good health until a week previous to his inspection, when he noticed a rash upon the side of his chest followed by an eruption in the axilla and inner side of the arm, and another similar patch on the back accompanied by severe pain. When examined there was a herpetic patch about one and half inches square just below the clavicle. The whole of the right axilla and three quarters of the right arm, as well as another small place on the back....were covered with the rash. There could be no doubt about it being a severe case of herpes zoster. Inspection showed the aura to be less distinct than normal, and of a grey blue colour. On the left side it was quite natural, but very narrow, the outer being three inches in breadth and the inner two and a half....on the right side, however, the aura was normal round the head, but as soon as the arms were raised, the appearance under the right arm and a little way down the trunk was very peculiar....Against a black background, it looked as if it consisted of a haze honeycombed with dark holes. The effect produced is difficult in the extreme to describe, and the diminution of the intensity of the granular part of the aura resulted evidently from a loss of substance. Besides, the

---

148 . Ibid, p. 51 - 52. The rays described by Kilner should not be confused with the 12 Rays described at the beginning of this Chapter.

inner and outer auras appeared to be completely amalgamated, since not a vestige of differentiation could be detected.[149]

The Aura, then, is a dynamic emanation constantly responding to the workings of the inner and deeper energetic processes which have been described above. When the normal functioning of those processes becomes unsettled, it appears that equivalent disturbances are exhibited in the shape, size, colour, characteristics and functioning of the auric field.

Having, in the previous Chapters, given a summary description of the subtle anatomy and its functions, we now turn to the matter of disturbances to it which may result in ill-health.

---

149. *Ibid*, p. 228

9: DISEASED ENERGY

The previous Chapters give an outline model of the human Subtle Anatomy as a closely-interrelated and interacting series of energy fields and flows, driven by conscious, unconscious and subconscious processes. At one very distant end of the spectrum, it is proposed, is found the little-understood phenomenon of pure consciousness at least one characteristic of which is the *existential will-to-be*. At the other are found the formative forces which directly substand the physical body. From this point of view, consciousness does *not* arise from material causes as an after-effect of evolutionary processes, but is a primary cause - probably *the* primary cause - which drives the physical universe into being. Nevertheless, the means by which primary consciousness comes into manifestation is greatly conditioned over vast periods of time by the process of evolution; evolution is not only the evolution of form, but of forces, energies, fields, and of existential consciousness itself as the underlying driver of the whole. Just as energy and matter are stated by Physics to be different forms of the same thing, so the concept of a triad of consciousness, energy and matter may be the basis for a more detailed and profound understanding of the fundamental characteristics of 'the same thing'.

The experienced phenomena of mind arise, at minimum, from the individual interacting with his environment - the internal environment of sensations generated by the nervous system, and the external environment of people and the world in general. In this context experience is of particular importance; experience interacts with the individual's present circumstances to determine action and reaction. The resulting whole - the sense of self or identity, how the individual presents him or herself to others, and the conditioning of present actions by experience - are amongst the factors which combine to create what is commonly described as the personality or character. Conscious events, however, are also built upon a substructure of unconscious and subconscious processes.

The unconscious is a vast but poorly-understood arena of forces, vectors and determinants which influences, controls, directs and even erupts violently into the individual and group (social) consciousness, and does so, seemingly, without directly revealing anything of its nature. The unconscious appears to be not directly observable, but its topography and morphology may be deduced to a certain extent from dreams, linguistic, semantic and cultural artefacts, disorders in the functioning of the personality, and, in the larger context, the functioning and dysfunctioning of society and humanity as whole.

Subconscious processes include those such as autonomic and, in particular, instinctual functions (survival, sex drive, etc). These may interact with conscious processes in various ways, to produce, for example, conflicts. One result of such conflicts is the development of social ordering and control mechanisms - laws, morality, admissible and inadmissible behaviour, prohibitions, and the punishments which result from transgressing them.

In general one can propose four directions from which difficulty - illness, originating in what we may call *dis-eased energy* - may arise. These can be categorised, in the broadest sense, as Formative; Psycho-Spiritual; Integrative; Relational.

1. Formative: Disturbances may exist or originate in various fields *prior* to manifestation in the Physical. In this case the disease process exists as a potential which, according to circumstances, may be transferred into the fabric of the paraphysical body and thence to the physical body. These disturbances are basically latent or so sufficiently controlled as to have little influence on the individual's health. As stressors build up in the system, so the formative disturbances may gain power and begin to erode the forces which control them and keep them in check. In time they may emerge as key factors in any number of diseases, but most notably in the chronic diseases. Where the controlling energies are innately weak, so the effects of formative disturbances may make themselves known earlier, for example, in birth deformities and the early appearance of severe or potentially deadly diseases.

2. Psycho-Spiritual: Disturbances which originate in the higher subtle bodies, hence, the spiritual, mental or emotional basis of disease. These may also result from external events which impact the individual, or even the group, psycho-spiritual state. Hahnemann refers to these as *'diseases spun by the soul.'*[150] The primary point is that these are disturbances of non-physical origin which arise from difficulties in the process of self-expression or self-realisation and may therefore be considered, centrally, as existential or ontological in nature.

---

150 . Hahnemann (1996), p. 202 'Emotional Diseases Spun and Maintained by the Soul'

3. Integrative: Disturbances to the linkage and interface between different structures in the Subtle Anatomy, or between Subtle Anatomy and para-physical anatomy; or between paraphysical anatomy and the actual physical anatomy. Examples are Chakra - Nadi, and Chakra - Gland, Integrity. Just as the healthy Physical body forms a co-ordinated integral balanced by homoeostatic forces, so the same may be said of the healthy Subtle Anatomy; more properly, one is a reciprocal of the other. The two systems inter-relate to form a dynamic complex of energy flows through corresponding fields into form and back again.

4. Relational: Disturbances resulting from the individual's relationship with the physical world. This category includes the wide range of impacts and problems generally described by orthodox medical science, for example, infection, malnutrition, toxic acquisitions, malignancies, and so forth. From the Radionic point of view, it is the effect of these on the energy system which is of key interest, along with the extent to which physical symptoms may be removed or reduced by actions on the energy system only, and the extent to which weakness in the energy system allows ingress of such external factors.

Even more concisely, these four categories may be described as developing from three sources, namely, as diseases of *origination*, diseases of *integration*, and diseases of *manifestation*. In very difficult circumstances all may combine to serious or deadly effect.

BASIC CATEGORIES OF DISEASE
In order to obtain a clearer understanding of the sources of disease, it is possible to suggest a group of twelve categories which help classify the myriad illnesses into general types, as follows. This should not be considered as a final, definitive or rigid system, but may serve as a useful starting point for the practitioner:

1. FLOW
2. STRUCTURE & INTEGRITY
3. PATHOLOGICAL INHIBITION
4. POLLUTION
5. INVASION
6. REACTION
7. MORBID
8. STRESSORS - RELATIONAL & EXTERNAL

9. DEPLETION & IMBALANCE
10. MORTAL, ACUTE & SUB-ACUTE
11. OCCULT
12. TRANSITIONAL

I shall now briefly describe each category; each category contains a number of sub-topics. These form the core of the list of Factors which may impact Locations in the human Subtle Anatomy. A summary table of the Factors, grouped into the twelve Categories, is given in Appendix 4. *The reader should bear in mind that to a high degree of correspondence, any of the Factors may affect any of the Locations.*

To give an example, CONGESTION (blockage, obstruction) might be found in the Respiratory system, with the usual accompanying symptoms such as excessive production of mucus, inflammation of lungs or bronchi, breathing difficulties, pain, cough, and so forth. This disease might be variously described as Bronchitis, Pneumonia, COPD[151], etc, according to medical diagnosis. But at the same time Congestion might also be found in the Astral Body (congestion of emotional energy on account of some negative emotional or psychological artefact). It might be found in the Mental Body (congestion of the mental process due to some negative psychological factor or complex, e.g. a *thought-form* to which the patient is strongly attached, which in turn produces an inhibition in the personality); perhaps in the Causal Body, where there is a hindrance to the sense of purpose; perhaps in the Atmic Body, where there is an obstruction to the individual's sense of *soul* expression, and so on. Therefore one might (by analysis) find not only Respiratory Congestion but also Congestion in any number or combination of levels in the Subtle Anatomy, and typically these *may* be instrumental in the appearance of the resulting physical illness. This does not necessarily say that because you have an emotional disturbance you *will* become ill, or ill in a certain way; or that because of a certain psychological disturbance you have created your own illness, i.e. you are to blame for your problems.[152] On

---

151. Chronic Obstructive Pulmonary Disease.
152. Obviously if an individual smokes 60 cigarettes and drinks a bottle of whisky a day one might well deduce a linkage with the cancer or cirrhosis which may eventually appear and thus conclude, not unreasonably, that the individual is the maker of his own ruin. On looking deeper it will likely be found that this kind of ultimately self-destructive behaviour is a manifestation of some underlying problem which is not so easily discerned.

the other hand, just because you have a certain symptom it does not necessarily mean that this is also reflected at some other level in the system. As described below, the arcana of possibilities is intended to reflect or at least indicate the complexities of the human situation, not reduce it to simplistic quasi-causal linkages.

1. FLOW
CONGESTION; OVERSTIMULATION; UNCOORDINATION; COORDINATION BETWEEN; TIME-BASED CYCLES & FUNCTIONS; AURIC ENERGISATION CYCLE

Here we are concerned with disruptions to the ordered, controlled, balanced and regulated flow of energies. As described in earlier Chapters, this includes, at minimum, consciousness, prana, and the formative forces.

CONGESTION - blockage or obstruction. Here there is an impedance to the flow of energy, such that Locations 'downstream' of the congestion will be starved of energy to a greater or lesser degree, while Locations 'upstream' will tend to suffer from an excessive amount of dammed-up energy spilling back towards them. Obstruction, to a greater or lesser degree, of the entry and exit points of Chakras and the need to clear same was especially emphasized by Tansley (1972) but in the present overview, Congestion may be found anywhere in the system.

OVERSTIMULATION - excessive energy in any Location. Many symptoms produced by nervous over-excitement are well-known. Bailey, for example, states that:

'....too powerful an etheric body and the overstimulation of the centres concerned, may put too great a strain upon the nervous system and produce, as a consequence, definite nervous trouble, migraine, mental and emotional imbalance, and, in some cases, lead to insanity.'[153]

Anxiety, high blood pressure, habitual aggressive behaviour, panic attacks, hyperthyroidism, epilepsy, arrhythmia, IBS (Irritable Bowel

---

153. Bailey (1953), p.87

Syndrome), excessive stomach acidity and even cancer (in the sense of uncontrolled and excessive production of immature or primitive cells) along with many other symptoms and diseases may be signs of overstimulation in some part of the system. Conversely, symptoms of energetic depletion, such as Adrenal exhaustion ('burn-out'), may result from prolonged over-excitation and hence such a condition might be considered the reciprocal of overstimulation. Given the idea of disturbances to homoeostatic equilibrium in the Subtle Anatomy as a whole, symptoms found in one part of the system will tend to have their reciprocal or opposite correspondence in some other part of it.

UNCOORDINATION - here the energy flow *within* a Location becomes uncoordinated. Instead of energy flowing in a regulated and ordered manner it becomes irregular, spasmodic and unstable. At certain times there may be insufficient energy, at other times too much. Symptoms in various nervous diseases, such as chorea and other dyskinesias, may be signs of energetic uncoordination, as may arrhythmia (irregular heartbeat). Uncoordination in the Mental Body may reflect in incoherent thinking, and an inability to connect thoughts and ideas in a logical sequence, related to external reality.

COORDINATION BETWEEN - a very large range of possibilities presents itself. Essentially the idea is that of synchronized, ordered and rhythmic inter-relationship and functioning *between two or more* Locations. For example, between Stomach and Duodenum; between Small Intestine and Colon; between Pulmonary and Systemic circulation; between Sympathetic and Parasympathetic nervous systems; between various Endocrine glands, or between individual glands and the Endocrine system as whole; between Mental and Astral Bodies ('heart and mind'); between Chakras; between Meridians; and so forth. Many instances of uncoordination between two or more Locations may be found.

TIME-BASED CYCLES & FUNCTIONS - the human system is recognized as being very much coordinated to time. The so-called 24-hour Circadian rhythm is well-known, or if not, then certainly one of its major disruptions - jet lag - has been experienced by many. The 28-day female menstrual cycle is another example, and disorders of the same are common. The Ko - Shen Cycle in the Five Element Theory of TCM (Traditional Chinese Medicine) refers to the balanced diurnal flow of Yin and Yang energy between the 12 main External Meridians, and disruptions

ALPHA-NUMERIC
TRANSDUCER v3
(ANT v3) with
External Well

ALPHA-NUMERIC
TRANSDUCER
SCMFP
(ANT 'REMEDY
MAKER')

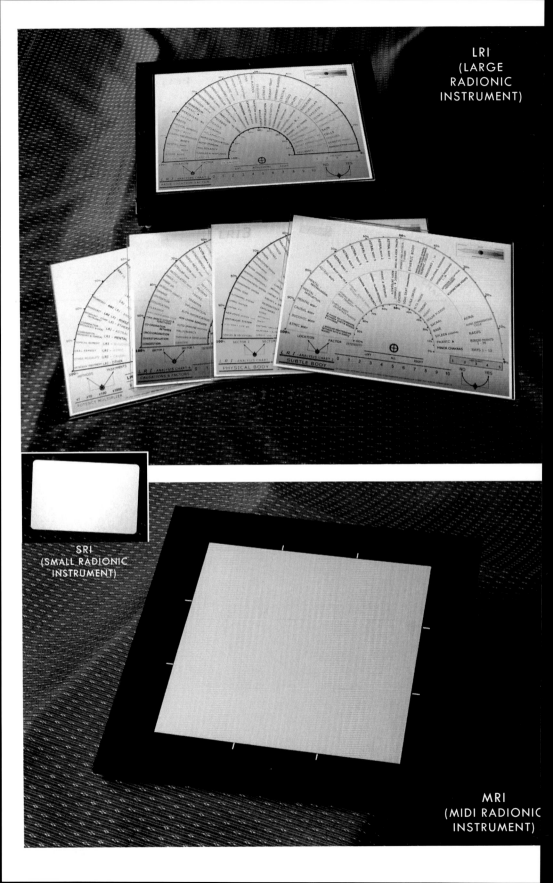

LRI
(LARGE
RADIONIC
INSTRUMENT)

SRI
(SMALL RADIONIC
INSTRUMENT)

MRI
(MIDI RADIONIC
INSTRUMENT)

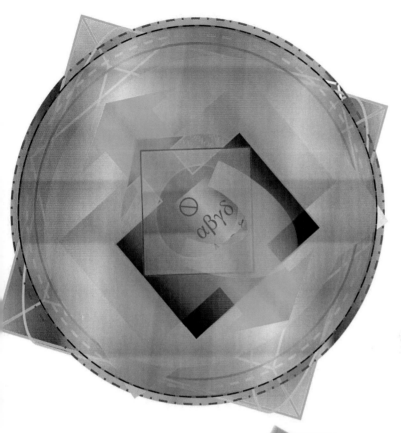

ARSENICUM
ALBUM
HOMOEOPATHIC
REMEDY

INFORMATION
ABOUT THE
COLOUR PLATES
CAN BE FOUND AT
THE END OF THE
BOOK

SPIGELIA
MARYLANDICA
HOMOEOPATHIC
REMEDY

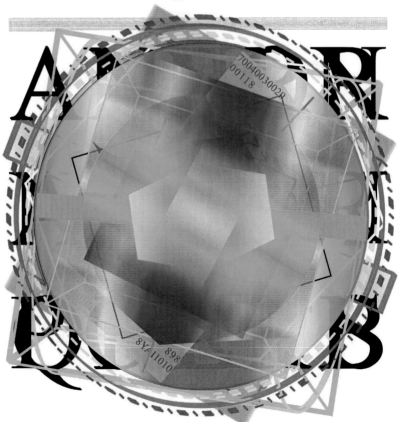

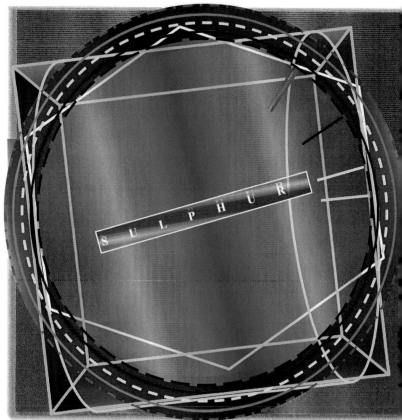

SULPHUR
HOMOEOPATHIC
REMEDY

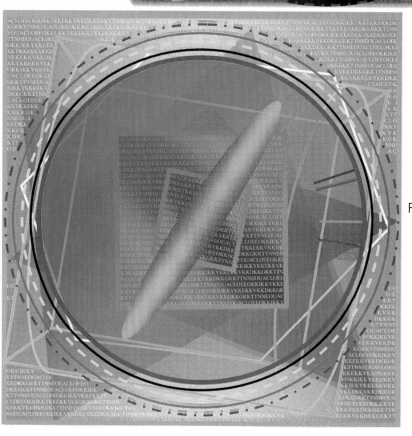

FOLLICULINUM
HOMOEOPATHIC
REMEDY

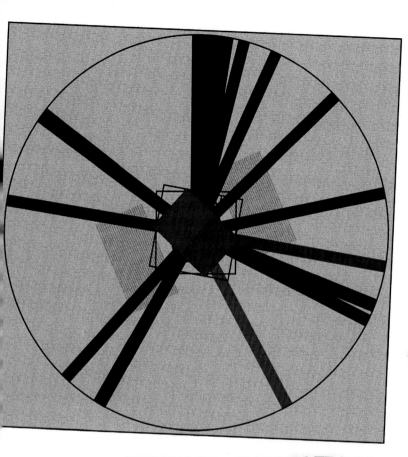

BORIUM
METALLICUM
HOMOEOPATHIC
REMEDY

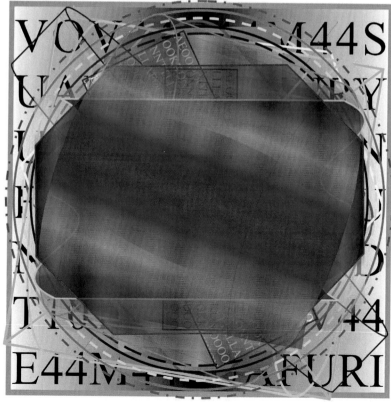

MERCURIUS
PRAECIPITATUS
ALBUS
HOMOEOPATHIC
REMEDY

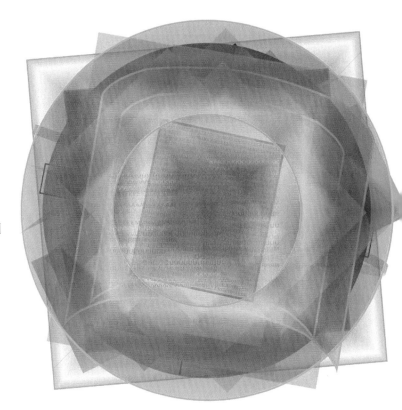

ETHERIC
BODY -
CONGESTION

VISUAL
SYSTEM -
NORMALISATIO

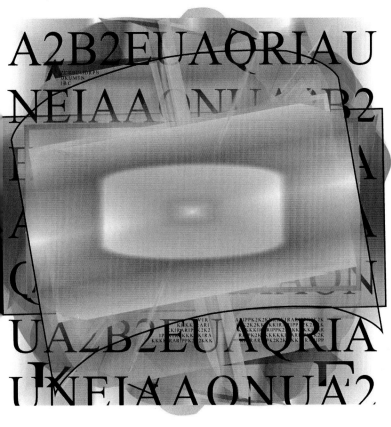

ETHERIC
BODY -
INFLAMMATION

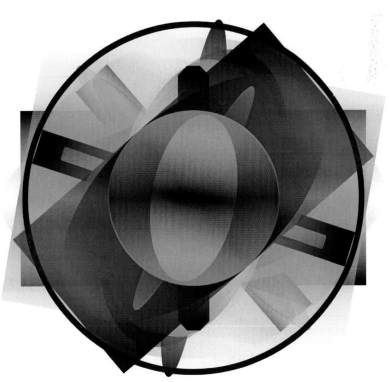

MUSCULAR
SYSTEM -
NORMALISATION

FEAR OF
CANCER
(PSYCHOLOGICAL
STATE)

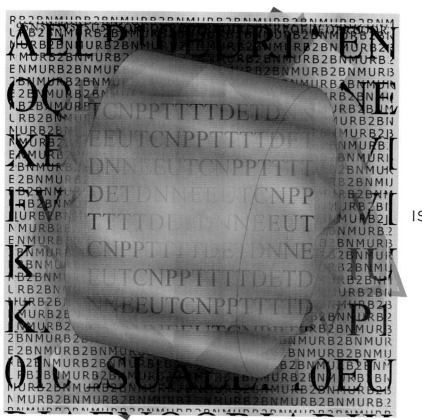

VIRAL
ISOMORPH
4

to this are considered to give rise to disease states. It should be noted that cycles governing cell division and replication are apparently not well understood at this time, although hormonal triggers are involved; in turn, the activity of the endocrine system is to some extent regulated by, or synchronized to, the Circadian and other rhythms.

Flow disturbances may be indicative of deeper or connected problems and the practitioner should always analyse the situation carefully before proceeding with treatments.

AURIC ENERGISATION CYCLE - there may be disturbances to the regular re-energisation cycle of the Aura. The rate at which the aura is refreshed will vary from individual to individual.

2. STRUCTURE & INTEGRITY
(a) DAMAGE, DISTORTION, DISLOCATION, CLEAVAGE; (b) INTEGRITY (VARIOUS CATEGORIES), (c) PHASE, (d) ANGLE

(a) DAMAGE, DISTORTION, DISLOCATION, CLEAVAGE
Here we are concerned with defects in the fields which result from stressors of different kinds, or in more general terms, *defective structures*. Every form has a certain tolerance to impact, but if the energy is sufficient then the form will be distorted, damaged, destroyed or otherwise mutilated. A car may absorb a certain amount of impact in a small crash and not suffer damage, but if it is hit at high speed by a large truck then the bodywork, chassis or other subassemblies might be distorted, parts will be thrown out of correct relationship with one another (dislocation), panels and other components will be literally bent out of shape (damage), and to a greater or lesser extent parts might be severed from one another (cleavage). By analogy similar things can happen to the fields of the Subtle Anatomy. In the healthy person these have a normal form and relationship with each other. In disease there may be changes to the fields which, as a result of the unsustainable impact of various forms of stressors, change their structure and thus their ability to function correctly.[154]

Thus we assume there is a normal form for all the fields of the Subtle Anatomy and, within a certain range, for all humans. If some

---

154. Kilner, *op. cit.*, provides numerous observations of distortion and disturbance to the shape and colour of the aura and its components in his case histories.

structural deformation is detected then it may be necessary to give treatments to try and return the field to its normal state, i.e. to try and normalise it. Many people suffer from low vitality, and fatigue syndromes such as CFS[155], a disease of uncertain cause, are medically recognized. Here a possible cause, such as structural *damage* or *distortion*, may be causing a degree of disturbance to some part of the Subtle Anatomy, resulting in poor transmission of the various needed forms of energy, notably prana. This may also reflect in depletion conditions in the endocrine system such as 'low' thyroid or underperformance of the many hormone producing cells outside of the main endocrine glands.

Cleavage, for example in the Etheric Body, may indicate a degree of disconnection between the Etheric Body itself and some of the other fields with which it must integrate, such as the Meridians, the Physical-Morphic counterpart fields, the Astral Body, the Chakras, the Nadis, and so forth. There may be a degree of disconnection between an organ and its underlying paraphysical fields in some disorders; cleavage of the underlying field may play in a role at the onset of diseases such as Type 1 Diabetes.

Persons who have suffered from a severe physical impact may, amongst other injuries, have sustained a *dislocation* of some of the energy fields from the physical body. Cases are found of people whose bodies perform all normal functions under autonomic control but have a bare semblance of normal interactive consciousness or are in a state of coma, and these conditions may be of very prolonged duration. Here the idea is that certain fields or a combination of fields have literally been knocked out of position relative to the physical body, so instead of being superimposed and aligned correctly they are displaced. The result is that the required energy cannot follow its normal path of transmission. If the autonomic system is sufficiently undamaged then the body will continue as far as possible in survival mode but the more delicate mechanisms producing normal consciousness are not capable of functioning.

A further point to consider is that defects to the structures, if not perhaps immediately critical, may accumulate during a lifetime. They can, in principle, contribute towards ageing by excessively degenerating the viability of the linkage between the Physical Body and its underlying fields, impairing vitality and allowing various inimical energetic presences to come into play in a more aggressive manner. Most people with any level

---

155. Chronic Fatigue Syndrome. Epstein-Barr and other viruses may have a role in CFS.

of computer awareness would see the value of defragmenting a computer hard drive and removing junk files, but how many think of defragging themselves? Ageing and death are normal but chronic and degenerative disease with its destructive processes and illnesses[156] is generally not considered desirable.

(b) INTEGRITY

There are various Locations which as a basis for correct flow or energy must be well-integrated. Particular attention needs to be paid to them in analysis. By 'integrity' I mean that the interface (linkage) between the related fields is coherent - the 'parts' fit together seamlessly. This allows proper flow of energy - for example, Prana - between them. Integrity as a category stands somewhat outside the normal Location - Factor system used in analysis, since the lack of integrity, or even *dis*-integration, of the Location *is* the problem under consideration. A Table indicating a range of possible problems is given in Appendix 5 but typical are disturbances to integrity between a Chakra and its related Endocrine gland. In the case of, for example, the Throat Chakra and Thyroid Gland, this may result in over- or under activity of the gland, e.g. hypo- or hyperthyroidism, disorders of the Parathyroid glands, and so forth. Disturbances involving the Spleen Chakra, Pranic Triangle, and its integrity with the Etheric and Physical-Morphic bodies may be a common problem and a source of lowered vitality.

(c) PHASE AND (d) ANGLE

In the first instance there is the *Phase relationship* between the various Subtle Bodies and Chakras. The idea of Phase is well-known in

---

156. Meditators, Qi Gong and Yoga practitioners, and so on, have techniques, some of ancient origin, which are aimed at cleansing and ordering the subtle energy fields. I caution strongly against reductionist models and analogies which claim that humans are simply machines, computers, survival mechanisms, bio-robots, concatenations of behaviouristic phenomena, etc. Such reductionism may become dehumanizing, with undesirable consequences (witness, for example, the linking of Darwinism to Eugenics). In addition, machines, computers, etc., are artefacts which have emerged as a result of the development of certain aspects of human consciousness and are partial manifestations of the limitless well; many other technologies may be possible which go far beyond those which presently exist, but they too will be passing reflections of what we *are becoming*, not depictions of what we *are*.

Physics with regard to the study of waveforms. In Fig. 14, two waveforms in phase with each other are indicated in A. Because they are marching in step, one is exactly superimposed on the other and cannot be seen. In B, the waveforms are out of phase and marching out of step, and one can clearly be distinguished from the other.[157]

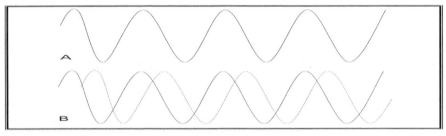

Figure 13:Phase relationships between waveforms

This hitherto unremarked problem refers to the Phase relationship between Chakras and Subtle Bodies, and also *between* Chakras and (if the time aspect is ignored) may be compared to the phases of the moon. Chakras have been described as opening and closing but a different image of the process may be useful. Chakras do not open and close but their 'surface' or 'face' is progressively revealed or obscured over a time cycle particular to each Chakra type - for example, approximately 5 full cycles per second for the Throat Chakra. This sequence resembles in many ways the phases of the moon, which pass from null visibility (New Moon) to total visibility (Full Moon) over the 29-day moon cycle. Each major Chakra has a definitive time period over which the Phasing process must take place for the individual to experience a balanced and proper flow of energy and proper relationship with the various Subtle Bodies, although those most notably affected by disturbances to the proper functioning of the Phase cycles are the Etheric, Mental and Astral (in that order). There may be some affect on the organ counterpart fields in certain types of illness such as cancers, leukaemias and anaemias. Correct co-ordination of Phase cycles between all major Chakras is a point of extreme importance.

---

157. The phenomenon of phasing is actually a well-known electronic effect used in music production. *Itchycoo Park* (1967) by *The Small Faces* was one of the first records to feature it and this can be heard on both the lead vocal and certain drum fills. The listener may note it for the first time at approximately 1:00 into the track.

The second problem described in this section, *Angular relationships* between Rays and Subtle Bodies, is a difficult process to describe but by way of analogy the idea of a train moving past an individual can used. If the whistle is blown while the train passes, a shift in pitch is heard - the well-known Doppler effect.[158] As the train moves towards the observer, the pitch of the whistle rises and as it moves away the pitch drops. If both individual and the train were moving side by side at the same speed, no pitch change would be discernible.

As already noted each individual is attuned to the calibre and characteristics of certain Rays, with a particular Ray dominating each of the main Subtle Bodies and systems. The Ray can be considered to be a fundamental vibrational pattern which links the individual to certain characteristics e.g. a Ray 5 Mental Body would give the individual a typically enquiring, 'scientific', concretised or 'materialistic' outlook. Circumstances may produce a situation where the individual becomes out of synchronisation with their fundamental Rays; thus we have the idea of lead and lag i.e. over-qualification or under-qualification by the Ray and its characteristics. This comes about as a result of a disturbance in synchronisation and the relationship between the individual and his or her rays can be described in terms of angle i.e. degree of offset. In a normal situation this would be considered to be zero; in over-energisation, plus so many degrees and in under-energisation, minus so many degrees. Such disturbances can give rise to a wide range of problems in the expression of personality, such as exaggerated or extreme characteristics, or tendencies which may drive the individual into situations of difficulty.

3. MIASMS AND MIASMATIC INHIBITION

The 'miasm' theory was developed first by Hahnemann, founder of Homoeopathy, in his attempt to identify a basis for chronic disease. In Hahnemann's view the miasm is a long-term, ingrained stressor to the Dynamis, his 'catch-all' term for the subtle energy fields, arguably what is described here as the Etheric Body and related structures and energy flows. The Miasm tends to be fixed in its presence and according to homoeopathic tenets may only be removed using the appropriate anti-miasmatic homoeopathic remedies. As the matter is rather complex the subject will be discussed more fully in Chapter 11.

---

158. With regard to light this effect is known as Red Shift. Doppler effects are widely used throughout science as a measurement technique.

4. POLLUTION

POISONS, TOXINS, TOXAEMIA are the broad categories. For present purposes, Poisons are substances of inorganic and Toxins are substances of organic origin, both groups considered injurious to the body. Toxaemia means the build-up of bacterial toxins in the blood. The central point here is that according to the concepts of Radiesthesia all such polluting substances have their own vibrational signature or waveform. From the viewpoint of Radionics, these signatures would be present in the fields corresponding to the affected regions of the physical body proper and hence Toxins and Poisons have a dual presence, physical and energetic. The body may therefore be detoxified of the physical substance but the energetic signature may remain in the individual's field. It is also feasible that treatments to remove the energetic signature of such Toxins and Poisons will induce the body to detoxify itself. When the impaired vibrational quality of the paraphysical body is normalised, a result may be that the functioning of any afflicted Location will improve and as a consequence, it will throw off any offending or noxious materials, right down to the cellular level.

As is well known, a vast amount of pollutants are now present in the environment, many of them of man-made origin. We are regularly subjected to pollutants from many sources, beginning with everyday objects such as cleaning materials and even food containers, plastics, and so forth. To this can be added dangerous presences such as organo-phosphates and organo-chlorides[159], traffic fumes, industrial waste, and so on. It is arguable that at minimum 30 to 40 percent all well-designed Radionic treatments produce some level of energetic detoxification in the patient.

5. INVASION

INFECTION - MULTIPLE; BACTERIA; VIRUSES; RETROVIRUSES; PARASITES & PROTOZOA; FUNGI, MOULDS AND SPORES; INFECTION - OTHER; INFESTATION

This category obviously includes the wide range of pathogens and other, largely microscopic, invaders which attack humanity at all times and in all places, sometimes with devastating, crippling, or deadly results. The Black Death (14th Century Europe), Syphilis, Smallpox, the Spanish Flu

---

159. Years back the author had a business advisor who died horribly of organo-phosphate poisoning.

(1918 - 1920) and Tuberculosis, to name but five examples, all resulted in large numbers of fatalities. The human body is subject to continuous invasion by many types of inimical micro-organisms and the competence of the individual's immune system in repelling or destroying these invaders is crucial to the maintenance of health. The concept of the physical immune system and its actions is well-documented in the orthodox literature and needs no reiteration here, but it may be noted that there are, basically, two means of defence, specific and non-specific. In the case of the former immunity has been acquired through exposure, either to the specific pathogen or via vaccination. In the latter, various means, such as the complement system, provide a general defence. The over-arching concept may be described as self - / non-self, i.e. that the body can differentiate between the materials from which it is made and that which is foreign and hostile to it and can take action accordingly.

Various categories are suggested for analytical purposes, the basic groups being listed above. INFECTION - OTHER includes those groups of infectious organisms not covered by the other more obvious groups, or not yet recognized. INFESTATION includes larger organisms such as lice or bedbugs. The idea is that each microorganism has not only its known physical characteristics but also a unique vibrational pattern or *energetic envelope* which can, potentially, be detected by radiesthesic means. Many Radionic codes have been created to assist in helping the practitioner to identify individual species of pathogen. In practice, it may not be necessary to make an analysis in such detail as treatments may be aimed at eliminating a general class of infection in a particular Location, e.g. a fungal infection in the lungs, a bacterial infection in the colon, a viral infection in the liver, and so on.[160] What is crucial in the infective process - in the conversion from invasion to infection - is that the pathogen becomes able to insert its energetic envelope into the field of the infected Location, and, sometimes, various higher level fields. Thus, if the infection is sufficiently severe, the 'image' of a pathogen may be found in the Meridians, and Astral, Mental, Causal or other bodies. The infection changes, to a greater or lesser extent, the energy field of the host and may impair its functioning in many ways.

The development of an invasion into an infection normally has a prodromal period during which the immune system and micro-organism

---

160. Comparatively, the idea of a 'broad-spectrum antibiotic' is well-known. This type of anti-microbial drug kills a range of common pathogens, eliminating the need for potentially lengthy and costly lab work.

struggle for dominance. According to the virulence of the pathogen and the condition of the immune system, this may be of shorter or longer duration. Thus one may not feel well for some time before an outbreak of an infection-based illness, without knowing why until the typical symptoms - for example, of influenza - make themselves apparent. This situation may be reflected in the individual's field and lead to uncertainty in radiesthesic analysis, as the outcome of the struggle is not yet determined.

If the pathogen *is* able to establish itself - infection - then its energetic identity will then be more clearly 'visible' to the practitioner. Furthermore is proposed that like any other organism a pathogen requires its quantum of life force energy and has its own underlying relationship with the formative forces of Nature. In this case the practitioner may strive to disturb the functioning of the organism by acting against the natural process, which is to say, by attempting to severely disrupt the relationship between the organism and those energies which support its physical presence and by so doing, compromise its existence. If this can be done effectively, the ability of the host's immune system to complete the job may be enhanced.[161] It should also be noted that some level of immunity might be induced using energetic means; this has certainly been tried in Homoeopathy by using preventative doses of remedies judged to be similar to the symptom-picture of the disease.

---

161. It is not known to the author whether microorganisms can be killed *in vitro* solely by Radionic means. As must be apparent by now, Radionics is an 'internal' method where we attempt to manipulate formative forces and energies in various ways. Beyond drug therapy such as antibiotics, other approaches to the problem of destroying pathogens using 'external' methods, principally electromagnetic pulses delivered by various means, have and are being tried. One of the most well-known is the work of Royal Raymond Rife (1888 - 1971) although the reader may also look up Georges Lakhovsky (1869 - 1942), Dr Robert Beck (1925 - 2002), Hulda Clark (1928 - 2009), and others.

6: REACTION

DEFENSIVE: INFLAMMATION; AUTO-IMMUNE RESPONSE; AUTO-INTOXICATION; NON-LIVING DEPOSITS

AUTO-GENERATED: ALLERGY; FOOD INTOLERANCE; MALABSORPTION; HYPERSENSITIVITY - CHEMICAL; HYPERSENSITIVITY; HYPERSENSIBILITY

Reactive states in this category are generally responses to a different type of invasion, typically that of non-infectious organic material, for example, animal hair (allergens), or *in*organic materials such as chemicals. For convenience one may attempt to divide these reactions into two groups, Defensive and Auto-Generated, although in reality they may be entangled.

INFLAMMATION itself is the well-known reaction of tissue to any form of impact, be it infection, physical trauma, or material irritants, and is famously typified by heat, redness, swelling and pain. It may also involve a degree of loss of function in the affected part. Inflammations are generally classed into two categories, acute and chronic. In the latter case the healing process has failed and there is an ongoing problem, which may be *local*, as in the case of inflammatory bowel diseases, or *systemic*, as in the case of SLE (Systemic Lupus Erythematosus), a chronic systemic inflammation of connective tissue.

It is also possible for inflammations to exist unnoticed or undiagnosed in the body for long periods of time, having a general negative effect on the health. In analysis of the patient the practitioner needs to study any such observed inflammations carefully as they may indicate other, and perhaps serious, underlying conditions. In short the inflammation may also be a kind of holding pattern which keeps the body in a certain defensive state and allows some degree of equilibrium in the system to be maintained, albeit at a lower level than complete health would provide, yet controlling more serious potential problems. The point is that to simply wade in and treat an inflammatory state may be suppressive. If it is reduced through treatment, providing a superficial degree of relief, the underlying forces which brought it into existence may be funnelled into more vicious activity in some other part of the body, or may return with further aggressive force to the same place, at a later date.

AUTO-IMMUNE RESPONSE diseases involve the immune system attacking the body, indicating a breakdown of the self/not-self distinction. Apart from SLE, some other autoimmune diseases include various forms of anaemia, rheumatoid arthritis, glomerulonephritis, Hashimoto's disease, etc. From the point of view of Radionics, these diseases may have a miasmatic origin, and in particular may originate in, or be greatly exacerbated by, the four environmental miasms which will be described in Chapter 11. No doubt prototypes - or even archetypes - of these diseases have existed for millennia but in recent times they have become more widespread and may be complexed with other problems.

AUTO-INTOXICATION refers to the build up of waste material at some level, for example, in the colon. Here waste matter may accrue and contribute towards a toxic environment where bowel flora become imbalanced, allowing overgrowths of potentially inimical organisms such as Candida. Conditions such as 'leaky gut' syndrome may develop, where toxic material permeates the gut wall and enters the bloodstream, resulting in a wide range of symptoms which may be hard to link directly to the basic cause.

NON-LIVING DEPOSITS refers to accretions of inorganic material, such as arterial plaque (atheroma), calcified material such as kidney and gall stones (renal and biliary calculus). Calcification may also affect various endocrine or lymph glands.

ALLERGY may result from some substances being so continuous a provocation as to cause a re-programming of the body's reactions i.e. the well-known allergic response, which is a habitual over-reaction (overstimulation) of the immune system to the presence of a particular substance such as pollen, cat hair, certain metals, dust, cosmetics, artificial fabrics, and so on. Resulting allergic symptoms may be wide-ranging and extremely severe.

FOOD INTOLERANCE is a non-allergic response to a foodstuff inimical to the system and may be much more difficult to identify than allergy because of the length of time between ingestion and reaction, i.e. of much longer duration than in an instance of allergy. The link between a food and the wide range of possible symptoms produced by intolerance to it may therefore be more difficult to establish. In addition it has been noted that we often crave foods to which we are intolerant, as if the system is desperately trying to obtain some needed nutrient from the food but cannot obtain it on account of the inability to metabolise it.

MALABSORPTION specifically refers to problems in the small intestine which impair the ability to take up certain nutrients, for example, certain vitamins. This condition may have its origins in an underlying miasmatic state and may result in more obvious symptoms (vitamin or nutritional deficiency).

HYPERSENSITIVITY in general terms means the tendency to react out of all proportion to stimulus. The idea of the emotionally-hypersensitive person is well-known, the person to whom, for example, the slightest negative comment might cause a catastrophic collapse of self-confidence, or, comparatively, explosive and even violent rage. Hypersensitivity may develop from any number of causes but excessive stress draining the nervous system combined with adrenal exhaustion might be one such. Bullying of a child at school, breaking down the developing self-image, might be another. One might find Hypersensitivity at many levels throughout the Subtle Anatomy: in the Teeth (e.g. to heat and cold); Adrenals and Nervous System (e.g. to stress); in the Aura (to the presence of other people); in the Astral Body (emotional hypersensitivity); in the Mental Body (to insults, slights etc); in the Causal Body (to setbacks); in the Atmic Body (experienced as despair and despondency about the reason to live and to *be*, in the existential sense); and in the Chakras and Meridians.

HYPERSENSIBILITY is a continual state of openness towards all stimuli, where the normal boundaries protecting the psyche have become lowered or weakened. This can result in many forms of psychism and displays of 'psychic abilities' such as the ability to sense or even read others' thoughts and emotions, experience of premonitions, forebodings, awareness of spirit entities, and so forth; or the development of an exaggerated aesthetic (as a protection). The counterpart can be severe exhaustion or even breakdown of the normal processes of the psyche, sometimes with production of hysterical symptoms and nervous under- or over-activity: depletion and overstimulation combined.

Finally, *CHEMICAL HYPERSENSITIVITY*[162] appears to be particularly modern condition, an acquired hyper reactivity to all forms of chemicals in the environment, particularly those found in household products and cosmetics.

7. MORBID
MALIGNANCY; TUMOURS & NEOPLASMS; CANCER

Although more commonly thought to mean tumours and other growths, 'malignancy' is a medical term generally used to indicate a pathological state in an organ or system, '*describing any disorder that*

---

162. Also MCS, Multiple Chemical Sensitivity.

becomes life-threatening if untreated.'[163] If malignancy is indicated during Radionic analysis then very careful investigation of the situation is obviously required. If there is any doubt, the practitioner should diplomatically refer the patient to an orthodox medical practitioner and also to try not to alarm the patient with any of his suspicions.

The body may create various forms of neoplasms (tumours) which may be benign or malignant, but of these malignant tumours and cancer are the ones which are most prominent. Cancer itself is defined as:

'a cellular malignancy whose unique trait - loss of normal controls - results in unregulated growth, lack of differentiation, and ability to invade local tissues and metastasize.' [164]

Such pathology is often the endgame of the human condition. It is the result of a more or less severe disturbance to order, organisation and process in the body. It may be local or systemic; it may be contained or palliated for a long time by treatment, but ultimately it tends towards degradation and breakdown of the body, and death is the typical outcome. Some part of the physical fabric of the body deteriorates beyond the point of restoration and from the Radionic point of view, delinking of the formative forces and the consequent degeneration of the counterpart energy fields of the related organs and their substructures are the fundamental causes. To reiterate, it is proposed (following the ideas put forward in Chapter 7) that Nature builds up form by precipitating waveforms to create matter. The 'consciousness' of Nature acts as a coefficient which maintains form by determining that such waveform hierarchies always 'collapse' in the same way, the result of which is a predictable material reality. Hence it may be proposed that a principal characteristic of the consciousness of Nature is neither energy nor matter but *information* - it is, in one of its aspects, an absolutely vast information field which describes the physical Universe in its entirety. It is inextricably involved in the creation of physical reality from each moment to the next.

Complexes of highly-organised matter such as organic molecules and macromolecules (including DNA) therefore originate in nested hierarchies of waveforms. If the body is totally delinked from the

---

163. Oxford (1994)
164. The Merck Manual, Sixteenth Edition (1992) p. 1263. *'Today THE MANUAL is the most widely used medical text in the world.'* (Foreword, p. v)

formative forces, death will result. A pathology such as cancer implies a partial disruption of the formative process which nevertheless takes a somewhat typical form; the range and characteristics of the abnormal cells allow us to recognize cancer, as opposed to some other type of pathology, or sheer total chaos. There may be various insults to the system from a range of possible sources which may serve as triggers for the growth of tumours and the development of cancer, but the end result is the deep disturbance to the underlying relationship between field and form. The baseline of modern orthodox biological thinking is that the gene code determines the organism in its entirety ('genetic determinism'). From the present viewpoint DNA, and hence chromosomes, are themselves determined by higher-order forces which precipitate the biological material of life forms from the field in the general cascade of objectification, from particles to galaxies. Any attempt by the Radionic practitioner to deal with the problem of cancer should take this into account.

10: DISEASED ENERGY (2)

(*continuing with the list of Factors by analytical group*)

8. STRESSORS - RELATIONAL & EXTERNAL

RELATIONAL: FUNCTIONAL; PSYCHOLOGICAL; EMOTIONAL; PSYCHOSOMATIC; SHOCK & TRAUMA; REACTIVE RELATIONSHIP; PREGNANCY

EXTERNAL: ENVIRONMENTAL, GEOPATHIC, ELECTROMAGNETIC, IATROGENIC, VACCINATION

The all-important *Stressors*, dominating factors in modern life, are divided into two subgroups, *Relational* and *External*. *Relational Stress* generally refers to tensions resulting from interactions with other people. *External Stress* generally refers to impacts having their source in the environment. In general, stress may be defined as:

'any factor that threatens the health of the body or has an adverse affect on its functioning, such as injury, disease, or worry. The existence of one form of stress diminishes resistance to other forms. Constant stress brings about changes in the balance of hormones in the body.'[165]

FUNCTIONAL STRESS in the Radionic context refers to the effect of the pressures which are felt as a result of dealing with the problems of everyday life, as in *'I'm stressed out'*. Stress as a problem was first identified by Hans Selye in the 1930s:

'He (Selye) recognized that strain, or stress, plays a very significant role in the development of all types of disease. In his view, stress is the non-specific response of a human body to any demand made upon it. Selye called the process whereby strain influences the body the General Adaptation Syndrome. He concluded that there are three distinct phases in this process - alarm, resistance, and exhaustion. Selye included, among other diseases, high blood pressure, gastric and duodenal ulcers, and various types of mental disorders as "diseases of adaptation." Through his presentation of these and related ideas, he stimulated much discussion and controversy. He played an indirect though major role in the stimulation of ideas concerning the sources of "wellness" as well as of

---

165. Oxford (1994).

"sickness." He wrote of two types of stress: pleasant stress contributing to human well-being; unpleasant stress contributing to disease.' [166]

Selye identified the Adrenal Glands as the principal site of response to stress. In the Radionic model its effects may be observed by the practitioner in many Locations, for example, Chakras (particularly Solar Plexus, Heart, Brow, which are particularly concerned with emotional and personality expression); Meridians; the Limbic System; Adrenals, and so on.

In the modern world stress is everywhere, rampant and often effective in degenerating or destroying quality of life. Financial difficulties, over-competitive work and social structures, peer pressure, overcrowding of the urban environment, lack of contact with Nature and its cycles, and constant bombardment with 'news' creating underlying non-specific feelings of anxiety about the present and future are just some of the stress factors which over time contribute to undermining the health of the individual, group or society. Symptoms of many types, for example nervous and general energetic depletion, may result. [167]

PSYCHOLOGICAL FACTORS refers to the possible effects on various Locations of the many negative psychological states or characteristics which have been observed. For example, intolerance; addiction; anxiety; obsession; disposition to cheat, lie, steal; fanaticism (political, religious); guilt (religious, sexual); messiah complex; cruelty; greed; egomania; frustration; habitual stubbornness (etc etc) may all be judged to be psychological characteristics which can give rise to destructive actions or relationships. These may have various effects on the functioning of a wide range of Locations - for example, the Digestive Tract (IBS) or Respiratory and Nervous Systems (panic attacks), the Skeleton (postural misalignments of various kinds), Spine and related structures (lower back pain), Cardio-Vascular System (high blood pressure) and etc.

---

166.   http://collections.ic.gc.ca/heirloom_series/volume4/222-223.htm   (Library and Archives Canada)

167 . The hikikomori phenomenon (withdrawal from society) seems to be a result of societal pressures. *'Though acute social withdrawal in Japan appears to affect both genders equally, because of differing social expectations for maturing boys and girls, the most widely reported cases of hikikomori are from middle and upper middle class families whose sons, typically their eldest, refuse to leave the home, often after experiencing one or more traumatic episodes of social or academic failure.'* http://en.wikipedia.org/wiki/Hikikomori

From the Radionic point of view these impairments are different from the *emotional responses* which might be related to these characteristics, such as anger, rage, hatred, sullenness, unhappiness, guilt, shame; here I refer to a type of inhibition of the normal functioning (in energetic terms) of an affected Location. Such impairment is more comparable to a psychosomatic effect, which might induce a restriction of function. By way of analogy, if a Location has a *normal* waveform then the effect of a Psychological or Emotional factor might be compared to functions such as *compression* (reduction of dynamic range) or *limiting* (strong curtailment of dynamic range beyond a certain point). Thus, comparatively, we have the idea of suppressed emotions, '*I was boiling with rage inside*' or '*I wanted to hit him for what he said*' (but did not). The expression has been suppressed, and in most people this suppressed energy has to go somewhere, however, and if the suppression is prolonged then there may be consequences in illness of various types.

EMOTIONAL FACTORS may be explained in terms broadly similar to those applying to Psychological Factors, i.e. the many and various negative emotional states and the effects of those states on various Locations. Examples are loneliness, shyness, anger, timidity, vanity, pitiless cruelty, jealousy, envy, inferiority complex, fear, anguish, and their effects on the individual and others.

PSYCHOSOMATIC FACTORS indicates a more direct linkage between the stressor and the physical result. Thus a psychological or emotional state produces a symptom which is not pathological in its nature or origin. Various forms of inhibition of the sexual function (frigidity, impotence) may, to a greater or lesser degree, have a psychosomatic element.[168]

SHOCK is a medically-recognized condition producing a range of symptoms and which may result from various types of insult, e.g. anaphylactic shock (severe allergic reaction); bacteraemic or toxic shock (presence of bacteria in the bloodstream); or emotional shock (neurogenic shock). To this may be added the idea of psychological Trauma - for example, Post-Traumatic Stress Disorder. From the point of view of Radionics several things are important. Shock and trauma may be carried by the system for long periods of time - even a lifetime - and have a disguised yet deeply undermining effect on the life of the individual. They may also be part of a stored of set of feelings and reactions which can be

---

168. The author once had a patient who could develop a temporary paralysis in the legs after seeing her ex-husband.

triggered by a memory or simulacrum - such as a depiction of similar circumstances in a film - of the original event. More importantly, shock and trauma may be involved in the onset of various illnesses, for example, cancer. The idea is that the balance of forces in the body becomes critically, perhaps irretrievably, disturbed. The concept of equilibrium between the forces and energies in the Subtle Anatomy has been mentioned. A connected idea or image is that of the balance between healthy energy and diseased energy, those energetic forces which, if brought out equilibrium, can cause a decisive re-orientation of the system in the direction of illness. To give an analogy, the 'cancer potential' might be present in an individual but is held in place by the more powerful controlling presence of 'healthy energy'. A sudden impact to the system, particularly a severe physical or emotional shock which the system cannot auto-compensate, may sufficiently disturb the situation with the result that the balance tips in favour of the 'cancer potential'.[169] Once again, shock and trauma may manifest at any level in the Subtle Anatomy, from the physical counterpart level right up to the Atmic Body - a 'shock to the Soul'.

REACTIVE RELATIONSHIP indicates that the person is involved with someone who causes them severe irritation or psychological disturbance. This could be husband and wife, employee and boss, neighbours, siblings. The relational stress is so great that it causes a range of symptoms, either expressed or repressed, which may affect the health of the individual. Such relationships and the related irritation may be of long duration, such as in an unhappy marriage, and may even lead to dire results such as murder, abandonment of children, suicide, and other actions with devastating long-term consequences.

PREGNANCY of itself is not considered to be a problem but there may be difficulties with a pregnancy which disturb the patient to some degree. The first of course may be in the earlier stages where the woman does not yet know she is pregnant; later may come various forms of complication. Thus pregnancy may, under certain circumstances, be observed to be a stressor to the patient.

---

169. There is the currently-popular idea of the 'tipping point', where things reach a kind of critical mass and a change of state occurs. My father often described to me, throughout his life, an inexplicable situation. 'So-and-so', he would say, 'fell of a ladder (was in a car crash) (etc) and he got cancer.' As a youth I often used to wonder how you could get cancer from falling off a ladder. This problem baffled me for years, but the action of the shock in disturbing the vital balance would appear to be a viable explanation for the unhappy outcome.

EXTERNAL STRESSORS

ENVIRONMENTAL, GEOPATHIC and *ELECTROMAGNETIC STRESS* forms a very large area of study and only the barest outline can be given here. In essence it is proposed that there is a wide range of inorganic energetic Factors in the environment which are potentially inimical to health. These Factors can disturb the fields and even the physical material of human and animal bodies in various ways, potentially facilitating or triggering the development of a wide range of diseases, some of them deadly. Many of the disruptive presences can be measured with various types of electronic test equipment[170] and although the intensity of the effect of these energies on the living organism is hotly debated - for example, the effect of mobile phones and the alleged tumour-inducing results of constant exposure to the signals - the existence of many of these fields and forces is not, since they are described by physics. Other presences can be detected by dowsers using standard Radiesthesic techniques, and some can be detected by both measuring instrument and dowser, indicating, as observed earlier, that some part of the spectrum of energies provoking a dowsing reaction have a physical aspect.

The classical situation is the action of intersecting Geopathic Stress lines in causing cancer. Two or more such lines cross at a point where an individual has his or her bed, and over a period of time this can cause a severe disruption to the individual's health. An admirable summary of the situation is given by Creightmore:

'The word "geopathic" is derived from the Greek words, 'Geo' meaning 'the Earth', and "pathos" meaning 'disease' or 'suffering', so literally 'suffering of the Earth'. The term 'geopathic stress' is used to describe negative energies, also known as 'harmful earth rays', which emanate from the earth and cause discomfort and ill health to those living above. Earth energies can be bad, good or neutral.

The surface of the earth is woven with a pattern of etheric threads identical in energy and importance to the acupuncture meridians of the human body. These are responsible for the health and growth of the natural kingdoms of the landscape, and any interruption to their strength and harmonious flow has subtle but profound effects upon the health of the local natural life....In the British landscape, besides the obvious effects of environmental pollution, the etheric matrix suffers disruption and

---

170. For example, Tesla and Gauss Meters, EMF, RF and Microwave Detectors, Geiger Counters, and related devices.

scarring from, for example, railway and motorway cuttings and embankments, bridges, quarries, tunnels, mines and underground bunkers, steel pilings, metal fence posts and road-sign stakes, buried gas, electricity and water mains, sewers, and building foundations.

The resulting etheric disharmony manifests as a lowered quality of the local natural life forces, often through the medium of what have been known in European geomancy as 'Black Streams' - local capillary meridians of energy associated with streams of underground water flow whose yin-yang balance has distorted on the side of excessive yin. Ascendance of degenerative over generative and regenerative influences occurs in places lying directly over such streams. These "black streams" are known in the Feng Shui tradition as lines of underground "Sha" or toxic energy, in contradistinction to the "white streams" that carry healthy, generative and regenerative energy or "Sheng Qi".

They may also however occur naturally, and a wide range of these and other naturally occurring energetic configurations in the landscape are known to have an influence on the quality of health of the local life forms....Granite districts are relatively high in non-corpuscular (natural) radioactive elements, such that the exposure to background ionising radiation of dwellers in moorland Cornwall or North-East Scotland is estimated at 25% above the United Kingdom national average, and 300% more for those who live in houses built of granite blocks.

Underground water streams, even when not 'black' or 'Sha-bearing', and geological faults are known to have an effect on the geomagnetic and etheric fields around them....The etheric earth forces have as a lower-octave reflex geomagnetic fields measurable with electromagnetic instruments. Where local disturbances in the geomagnetic flux occur, so-called areas of geopathic disturbance, there appears also some disruption to the biological regulating mechanisms of living organisms....Geopathically disturbed zones may differ from surrounding regions in the degree of ionisation, from altered electromagnetic field charges; in AC changes; in enhanced electrical resistance; in altered acoustic levels and radio reception; and in increased gamma radiation. Associated also with such areas are increased 'occult' phenomena. The relationship between haunted houses and ley-line crossings is well known....

As the Earth rotates on its axis, it functions as an electro-magnet generating electrical currents in the molten metals found within its core, and an electromagnetic field on the surface which oscillates at an average frequency of 7.83 Hz, which is almost identical to the range of alpha human brainwaves. Life on earth has evolved with this background magnetic field, and creatures are accustomed to living within its presence and are able to cope with the slight fluctuations over time caused by electrical storms and the sun's activity. Geopathic stress (GS) represents a distortion of this natural frequency by weak electromagnetic fields created by streams of water flowing underground, geological fault lines, underground caverns, and certain mineral deposits (notably coal, oil, and iron). For example, where the inner Earth's vibration of 7.83 Hz crosses a water vein 200 – 500 feet below ground, stress lines vibrating at up to 250 Hz can be created....

Any distortion of this 7.83 Hz level creates a stress with the potential to weaken the immune system of any mammal living above the distortion, leading to greater susceptibility to viruses, bacteria, parasites, environmental pollution, degenerative disease, and a wide range of health problems. Many dowsers use a 0 - 16 scale known as the Von Pohl scale (after its originator) to measure the strength of geopathic stress, in which 0 represents the healthy 7.83 Schumann frequency, and 16 an extremely strong locus corresponding to 250 Hz. For example, people who are sleeping on a GS locus of 9 or more (perhaps a combined score from the presence of several geopathic features) are likely to develop cancer.

In the sensitive or weak patient, or in anyone exposed for a sufficient length of time, geopathic stress may be sufficient to overcome the body's natural homeostatic regulation and lead into a disease spiral, presenting at first a confused non-specific symptom picture. Measurable physiological effects of geopathic stress include changes in the electrical polarity of the cell membrane with impeded ionisation across the cell wall; altered spin oscillation and proton resonance of protein molecules; faulty hydrogen bonding; disturbed mesenchyme base regulation, hormone balance and pH values.

The most frequently found symptoms occurring at an early stage of exposure to geopathic stress, perhaps immediately upon moving to a new house, are sleep disturbances. The siting of a patient's bed seems to be the most important factor, after which come favourite chair, desk, room in which most working time is spent, and so forth.

Pathological symptoms can include restlessness, difficulty in getting to sleep, excessive dreaming, excessively heavy sleep and sleep requirements, waking unrefreshed, cold or restless feet and legs in bed, asthma and respiratory difficulties at night, fatigue and lethargy, unexplained mood changes, aggression and depression.

....The two broad categories of geopathic disturbance are yin - the discharging field, and yang - the charging field, ranging from the geomagnetic baseline of 65,000 nano-Tesla by up to 8,000 nT either way. The yin fields are associated with underground water flows, underground caverns and rock hollows, the running water causing a decrease in the intensity of the rocks' geomagnetic field strong enough to influence living organisms on the surface. Where two underground streams cross the effect is enhanced.

The pathological states associated with the yin fields manifest first as the above-noted sleep disturbances and mental symptoms. Over time, in the idiom of TCM [Traditional Chinese Medicine], *Qi Xu (energy deficiency)* syndromes worsen to become *Xue Xu (Blood deficiency)* and *Wei (wasting and paralysing)* conditions - fatigue, neurasthenia, depression, arthritis, diabetes mellitus, cancers, multiple sclerosis, myopathies and neuropathies and other degenerative disorders. These zones in space, represented at their strongest as a crossing point of two unhealthy underground streams, represent energy sinks sacred to the degenerative and dissolutive forces. The yang fields are especially associated with fault zones and with coal and oil deposits. Found in such regions are changes in ionisation, infra-red emission and AC & DC current; low frequency atmospheric pulsations with increased probability of lightning strikes; and low-level radiation emissions. As might be expected, yang fields lead to *Qi Shi (energy excess)* states such as hypertension, cardiac problems, strokes, migraines, epileptiform fits, gastritis, alcoholism, mania and schizophrenia.

Global geomagnetic grid crossing points can be associated with both yin and yang fields. A survey of the world's literature concerning GS shows a remarkable concordance of experience regarding the medical symptoms associated with exposure. For example, a list of known symptoms from the Chinese Feng Shui tradition that I was given in 1996 was identical in every respect to a list that I had myself previously compiled from the Western literature and my own experience.

CANCER is the most notorious of these, and tumours are known to develop almost always at exactly the spot where two or more GS lines cross a person's body as they lie asleep in their bed. All mammals are considered to produce cancerous cells on a continual basis, though they are also continuously destroyed by the body's immune system. Stress on the immune system caused by GS is seen as responsible for the resulting overgrowth of cancer cells. Professional dowsers tell many stories of *patients whose tumours have 'mysteriously' disappeared after moving their sleeping position away from the GS lines.'* [171]

Amongst the various groups of Environmental and Geopathic Stress phenomena the practitioner should consider can be included:

1. Cosmic rays penetrating to Earth from space - many forms of energy traverse space, emanating from the sun and further away. Some of these are well-known, such as bursts of solar electromagnetic energy which may penetrate the Earth's magnetosphere and, for example, knock out power grids and cause disruption to communications systems. This includes excessive amounts of solar radiation (light) which may reach the surface of the Earth as a result of reduction in the ozone layer and are said to be implicated in the formation of various forms of cancers, particularly skin cancers.

Other forces and energies proposed by science but not yet detected or explained, for example, gravity waves, dark matter and dark energy, may also have effects on the health of humans.

Finally, while astrology is generally dismissed by science as bilge, it may be noted that the planets and other objects in the solar system are electromagnetic and gravitational force-bodies rotating round the sun and their fields presumably interact with systemic and extra-systemic fields in an ongoing process, producing various effects which influence humans and other planetary life forms. Just as geopathic stress has a physical presence detectable by conventional instruments as part of its spectrum, so the same may apply to putative astrological forces. The characterisations and interpretations of astrology may, it can be argued, have a basis in physics.

2. Subatomic particles passing through space e.g. neutrinos.

Large quantities of such particles traverse the Earth and pass through the bodies of living beings. These may or may not have effects on health.

---

171. Creightmore (2007), p. 2 - 4. Anyone interested in this topic should read the full article at www.landandspirit.net/index.html. The author (Creightmore) generously appends, 'Reproduction of this article, in whole or in part, is expressly encouraged (with appropriate acknowledgements please).'

3. Moon cycles

The influence of the moon on the earth is well known and the full moon is thought to influence the mental state of susceptible individuals, particularly those who are mentally disturbed - hence the expression 'lunatic.' According to Doris Frankish,

'Georheology, a science developed by the late Scottish dowser Andrew Davie, deals with spontaneous fires, sudden deaths, murders, suicides, alcoholism, machine and concrete failures, and areas and times of hazard can be calculated from moon tables. He believed that iron-bearing rock sensitised by solar flares caused electromagnetic disturbances, which can be intense on fault lines. When the moon changes phase on the same angle as the line, there is a sudden switch in polarity, which causes a backlash of energy. Anything can happen on the equidistant node points of the line, and incidents can be cyclic in nature. The process can cause molecular disturbances in the DNA of the human body. Colour is an important part of the action, with materials on the red end of the colour spectrum being the source of the fire. Any fibrous substance can ignite, depending on a set of conditions. Hay, straw and paper are probably the most susceptible to spontaneous combustion, but wood, wool and other fibrous materials are also liable to be affected. Humans, animals and other organic materials are known to be at high risk.' [172]

4. Interaction of cosmic rays with local fields; effects of subsurface materials.

In general the idea is that incoming cosmic rays may be reflected back from the subsoil by certain types of geological materials. The resultant intermodulation creates interference patterns which may be detrimental to health. In this respect, Lakhovsky writes:

'I have applied the same method of analysis to the principle cities of France and those of neighbouring countries. The results have been grouped so as to indicate the density of cancer as a function of the geographical nature of the soil.

These investigations have clearly established the fact that a low cancer density is found in localities built on sand, limestone, gypsum, sandstone, certain primitive rocks and recent alluvial deposits rich in gravel

---

172. Doris told the author in 2011 that she is writing a book on Georheology. This excerpt is from a lecture given to the BDA (British Dowser's Association) in 2008.

and sand. One the other hand, a high cancer density is associated with localities built on plastic clay, Jurassic marl, chalk, iron ores, carboniferous beds and slate.

It will also be seen that the cancer density in France is not distributed at random, but is related to natural regions corresponding to the geological nature of the soil....we know that waves (cosmic radiation) penetrate into the soil all the better as the insulating properties of the soil are more marked, which is in accordance with our knowledge of the propagation of waves....the conducting soils act almost like metallic screens and absorb waves to a maximum degree....the dielectric (insulating) soils facilitate the penetration of waves to a great depth. Thus it follows that these soils, permeable to waves, such as sand, sandstone and gravel, which absorb radiation to a great depth, do not show any appreciable reaction on the cosmic field at the earth's surface....but when the radiation is only superficially absorbed as in the case of conducting soils impermeable to waves such as clay, marl, carboniferous beds, iron ores, this rapid absorption gives rise, at the surface of the conducting stratum, to intense currents which react on the superficial cosmic field....as the development of cancer is supposed to be connected with oscillatory disequilibrium caused by variations in the field of cosmic radiation, it follows that the incidence of cancer is low on insulating soils and high on conducting soils which modify the field.'[173]

Furthermore,

'The German dowser, Baron von Pohl, was asked to dowse the small town of Vilsbiburg in 1929, having then the highest per capita cancer death rate in Bavaria. He discovered a 100% correlation between the beds of cancer victims and the paths of Sha streams passing through the town. He repeated the procedure in Grafenau in 1930, with the lowest cancer incidence in the province, and again found 100 per cent correlation. He developed a scale to rate Geopathic Stress of 1 to 16, where a combined tally of 9 or above from streams crossing gives rise to cancer.'[174]

---

173. Lakhovsky (1935), p. 139 - 145. There are many more potentially carcinogenic stressors in the modern environment, so any correlation between soil and subsoil types and incidence of cancer may be more difficult to establish nowadays.
174. Creightmore, *op. cit.*, p. 28

Within this general context, it should be noted that no matter what form of treatment a person is given for cancer or other forms of serious illness - including all forms of orthodox treatment - geopathic stress may act as a maintaining cause or even block to its progress. If the presence of GS is detected, action should be taken to counteract it *as a priority*. This may be as simple as moving the patient's bed to a safe place. As Creightmore concludes, '*....how much suffering could have been avoided if the understanding of the importance of the influence of geopathic stress upon life on Earth was more widely recognised?*'

5. Global geomagnetic grids and Ley Lines

In the 1960s Dr Ernst Hartmann, a dowser, proposed the existence of a 'global-net' energy grid, now known as the Hartmann grid. Here intersecting lines are found running North-South at 2 metre intervals and East-West at 2.5 metres. Line width may vary, being up to nearly a metre. Similarly in the 1970s Dr Manfred Curry and Dr Wittman found a second global grid at 45 degrees to the Hartmann lines, of a broadly similar size and scale. The New Zealand researcher, Bruce Cathie, has also written several books on global energy grids that he has detected and has indicated links between these and UFO sightings. Ley lines

'*are lines of energy running over-ground in straight lines, often reflected in ancient trackway lines and alignments of prehistoric and historic sacred sites in the landscape....[and] are properly defined as straight over-ground energy lines that echo the sinuous paths of larger underground rivers.*'[175]

The effect of intersect points of the Hartmann and Curry grids with other negative energies may need to be taken into account in any study of local geopathic stress phenomena.

6. Geological Faults, Mineral deposits, Underground Water - 'black streams'

The effects of these have been generally covered above. It should be remembered that according to the tenets of Radionics all of these characteristics of the Earth itself will have not only a physical but also an energetic presence with related etheric counterpart fields. These may also

---

175. Creightmore, *op. cit.*, p. 19. The classic work on Ley Lines is Alfred Watkins' *The Old Straight Track* (1925), a book which came to prominence in the 1960s.

cause disruptions in the calibre, quality and uniformity of the Earth's pranic (Qi) field from which living beings (including humans) draw their own pranic intake.[176] The Earth's pranic field is, in turn, refreshed by inflows of cosmic prana ejected by the sun and carried across on the solar wind.[177] In short this proposes an esoteric system of enormous complexity in which man, planet, sun, solar system and cosmos are intimately linked, this over and beyond that already proposed by astrophysics.

7. Industrial, military and medical ionising radiation sources; Microwave and radio wave transmissions; the entire spectrum of AC pulsed electromagnetic fields

Here are, essentially, man-made forms of electromagnetic radiation from radio waves to gamma rays (nuclear radiation), i.e. across the entire electromagnetic spectrum. The more obvious effects of these require no discussion; everyone knows that nuclear radiation can kill and microwaves can cook. However a modern phenomenon is that of *Electromagnetic Stress*. Beal tells us:

*'Many persons, primarily women, have become chronically miserable, easily fatigued, and painfully hypersensitive with a variety of manifesting symptoms, due to stresses brought about in part by **long-term** environmental factors. These factors may involve undesirable exposures to chemical/particulate pollutants, electromagnetic/electric fields and other irritants, which interfere with the normal body immune system, coping abilities, healing efforts and healthy lifestyle. Recent medical research, regarding system metabolic functions, primarily involves previously undiagnosable thyroid-related symptoms in persons who are **thyroid-resistant rather than thyroid-deficient**. For example, in addition to fibromyalgia being a phenotypic expression of thyroid hormone resistance, so too appear to be chronic fatigue syndrome (CFIDS), gulf war syndrome (GWS), **electrical hypersensitivity (EHS)**, multiple chemical sensitivity (MCS), premenstrual syndrome (PMS) and breast silicone implant rejection syndrome. Persons afflicted with these seemingly-related dis-eases are* especially affected by the many forms of stress we encounter every day, e.g., psychological, physiological, spiritual and environmental.

It appears that long-term, <u>uncontrolled</u> EMF [electro-magnetic field] exposure may act as a promoter, an immune system irritant (in

---

176 . See comments above in Chapter 5
177 . See in general Wachsmuth (1923).

addition to any chemical sensitivities present), thus overloading the body's defence mechanisms. Environmentally-ill persons with compromised immune systems often find that EMF transients are one more irritating factor to avoid. The manifesting symptoms may then vary over a wide range, depending upon individual immune system factors....not just cancer or alzheimer's increases, but increases in a host of dis-eases often considered 'minor', e.g. allergies, headaches, fatigue, insomnia, etc.....Individuals with multiple sensitivities, including EMFs, have reported reactions to various types of electrical equipment, including power lines, transformers, electronic office equipment such as typewriters and computer terminals, video display terminals (VDTs), household appliances (such as hair dryers), telephones, battery powered analog watches, digital clocks and other digital electronic devices, and fluorescent lights.'[178]

8. Cancer houses; Sick Building Syndrome

The existence of 'cancer houses' has long been noted - houses where several generations of people have developed cancer. Possible causes have been described above. A more recent phenomenon is Sick Building Syndrome - usually office blocks and similar closed-environment buildings where occupants develop a variety of symptoms such as fatigue, allergic responses, irritation of nose and eyes, cold and flu-type symptoms, and so on. These tend to be air-conditioned buildings containing (or constructed from) a large number of artificial materials with toxic components, electro-magnetic fields (e.g. wireless computer networks) and possibly quantities of pathogens such as moulds, bacteria and viruses which lodge in the air conditioning system.

SUMMARY

The practitioner needs to be aware of these Environmental stressors and the above list is not final. For example the development and widespread ingestion of GM (genetically-modified) foods may yet prove to be another powerful stressor. The point is that the aetiology of illness in any patient may be affected by, triggered by, or maintained by any one or combination of the above, and, if any of them *are* in play, and to reiterate,

---

178. Beal (2005). http://emfinterface.wordpress.com/ Beal states that he developed 'an unusual allergy from exposure to the strong EMFs present' while working on the Space Shuttle External Tank Project at Martin Marietta Manned Space Systems (now Lockheed Martin).

unless these are dealt with other treatments may be severely impeded in their action or blocked altogether.

IATROGENIC[179] AND VACCINATION STRESS

Here are two potential categories of energetic stressor having their origin in the use of medical drugs and immunological procedures; resulting, in effect, from orthodox medical treatment. It will be understood that in many instances a person has received both a multiplicity of vaccinations and may at some other - usually later - stage in life receive a range of medical drugs in various combinations, often for long periods of time. Some of these combinations may have known side-effects and others may not, in short, there is a considerable possibility that unknown or unanticipated side-effects and reactions may arise. Lipton reports:

'Adverse drug effects....are a primary reason why a leading cause of death is iatrogenic illness, i.e. illness resulting from medical treatment. According to conservative estimates published in the Journal of the American Medical Association, iatrogenic illness is the third-leading cause of death in this country [the USA]. *More than 120,000 people die from the adverse effects of prescribed medications every year. However....a new study, based on the results of a ten-year survey of government statistics, came up with even more dismal figures. That study concludes that iatrogenic illness is actually the* leading *cause of death in the United States and that adverse reactions to prescription drugs are responsible for more than 300,000 deaths a year.'*[180]

From the point of view of the Radionic practitioner, these substances and materials have their own energetic signatures which may become embedded in the fields of some or various Locations in the Subtle Anatomy. Thus, from the energetic point of view, the innate disease picture (the actual pathology) may become quite deeply complexed by the added combinations of medical drugs used in the attempt to regulate or control it, and any negative effects of those drugs on the energetic system. A primary result might be to block or impede Radionic or other vibrational treatments to a greater or lesser degree, in this way defeating the efforts

---

179. *'describing a condition that has resulted from treatment, as either an unforeseen or inevitable side effect.'* Oxford (1994)
180. Lipton, *op. cit.*, p. 77. Lipton supports the statistics with the relevant citations.

of the practitioner. Nevertheless orthodox medical treatment should not be changed or discontinued except as advised by a Doctor. In normal circumstances the practitioner has to work with, around, or within the confines of medical therapies.

Vaccination is of course considered to be one of the major triumphs of the modern medical endeavour and whatever may be the on-costs of the vaccination program to the individual's Subtle Anatomy, the deleterious effects of diseases which might be otherwise be contracted (in the absence of vaccination against) may be far worse. As many people will appreciate, the vaccination discussion is lengthy and controversial and no doubt will continue for many more years.

9. DEPLETION & IMBALANCE

NUTRITIONAL DEFICIENCY; VITAMIN & MINERAL DEFICIENCY; ENZYME & CATALYST DEFICIENCY; HORMONE IMBALANCE; ELECTROLYTE IMBALANCE; ACID-BASE BALANCE; DEHYDRATION; MALABSORPTION; OTHER DEFICIENCY

Common to the subcategories above is the idea that one or more substances essential to the correct functioning of the organism are not present, not present in sufficient quantities, somehow prevented from being taken up and used, or the body has a reduced capability to manufacture the required substance. In general the solution, where possible, is to ingest the appropriate substance and thus rectify the problem, for example, if you are dehydrated, you drink water and electrolytes; if you have scurvy, you take vitamin C or some foodstuff containing it;[181] if you have an underactive Thyroid ('low' Thyroid) the Doctor might prescribe Thyroxin; and so on. Charts could be constructed which indicate, for example, the range of vitamins typically required by a human and the pendulum may indicate which are deficient for any patient.

In some patients the problem may be chronic and may not be solved by supplementation. There may be some form of energetic inhibition - for example the presence of a miasm, congestion of the Thyroid,

---

181. E.g. Vitamin C deficiency produces scurvy, which killed many seafarers. In 1747 James Lind, a surgeon in the Royal Navy, demonstrated that crew taking oranges and lemons as a supplement to their diet did not develop scurvy whereas those on standard rations, did. The term 'Limey', referring to the British, originated in British sailors being given lime juice as an antiscorbutic.

uncoordination of the Endocrine or Digestive Systems, toxic energy patterns, unrecognised depletion of the Adrenals - which inhibits the proper take-up and use of vitamins, minerals and nutrients or prevents the correct hormone balance being established, and so on. In other instances a necessary substance is not produced in the appropriate quantities by the body. General depletion states, where the patient complains of low energy, total exhaustion, inability to function and other weaknesses may involve various deficiencies which are not correctable by supplementation, no matter how large the amount of supplements taken. This is because the key to the problem lies in some form of energetic dysfunction or blockage. In such cases treatment of the underlying problem - which may not be discernible using normal analytical techniques - may result in an improvement in the apparent symptoms. Thus careful analysis of possible deeper-level causation needs to be made where problems of depletion are detected.

10. MORTAL, ACUTE & SUB-ACUTE

ABSCESS; ADDICTION; ADHESIONS; ANEURYSM; CYST; FISTULA; FRACTURE; HAEMORRHAGE; HERNIA; HIATUS HERNIA; OEDEMA; PERFORATION; PROLAPSE; SCAR TISSUE; SCLEROSIS; SPASM; THROMBOSIS

This category contains a wide range of impacts to, and problems in, the body. Those listed above (as examples) are as defined in the orthodox medical text books. Some obviously create situations of great urgency. Others can be 'hidden' in the body for long periods of time yet may, nevertheless, cause serious problems. They may undermine the patient's general health and create a range of secondary symptoms, the source of which may not be apparent in a superficial examination. Some may, potentially, be life-threatening - i.e., *Mortal* - such as aneurysms, yet may not be apparent without expensive diagnostic procedures such as CT scan.[182] The practitioner might pick these up by dowsing as they would exist as definite energetic abnormalities at various levels in the Subtle

---

182. For example the author has a friend who developed severe back problems in his mid 50s. After a scan it was found that several vertebrae in his lower spine were partially fractured. He remembered falling badly on his lower back on some concrete stairs at around the age of 19. Thus the problem had apparently been there for years as a potential but only with the onset of appropriate circumstances had the weakness become apparent. In another instance the author actually witnessed someone he knew break his upper arm in an arm-wrestling contest. The doctors reckoned that there was a pre-existing partial fracture which the mechanical stress had completed.

Anatomy, some possibly so deeply-embedded in the system as to be found in the Causal Body and higher Chakras.[183]

Some of these problems if detected might require orthodox intervention such as surgery and on that basis the practitioner should, using some discretion, suggest that the patient speak to a Doctor since, clearly, in some circumstances, there might be an element of urgency.

11. OCCULT
PSYCHIC INTERFERENCE; PSYCHIC ATTACK; BLACK MAGIC ATTACK; ACTIVATED SHELL; POSSESSION; COSMIC EVIL

The subject of the Occult is of course controversial. Here I refer to aspects of the so-called paranormal, centrally but not entirely, to those where humans attempt to manipulate supposed occult forces to their advantage in order to attack, hurt, control or even destroy others. No doubt we are all very modern people who have been thoroughly sanitized by rationalism and we do not believe, or have been lead to believe, or even prefer to believe, that such things do not exist outside of the movies, the worlds of the imagination, and the risible phantasms of the religious-minded. Nevertheless, a deep fascination with the supernatural - *The Exorcist* (1973), for instance, being one of the highest-grossing films of all time - remains beneath the surface of everyday life.

I myself, and in spite of many experiences (being a profound sceptic) largely took a dismissive point of view of the occult. I was eventually confronted with the problem presented by several persons, individually coming for help, who were either mentally unbalanced or *really were under the influence of some malign and unusual force or process*. In these instances you have to decide. You have to assess the patient very carefully and only if you can comfortably dismiss all supposedly 'conventional' explanations (hysteria, paranoia, delusional states, repressed psychological artefacts creating images in the mind which appear to be autonomous, compensations for inadmissible psychological assaults, projection, excessive drug use, etc) may you look at

---

183. This latter has been noted by the author in the case of a long-term heroin addict, who was at the time in early middle age. He recounted that he had discovered Heroin as his drug of choice when around 15 years old and had made a life out of it, continually relapsing in spite of repeated attempts to get clean. In short, Radionic analysis suggested that addiction was, as it were, something 'in his soul', or his 'life path', as opposed to being, let's say, a rather more superficial 'lifestyle choice'.

the occult realm as a possible Factor. In some of these persons there may be an element of psychic susceptibility which makes them easier to victimize; but not in all. In this short survey I will look at several forms of occult disturbance which the practitioner might have to take into consideration. Dealing with them is another matter and if there are any doubts, such cases should be passed to others, who, hopefully, know what to do.[184]

PSYCHIC INTERFERENCE is common and is not really a 'deliberate' occult manipulation. Here the victim is in contact with a person or persons who more-or-less unconsciously project malign or negative thoughts at them. These persons may emanate jealousy, envy, hatred, a peer group obsession with someone who does not 'fit', and a wide range of possible other selfish and destructive attitudes towards the victim.[185] If not directly aware of these attacks the victim may nevertheless respond - albeit unconsciously - and experience various symptoms such as depression, life and career problems, 'nothing going right' etc. Politics and corporations are often full of such rivalries, which boil up in the ferment of an incestuous and intensely-competitive environment. Here the poisonous mental atmosphere undermines the victim, perhaps by a sort of insidious and subconscious *negative* suggestion, slowly destroying his self-confidence, self-image and ability to cope. The individual's situation may become confused and may result in accidents and errors which are put down to chance. But the probability of their happening may be increased by the circumstances; it is as if the so-called *Evil Eye* has been invoked. Many know the expression *'shit happens'* but the apparently random circumstances under which it is considered to have happened may need to be examined. Perhaps the negative thoughts of others help create a kind of harmful synchronicity, where sequences of damaging events arise 'as if from nowhere' or seemingly 'by chance'. Such situations may have the potential to develop an extraordinarily highly-charged social momentum, beneath which can often be found extreme and unbearable group (social) tensions which are at least partially alleviated - or diverted - by projection onto some imagined 'evil' force. The Salem Witch trials of 1692 - 93, in

---

184. Do not think that this necessarily includes the author.
185. Resulting in, for example, bullying, including the very modern phenomenon of *cyber-bullying.*

which nineteen people were executed for witchcraft, are a famous example of mass hysteria.[186]

In *PSYCHIC ATTACK* the situation has been intensified by the additional component of deliberation and ritualised processes, where the attacker creates and projects negative images towards the victim with a view to undermining or destroying him or her. Here we are on the road to real *BLACK MAGIC*, where the attacker may use, or pay others claiming appropriate skills to use, an array of techniques which appear to be able to produce really disastrous results. In this case someone, more or less skilled, is using various Black Occult methods to attack another person or even a business or other organisation.[187]

Skilled Black Magicians may be able to produce a range of dire effects, such as occultation of the Atmic Body (i.e. 'soul stealing'),[188] installation of powerful negative thought-forms or even entities in the Mental and Astral Bodies and Aura (possession), distortion, tearing, inversion and reversal of the Chakras - and so on. Here I am describing the result of such magical actions in terms of the Radionic model; the Magician may not at all understand it in this way. These afflicts in turn may produce a large range of physical symptomology which is a result of the impairment or breakdown - i.e. dis-integration - of the substanding energy fields and not the product of any 'normal' illness. These could include a variety of what might be called 'pseudo-symptoms' such as heart and blood pressure problems, disturbed sleep, nightmares, pains of many types, nervous problems - phenomena which look as if they might be

---

186. The grim and brutal film *Witchfinder General* (1968) is also a good illustration of this phenomenon. See also Sir E. E. Evans-Pritchard's seminal study, *Witchcraft, Oracles and Magic amongst the Azande* (1937), in which a purely 'societal' explanation for supernatural phenomena is proposed. Referring to the earlier discussion of the 'group' Astral Body, such mass phenomena may involve entrainment of the outer layers of the Astral Bodies of the individuals concerned (Astral 1 and 2), feedback of emotional energy leading to ever-higher levels of excitement with corresponding loss of reason and rationality.

187. Interested persons could read *PSYCHIC SELF-DEFENCE* by Dion Fortune as an introduction to this dark and calculated underworld. Note that Black Magic is not the same as Satanism. Satanists worship an evil presence, (i.e. commonly named Satan), whereas Black Magicians may not necessarily worship anything, except, perhaps, their own ego. Black Magic is in fact rife in various parts of the world.

188. Here the victim becomes a hollowed-out version of himself, existing in a sort of twilight state as a type of pseudo-person, losing contact with reality, resembling the person you once knew but is not that person, being out of contact with his 'real' self i.e. his soul essence; and thus, 'knocked out' in a very real sense.

psychosomatic or stress-related but are actually reactions by the victim to the attack. In worse cases there may be actual real pathological symptoms or even death; for example, a potentially disastrous health problem might be triggered, with deadly results. Bailey informs us:

"The Left-Hand Path is that followed by the Black Magicians, and by the Brothers of the Shadows. It originates in the use of the forces of nature for selfish ends; it is characterised by intense selfishness and separativeness, and ends in Avitchi, the 8th sphere, the home of lost souls, or those shells of the lower man which have become separated from their egoic or individual life principle." [189]

ACTIVATED SHELLS may be found in various people, such as psychics, mediums, meditators, psychic researchers, and people who take pleasure drugs, i.e. people who might open themselves up, usually unintentionally, to the arena in which such psychic forces are at play. But Shells are not restricted to these categories. For example children in stressful situations who try to escape by conscious or unconscious out-of-body projection may pick up such Shells. MacIvor and Laforest state:

'when we finish life on the physical plane, the physical body disintegrates...our astral body continues its existence on the astral plane for a number of years....when we 'die' on the astral plane and our soul passes on to....higher realms, the astral body is left to float about and disintegrate. This is a normal occurrence. Quite frequently....the astral shells become activated by....a thought form of primitive intelligence. This combination is termed an activated shell....to maintain its viability the activated shell must attach itself to the etheric double of a living person, where it absorbs the vitality and vitamin resources of that individual. It is capable of disturbing the whole system, even affecting thoughts and emotions. While the activated shell might be described as an invasion of the individual's energy body, it is not the same thing as "possession" in the manner understood by occult science and rather sensationally popularized in recent books and movies. Whatever the true cause or nature of possession, the individual seems to lose a certain degree of conscious control over his or her personality or actions. It has been theorized that another "intelligence" takes over, at least temporarily. This is not the case with activated shells, which are simply energies imbued with thought

189. Bailey (1925), p. 642 *n.*

forms, not an intelligence per se. They have no ability to take over an individual's personality or actions. The activated shells may only be detected indirectly through pain, allergy, infection, and so forth, or perhaps through some general mental or emotional state such as depression or irritability. One is not usually aware when one has an activated shell, nor is one necessarily specifically aware of their departure when they are eradicated through treatment....A clearing up of symptoms is one noticeable result, but this often happens gradually over a period of time....activated shells may enter through any one of the seven major chakras either singly or in small groups....shells penetrate no further than the etheric body....pain, allergy, infection....or....some general mental or emotional state such as depression or irritability [may result].'[190]

POSSESSION is a further stage. Here an entity of some form, either *invoked,* or *created* by an attacking human with the appropriate skills,[191] or *native* in the shadow worlds, attempts to control, or 'overshadow' a human, introducing an element of automatism in the victim's behaviour, i.e. they are not in full control of their actions. As an extreme example, the phenomenon of one person displaying multiple personalities (Multiple Personality Disorder), is known. While this is considered to be a purely mental phenomenon by psychiatrists, in some cases the solution to the problem may simply be that there are indeed multiple personalities occupying the same body except that all but one - i.e. the owner of the body - are discarnate (possessing entities). This type of situation may of course combine both aspects, i.e. mental illness weakening the protective outer layers of patient's subtle energy fields - the Aura, for example - facilitating invasion by non-physical beings. Steiger writes:

'As a result of my forty-two years of investigation and research, however, I have found that the traditional haunting scenario is but one of many types of frightening phenomena created by a host of spirit beings who live in the Shadow World. What is more, a good many inhabitants of the Shadow World may have absolutely nothing to do with the spirits of the dead or the question of life after death. Some entities appear to be*

---

190. McIvor & LaForest (1979), p. 110 - 111
191. One of the typical problems is that the would-be Black Occult Master convinces himself that he is really good at the art and unleashes some type of force-entity which is far more powerful than he imagined in his conjurations and then, as it were, 'all hell breaks loose.' Not for nothing do we have the ancient Greek myth of Pandora's Box.

multidimensional beings, intelligences that enter into our dimension of reality for purposes that may be beyond our capacity to imagine. Some may be benign, perhaps seeking to bring us higher awareness of the complex universe in which we reside. Others may be cosmic tricksters and troublemakers bent on mischief. And, unfortunately, there are some beings who do not appear to have our best interests at heart....they may have entered our world with the intention of possessing our bodies or capturing our souls.

Among the spirit and multidimensional beings that I have isolated in my research are following: Spirits of the Dead....Poltergeists....Phantoms....Animal Spirits....Nature Spirits....Deiform Spirits....Spirit Residue.... Spirit Parasites....Spirit Mimics....' [192]

Saraydarian clearly differentiates between obsession and possession:

'Obsession and possession are two important words often incorrectly used. Obsession is etheric, astral or mental inhibition. Post-hypnotic suggestion is a kind of obsession or inhibition. Obsession on the etheric level is a mechanical habit which is the result of some distortion in the nervous and the corresponding etheric body. Emotional obsession is an emotion caught in the astral plane which controls other emotions. Such an obsession can be local or isolated, or it can have its roots in the emotional body of a society from which it derives its power. Accidents and events charged with strong emotion can be registered like a photograph by the astral body. They serve as obsessing neuroses. In the mental plane, obsession is an inhibited, trapped thoughtform, with or without entities attached to it.

Possession is different. Possession is done by an entity who has many obsessions and tries to occupy the nature of a man and use it partially or completely as a mechanism for his expression. Thus, a possessed person is occupied not only by an entity but also by the obsessions of the entity. An advanced case of possession occurs when more than one entity possesses a man, all locating themselves in certain etheric, astral and mental centers according to their levels and intentions.

There is also a kind of possession which is carried on at a distance, when a powerful person controls another person through his etheric emanations, emotions, or thoughts. Some people fall very easily victim to

---

192. Brad Steiger (2000) p. 13 - 18

this kind of possession....such possessions occur only if there is a karmic tie or psychological resonance between the persons.

People think that obsession and possession can be either good or bad, constructive or destructive. That is not true. Obsession and possession are kinds of diseases. The basic argument against them is that that which obsesses and possesses imposes itself over the person against his free will and controls him. If anyone is controlled, either by good or by evil, it does not make a difference in the long run. Even if obsession and possession are positive, they deprive a person of his divine rights of freedom and conscious evolution. No one can be beautiful, good and just by masquerading in the role of beauty, goodness and justice. That is why even beauty, goodness, and justice must not be imposed but evoked. [193]

Finally *COSMIC EVIL* brings us to the idea of a titanic struggle underlying the human situation, a Manichean and ancient battle between colossal discarnate forces of good and evil which are also in deadly combat to win control of the human spirit and destiny. This battle ebbs and flows, but has been depicted countless times throughout all cultures and forms and is an absolutely archetypal theme which appears over and over again in the arts and religions and in almost as many forms and guises as there are individual humans; the *conflict within each is also the common property of all.*[194] On the mundane and historical levels there is the matter of human evil. Bailey states:

'*A gigantic thought form hovers over the entire human family, built by men everywhere during the ages, energised by the insane desires and evil inclinations of all that is worst in man's nature, and kept alive by the promptings of his lower desires. This thought form has to be broken up and dissipated by man himself...*' [195]

---

193. Saraydarian (1990) p. 333 - 334

194. For example the original *Star Wars* trilogy (1977 - 1983) is a perfect play upon archetypes. *Night Watch* (2004) explicitly portrays the world as being held in an unforgiving balance between the forces of good and evil. For all of us dyed-in-the-wool postmodernists who *really believe* in purely rational explanations for all the bestial phenomena (ongoing) of the last 100 years, *The Usual Suspects* (1995) advises '*The greatest trick the Devil ever pulled was convincing the world he didn't exist.*' See Campbell (1973) for a detailed study of archetypes in religion and mythology.

195. Bailey (1925) p. 948.

Beyond this is are the great universal forces of Good and Evil, characterised (to give but one example) as God and the Devil (Satan) in theology, which pull like great attractors in the phase space which is human consciousness; now it goes this way, now that, and with it human hope and despair ebb and flow without cessation. The influence of the greater evil on humanity is more subtle in its operation, although not less inversely spectacular in its products:

'The question of whether Hitler himself was influenced by so-called occult forces has been hotly debated and is so to this day with conventional 'material' historians denying any such involvement and esotericists claiming the control of external malign presences.

However this argument only echoes the general misconception about the nature of the hierarchy of energies which influence humanity and the externally-formed world. Hitler himself had an extremely powerful personality which actively sought redemption for many deeply-perceived slights and psychic wounds and he possessed, in addition, the ability to project his inner deficits into his national situation. The desire for redemption and self-justification at any cost - any being the operative expression - opened the door to those discarnate minds who are the quintessence of evil in all its aspects and which search for and feed off negativity across all planes and dimensions as they are able to find and leech on to it. Thus they the truly lost had found a kindred personality in the questing Hitler and were able to insert and activate many absolutely destructive concepts onto the Earth through this doorway and that provided by the others who followed him as his close associates.

Those masses who bought into the Nazi ideology were simply deluded and also ready to be seduced on account of social and political circumstances which are well-documented and need no further elaboration here, which, nevertheless, does not excuse them of their responsibilities as human individuals. Hitler himself was not especially aware of the interventions which occurred in his mind process although suffice it to say he was unusually receptive and this, combined with his personality attributes, made him a highly-suitable candidate even when compared with any of the pantheon of evil personalities who have walked the planet across the ages.

As a result it is perfectly convenient to view Hitler in purely material-historical terms and deny the occult aspect because the usual accoutrements of the occult dabbler were in truth largely absent. Hitler personally did not need such paraphernalia as he was to the average black magician as a virtuoso is to the jobbing musician.' [196]

Obviously this short discussion of the range of the so-called Occult goes at some point beyond the remit and scope of action of the Radionic practitioner, which does not mean, however, that we should limit our field of awareness. But humans are not only the initiators of destructive forces but also their target, and this often unconsciously, the incoming negative energy sweeping all before it in an unrecognised yet irresistible tidal wave of disturbance. Some of the collective psychic catastrophes we experience may even simply be the turbulence set up by the passing wake of cosmic forces and conflicts of which we have as yet the barest conception.

12. TRANSITIONAL
ASTROLOGICAL DISTURBANCE; HEALING REACTION; KARMIC CAUSATION; IRREVERSIBLE PATHOLOGY; DEATH APPARENT

Here we are concerned with the results of changes of state in the individual. In the ongoing turbulence of this age many are going through unimaginable transitions, uprooted from the life they once knew and thrust by circumstances into areas of experience with which they may never have wished to deal. Some lives collapse and are destroyed in the process; others manage to use the moment to transform themselves.

ASTROLOGICAL DISTURBANCE as a possibility has been referred to above in the section on Environmental Stressors. Proposed effects of astrological alignments may affect not only individual but also group and even planetary circumstances. Depending upon the practitioner's view of such matters, it may be useful to ask if there is some astrological configuration which is impeding the progress of any treatment or even instrumental in creating the patient's problems. In *Teletherapy*

---

196. One of my correspondents (2002), who wishes to remain anonymous. Compare Fest (1979) p. 174, *'In Mein Kampf he* [Hitler] *had already come out against pseudo-academic folkish occultism, and finally....*[in] *1938 he publicly repudiated all such goings-on, which* 'could not be tolerated in the movement.' 'At the pinnacle of our movement stands not mysterious premonition, but clear knowledge and hence open avowal. But woe if, through the insinuation of obscure mystical elements, the movement or the state should give unclear orders....Our 'cult' is exclusively cultivation of that which is natural and hence willed by God.' One can only conclude that in a world which produced a statement such as this, anything can be rationalised. For an in-depth exploration of Hitler and the occult forces thought to be behind Nazism, see Pauwels and Bergier (2001).

Bhattacharyya advises that certain gems and crystals may be used to offset such negative influences.

HEALING REACTION (known in homoeopathy as an 'aggravation') refers to a possible temporary increase in the patient's symptoms following the use of a vibrational remedy. In short, the patient may feel somewhat worse before they feel better. Here the objective is to normalise the patient's fields and in the process to enable them to throw off the diseased energy. It is the process of normalisation itself which temporarily produces the increased disturbance. The reaction is usually of short duration (typically, and usually maximally 24 - 48 hours) and will tend to vary in intensity with each patient. The important point is not to confuse the healing response with the actual illness itself, since the practitioner may feel the need to add in more treatment to deal with the 'new' symptoms - which are not actually new. Therefore it may be necessary to give treatment and wait. Such healing reactions should not be confused with the concept of side-effects, which latter are direct but unwanted physiological reactions resulting from the presence of a drug in the patient's system. [197]

KARMIC CAUSATION suggests that the individual may be working through the effects, or results, of actions in a previous life. Bailey has a great deal to say about karma and the reader may wish to study (for example) Chapter 3 of *Esoteric Healing*; the meta-argument is that all present circumstances result from past karma, whether that of an individual, an associated group, a particular race, a nation, or humanity as a whole, in some degree or combination, reaching back, ultimately and impenetrably, into the origins of the Cosmos itself. Within this perspective it is claimed that a) present circumstances of turmoil are at least in part the result of the conscious processing, which is to say the working-off, or compensation for, centuries or millennia of past karma which have built up like a huge shadow over the human race and b) that there is not only 'bad' but also 'good' karma, these being denoted the *karma of retribution* and the *karma of reward* respectively.[198] Comparatively, note that in Jungian psychology the idea of the shadow has huge importance:

---

197. Hahnemann, *op. cit.*, comments on the homoeopathic aggravation in, for instance, §160 and §161.
198. Bailey (1953), p. 295

'The shadow is that hidden, repressed, for the most part inferior and guilt-laden personality whose ultimate ramifications reach back into the realm of our animal ancestors and so comprise the whole historical aspect of the unconscious...if it has been believed hitherto that the human shadow was the source of all evil, it can now be ascertained....that the unconscious man, that is, his shadow, does not consist only of morally reprehensible tendencies but also displays a number of good qualities, such as normal instincts, appropriate reaction, realistic insights, creative impulses, etc.'[199]

In short, one may comment, actions have consequences, the outcome of which may be positive or negative; but such is the complexity of the world that the outcome of many actions may be both positive *and* negative, since simple ideas held up as moral or ethical are continually challenged by shades of grey, there often being no clear-cut ('good' or 'bad') answers to any particular dilemma.

In the West, the concept of the action of karma as a direct cause of present problems in an individual has come into vogue in recent decades. The practitioner should exercise extreme caution when attributing the illness of a patient to his or her karma and in the author's opinion it is unlikely to be a Factor in all but a few cases. The focus should be on the present situation and not on unearthing a putative past which is likely to be unverifiable and might in fact, if suggested to the patient, make matters worse. It is what you can do right now in this lifetime that counts; what you may (or may not) have done in some previous life cannot be apprehended directly, for the most part. This does not, however, dismiss the fact that in some fraction of persons there is the need, and, probably, capability, to deal with a karmic matter which presents itself in the life path. It might be thought that if such a situation occurs then it is a psychic event which is ripe for attention and as a result of the life process has 'chosen' its moment to manifest and may be dealt with accordingly.

IRREVERSIBLE PATHOLOGY is a situation, in essence, which has gone beyond therapeutic intervention. There might be two basic categories. In the first instance an illness has necessitated surgery, with the removal of some organ or part of the body (such as an amputation). This is a situation which cannot be reversed. In the second, the patient is incurable by any means and any method of therapeutic intervention can

---

199. Jung (1995), p. 418

only palliate the problem at best. The point for the practitioner is to be realistic about what can be done. In any case where an irreversible pathology is indicated, if it has not already been medically diagnosed then the best course of action may be to gently refer the patient to an orthodox practitioner.

DEATH APPARENT refers to the end stage in an illness. Here the patient is in the process of dying, and no treatment can reverse the process. Nevertheless Radionic treatments have been given to ease the passage and to attempt to calm the patient. In addition, it can be added that treatments have been continued for a short while *post mortem*, before the deceased has 'passed on', in order to reduce the ongoing impact on the energy field of some of the more 'physical' aspects of the illness. Atheists may reject the idea that there is 'anywhere' to pass on to, but the author is certain we will all get a chance to find out.

11: DISEASED ENERGY - MIASMS AND MIASMATIC INHIBITION

INTRODUCTION[200]

Section 3 of Chapter 9 refers to the concept of Miasms and Miasmatic Inhibition. This Chapter gives a basic explanation of the Miasms and their possible impact, potential or actual, on human health.

To give the reader a simple and approximate idea, the idea of the miasm might generally - but only very generally - be equated with the concepts of predisposition and diathesis[201] found in orthodox medicine. From the energetic point of view, the origin of the miasm concept has its source in the work of Samuel Hahnemann (1755 – 1843), founder of Homoeopathy, and was initially proposed in *The Chronic Diseases* (3 volumes, 1826 - 1837). Perhaps the most fundamental concept in Homoeopathy is that of the *Vital Force,* also referred to as the *Dynamis* or *Life Force*. According to Hahnemann, the Vital Force[202] is inseparable from, and entirely contiguous with, the physical body. Its free and unimpeded flow throughout the physical organism is absolutely essential to health:

'The material organism, thought of without life force, is capable of no sensibility, no activity, no self-preservation. It derives all sensibility and produces its life functions solely by means of the immaterial wesen (the life principle, the life force) that enlivens the material organism in health and disease.'[203]

---

200. Part of this Chapter has been taken from an article by the author originally published under the title *A Study of the Miasms for Radionics* in Scofield (2003). This extract has been somewhat revised.

201. *'A higher than average tendency to acquire certain diseases....'* (Oxford, 1994). I give this analogy to help the unacquainted reader to get a basic idea about Miasms, which are, in fact, a rather difficult and profound concept. The term 'Miasm' was also used in earlier times to describe 'bad and unwholesome' air, which, for example in marshy districts, was thought to give rise to diseases such as Malaria. Its continued use in the homoeopathic context is probably inappropriate but no better or other term has been accepted at present.

202. It is arguable that the term *Dynamis* basically refers to the Etheric Body and its subdivisions, including the accompanying flow of Ch'i or Pranic energy, for example as described in this book.

203. §10, *The Organon of Medicine* - Hahnemann (1996). *Wesen* can also be translated as *being,* or *essence*. Hahnemann adds in a footnote to this paragraph *'Without the life force, the material organism is dead and only subject to the power of the external physical world.*

This viewpoint, it probably almost goes without saying, is opposite to the materialist basis of modern science, which generally maintains that life arises from 'dead' matter, as discussed earlier. The conceptual origin of the medical viewpoint you hold, one may think, then determines the method of intervention; in orthodox medicine, *basically*, physical methods such as pharmaceutical drugs, surgery, etc., only, are allowable as therapies because science dictates that only physical matter is 'allowed' to exist. In Homoeopathy illness arises from non-material causes:

'When a person falls ill, it is initially only this spirit-like autonomic life-force (life principle), everywhere present in the organism, that is mistuned through the dynamic influence of a morbific agent inimical to life. Only the life principle, mistuned to abnormality, can impart to the organism the adverse sensations and induce in the organism the irregular functions that we call disease.' [204]

From *this* viewpoint, any sufficiently strong impingement of the life force will produce observable symptoms; just as the free-flowing, unconstrained Dynamis can be directly equated with a healthy human, so, equally, a disturbed, constrained Dynamis can be directly equated with the symptoms experienced by the sick human. In short, disease is not caused by any *direct* physical impact on the material of the physical body. The primary effect of any such impact is on the life force, which, if it cannot react in such a way as to *autonomously* restore its normal functioning, becomes impeded or inhibited in its expression - *'mistuned to abnormality'*. This disturbance to the life force, according to its nature, is then transmitted to the material of the physical body, producing, or, one might say, *externalising* as the symptoms recognized as disease or illness.

It decays and is again resolved into its chemical constituents.' - although he does not appear to say anything about the existence, nature or origin of the life force, or the question of how it becomes conjoined to the physical body .

204. §11, *op. cit*. The 'morbific agents' being what would be termed *Factors* in Radionics. Radionics would probably take the view that there is a continuum from consciousness to matter, which are not, as it were, one thing and some other thing which temporarily conjoin to create a living being, as Hahnemann appears to describe it. The physical world and its phenomena are externalisations of consciousness manifesting through energy and matter.

Disease is an *internal, dynamic* process which can be detected by its *external* signs. These signs may be present on the physical, emotional or mental levels and can consist of functional or pathological disturbances, or both; and thus these abnormal conditions may include not only physical but also mental and emotional states.[205]

Careful observation showed Hahnemann that some disease conditions would persist in spite of him giving well-chosen remedies from his existing Materia Medica; acute symptoms would disappear, but in certain patients a true and ongoing state of good health and vitality could not be achieved. This led him to the conclusion that chronic illness results from an underlying condition which permanently and progressively impairs and ultimately breaks down the Dynamis. In short, the miasm is a hidden, ongoing and insidious pollution of the Vital Force; it is a presence which cannot be removed by any external or material means, medical or otherwise, and externalises in a progressive symptomology:

'....a miasmatic, chronic nature...that after it has once advanced and developed to a certain degree can never be removed by the strength of any robust constitution, it can never be overcome by the most wholesome diet and order of life, nor will it die out of itself....it is ever more aggravated, from year to year, through a transition into other and more serious symptoms, even till the end of man's life...' [206]

---

205. Developing the idea of 'mistuned', think of a symphony orchestra. If one instrument is out of tune, the audience might not notice it. But if several are out of tune, the result could become quite annoying. If all the instruments are out of tune, the character of the music would be destroyed. And if not only out of tune but out of time (synchronisation) - chaos!
206. *The Chronic Diseases* (Theoretical Part) by Samuel Hahnemann (page 35). I will give a simple analogy which may help with the idea of miasms as fixed pollutions of the Vital Force. Every house has a cold water tank into which water flows from the main supply. Let us suppose there is something which always stains the water red; the water will therefore always flow out of the taps discoloured red. There may be blockages in the pipes (Congestion) which can be cleared; there may be excess water pressure which needs adjusting (Overstimulation); there might be air bubbles in the pipes which means the water flows in an irregular fashion (Uncoordination); defective structures in the building might press on the pipes (Stress), leading to fracture (Damage) or deformation (Distortion), and so on. But none of these will stop the water flowing out discoloured red. The only way that can be done is by removing whatever it is in the tank or the supply to the tank which stains the water. By analogy, the source of that stain is the miasm. This is of course simplistic; but the important point is that there are other conditions which affect the Dynamis such as Congestion, Overstimulation, Uncoordination, the energy patterns of Toxins, etc., which can also produce serious symptoms. These however are not miasms, although they may be

If we accept Hahnemann's thesis, then identification and proper treatment of miasms as Factors in ill health must be an important consideration in Radionic work. The argument is that miasms present, in many cases, such a considerable problem that they can hardly be ignored. According to Gurudas,

'As originally stated by Dr. Hahnemann....miasms are the root cause of all chronic diseases and can be a contributing factor in some acute problems. They are the vibrational foundation of genetically inherited diseases in the body, which are passed on from generation to generation....as individuals age, their vitality weakens, which allows miasms to penetrate the physical body from the subtle anatomies and cellular level....It is essential that holistic health practitioners understand the profound impact miasms have on chronic diseases. Underlying miasms contribute to making one susceptible to various acute illnesses. What usually happens today is that the client is treated with natural remedies, yet the underlying problems are not even considered or examined...effectively treating the miasms is essential if the holistic health movement is to reach its full potential of restoring people to health in mind, body and spirit....a miasm is not necessarily a disease; it is the potential for disease. Indeed, miasms are a crystallized pattern of karma....There is a general misconception in homoeopathic circles that miasms represent an imbalanced pattern that blocks the person's vitality and the life force of a vibrational remedy. This observation is not wrong; it is just incomplete. Miasms are not just darkness or tainted energy; they are the lack of light or life force. The life force is the causal element that arranges the pattern correctly; thus, healing occurs when the life force penetrates into the void. Many times, individuals remove blockages but still do not permit the light or life force to enter, thus recreating the circumstances.'[207]

Although Hahnemann takes an entirely negative view of the miasms, it can be argued that they have valuable positive aspects. Many of

---

entangled with miasms or may even be the result of miasmatic inhibition. As a consequence any attempt to untangle the problem requires a great deal of care.
207. Gurudas (1986), p. 82 - 83

the greatest works of art, for example, may be a result, to some degree, of the individual's effort to overcome inner miasmatic forces. Many existential struggles depicted in the arts may actually be showing the conflict produced in the individual between the negative aspect of the miasm - the 'lack of light' - and the aspiration to achieve great insights, grasp of higher truths, transcendence of limitation, and the drive to self-realisation. Thus miasms may bring energy, motivation and fire and stand opposed to complacency and stagnation. Hence it can be argued that they have both positive and negative qualities. Use of the forces they ignite may hasten the way to a deeper understanding and quicken personal evolution.

Miasms may also act at a mass level. *Derived* from Hahnemann's thinking, contagious epidemic diseases (in particular) may also spread through contact between the individual's Etheric Body and the Etheric field and Pranic energies of the planet. This is to suggest that the energy pattern of the disease pollutes the planetary field and through contact with it - because, it is said, we draw Prana from the Earth's pranic field - this may then inhibit or pollute the individual Dynamis. The actual pathogen infects later, since the internal environment has been prepared for it and the microbe can then implant its energetic envelope into the infected host. Subject to the condition of the immune system, the pathogen will then prosper accordingly. Bailey also refers to the three *Planetary Diseases*, Syphilis, Cancer and Tuberculosis:

'.....They are planetary in scope, present in the substance of which all forms are made, and are responsible for producing a host of lesser diseases which are sometimes recognised as affiliates but are frequently not so known.' [208]

Group Astral, or emotional-psychological phenomena, are common and pervasive throughout the modern world, particularly since the ideas involved may spread very quickly through the mass media. Thus for example:

'A good number of people in the world today are in a Sycotic state. There is a sense of inadequacy and inferiority, of having a tough time with the self in the struggle for existence. The growth of psychotherapy, self-improvement techniques, etc., are all in response to this rise in Sycosis.

---

208. Bailey (1953) p. 199. Bailey does not mention the Miasm concept *per se*.

Unfortunately, however, most such methods manage to achieve the opposite because they only bring about a better adjustment to fixed ways of thinking and living. These are only ways of coping with the same feeling of inferiority rather than a true diminution of the feeling.' [209]

or perhaps even more trenchantly,

'The value of the nosodes of human disease products lies in the fact that each one in a different relationship possesses the sum total background of racial miasmatic development. In this connection I offer a suggestion in the social study of the much-discussed psychology of 'mob action', often syphilitic in its brutality and unreasonableness, sycotic in action and persistency, and psoric in the welding of many persons from various social strata toward a unified purpose. The explosive element represents the release of the suppressed miasmatic accumulation, producing an effect entirely against the routine of long-established custom.' [210]

One might therefore suggest that miasms function not only in the life of the individual but can also play an important role in the life of society and in historical development. Here the miasms are seen *not* as energetic primitives creating illness in the Physical Body in the classical Hahnemannian sense, but as mass emotional and psychological *delusional phenomena*. Artefacts in, or arising from, the collective unconscious would include components of miasmatic origin accreted over centuries, millennia, perhaps even aeons. These would manifest as forces, acting not as isolated random events but as interconnected, accreted and reinforced patterns which drive action, response and evolutionary processes in many ways. These may erupt into human consciousness under appropriate circumstances as a component in the creation of various forms of upheaval such as warfare, political movements, the breakdown of societies, the shattering of rigid socio-historical structures, economic contractions or expansions, the emergence of new religions, the

---

209. Sankaran (1994) p. 26.
210. Quoted in Vermeulen (1996) (*Synoptic Materia Medica II*), p. 126. This section concerns the homoeopathic remedy Bacillinum, a nosode of Tuberculosis, and the quote is attributed to 'Waffensmith, 1929'. Nosodes are homoeopathic remedies produced by potentising disease products, e.g. Tuberculinum, Syphilinum, etc.

development of new technologies, and even the appearance of new diseases, creating conditions for the materialisation of new forms of social organisation, in short, the historical process as it is called; over the longer time span, the evolutionary process. These miasmatic components may also be identified with the idea of *karma* - the results of past actions, lying buried, stored and unprocessed, in the collective memory of mankind, emerging from the unconscious as circumstances allow, to provoke a rebalancing of the psychic homeostasis of humanity. At the physical level they may be forceful determinants in the evolution and development of form, through their influence on morphogenesis.

A GENERAL OVERVIEW OF THE MIASMS

Hahnemann proposed three basic miasms, referred to sometimes as the 'classical' miasms. The principal agent is denoted *Psora*, which he describes as the *itch-disease*. In fact the eruption on the skin is the sign of the inner action of the otherwise-invisible Psoric miasm on the Dynamis. It is *suppression* of the eruption, particularly by the use of allopathic medicines,[211] which may then drive the miasm deeper into the organism and force it to manifest through a more serious set of symptoms at some later time. Thus the Dynamis always attempts to keep symptoms as far away as possible from important vital organs such as the heart and brain; suppressive treatment may force it to retreat from its best defensive position, creating the potential for the intensity of action of the miasm to increase. This may eventually result in a more concerted attack on the organism. To work this point over, in Hahnemann's view diseases result from an impingement of the Vital Force i.e. diseases are Dynamic (energetic) in nature and can only be removed by correcting the problem at the Dynamic level with a suitably homoeopathic (similar[212]) potentised (i.e. Dynamic) remedy. To put it another way, what are described by

---

211. I.e. orthodox medicines which remove the symptoms but do not cure the actual disease, which at its root is a problem in the life force. Hahnemann's contempt for the medical methods of his time is boundless and is expressed in the most severely critical of terms - see *The Organon*. Almost needless to say, it won him few friends in the medical profession.

212. A homoeopathic remedy is selected according to the Law of Similars, which is to say, *a substance which can produce certain symptoms in a healthy person will cure those symptoms in a person sick with them*. The most frenzied point of contention is the potentisation of the substance - repeated dilution and shaking (succussion), which elicits the usual complaint from scientists and sceptics 'but there's nothing in there, how can it possibly work?'

orthodox medicine as diseases are only symptoms, or constellations of symptoms; the disease itself is the disturbance to the Vital Force. Suppression therefore occurs when external symptoms are removed without corresponding correction of the disturbance to the Dynamis. This potentially creates conditions whereby the disturbance may be forced to manifest at some later time in further and more serious symptoms. In this sense it may also have been driven into a region of the Dynamis which corresponds to more critical and vulnerable systems in the body. In Hahnemann's words,

'Psora is that most ancient, most universal, most destructive *and yet* most misapprehended *chronic miasmatic disease which for many thousands of years has disfigured and tortured mankind, and which during the last centuries has become the mother of all the thousands of incredibly various (acute and) chronic (non-venereal) diseases...Psora...is...the* oldest *and* most hydra-headed *of all the chronic miasmatic diseases.'* [213]

Hahnemann states that Psora is highly contagious (on the energetic level) and that Leprosy was its original form of *physical* manifestation:

'...let no-one think that the Psora, which has been thus mitigated in its local symptoms, its cutaneous eruption, differs materially from ancient leprosy.' [214]

According to Hahnemann Psora may be considered to account for about 90% of all chronic diseases, but the two remaining fundamental miasms are also important: *Sycosis (*the *fig-wart disease)*, the miasm resulting from suppressed or improperly-treated Gonorrhoea, particularly where condylomata and other skin excrescences such as warts accompany the discharge; and *Syphilis (*the *chancre disease)*, where improper removal of the initial ulcer-like eruption leads again to suppression of the disease and its subsequent devastating consequences. It should be noted that each miasm has its initial presenting symptom as a form of eruption on the skin - in other words, far from the vital centres - and it is the suppression of this eruption which leads to the complication of the miasm, driving it deeper into the interior of the organism, enabling it to develop

---

213. *The Chronic Diseases* (Theoretical Part) (1993) by Samuel Hahnemann, page 35.
214. Ibid., page 40, Note.

into more ominous and threatening forms. These forms include many of the diseases described by orthodox medicine.

Since Hahnemann's time many efforts have been made to explain the miasms. Many books and articles have been written describing its symptomology in encyclopaedic detail, and this wealth of literature is freely available. The names used by Hahnemann for the miasms are also confusing, since the diseases themselves (e.g. Leprosy, Syphilis) are in a sense products of the basic related miasmatic deficiency of which Syphilis is only one possible, if perhaps typical - or perhaps even archetypal - manifestation. However, it can be proposed that the essential characteristic of each miasm may be summarized in a single keyword. Psora is the miasm of *DEFICIENCY*; Sycosis, that of *EXCESS*; and Syphilis, that of *DESTRUCTION*. Psora *fails to meet the challenges of life in some way* (deficiency); as a result it *compensates with overreaction* (excess); and finally *overreaches itself and fails* (destruction).

With an additional 150 years of research into human physiology and pathology - not to mention genetics - since Hahnemann's death, the concept of miasms may seem ridiculous. So let us turn to an expert assessment by a modern Doctor:

'Unfortunately, because the idea, as propounded by Hahnemann, is so patently, in our modern eyes, merely a beginning, the germ only, of a real understanding of the nature of disease, it has given rise to two equally irrational attitudes in recent times. There are many homoeopaths who take the view that the original thesis cannot be improved upon....there are also others who, by reason of its obvious incompleteness, dismiss the whole thing as nonsense....Despite the foregoing remarks, it is striking that the described characteristics of the original 'three' nonetheless do correspond with the three fundamental types of manifestations of disease, namely: - overproliferation of tissue (Sycosis), destruction and ulceration (Syphilitic) and functional depletion and imbalance (Psora) and regarded in this light, the theory is indeed a monument to Hahnemann's genius and acuteness of observation.' [215]

OUTLINE OF THE CHARACTERISTICS OF THE MIASMS

Some basic general manifestations of each type of miasm will be listed, but note that symptoms attributable to miasmatic causes have

---

[215]. *Miasms – A Review* by Dr Farley Spink. Journal of the Psionic Medical Society, Volume XVI, No 38, Spring 2000.

literally book-length coverage and only the most basic outline can be given here. Each miasm is said to have effects at the physical, emotional and mental (psychological) levels and the trained observer can see the miasmatic inhibition underlying the behaviour and symptoms of many patients. To begin,

PSORA (*DEFICIENCY*): Vitamin, Nutrititional and Catalyst (Enzymes etc) deficiencies of all types. Impaired immune response. Skin eruptions and itching. Functional disorders of the system, such as digestive disturbances. Anxiety, Fears, Restlessness, Neuroses. Excessive response to slight stimuli; reactions exaggerated out of all proportion to stimulus. Basic feeling of weariness. Existential anxiety. Symptoms aggravated at any time of day or night. In general Psora has the central characteristic of deficient response - the inability, at some level - to respond equally to a challenge or insult to the system.

SYCOSIS (*EXCESS*): Overgrowth of tissues, warts, condylomata etc; tumours, neoplasms, cancers. Chronic catarrhs and mucous discharges. Chronic inflammations. Obsessive mental states and fixed ideas. Deceitfulness, excessive charm, disposition to flatter and other disguised aggressive attitudes, typically manipulative, covering up lack of self-confidence.[216] Control freaks. Sexual perversions. 'Night people'. Symptoms generally ameliorated evening and night, worse day.

SYPHILIS (*DESTRUCTION*): Destruction and necrosis of tissue; ulcerations; neurological diseases; congenital disorders; systemic breakdown. Depression, suicide, murder, disintegration of mental function, psychosis, paranoia, violence. Symptoms generally ameliorated day, aggravated evening and night.

---

216. 'Pavel Sudoplatov, Stalin's spymaster, was an expert on the recruitment of spies in capitalist countries. *"Search for people who are hurt by fate or nature - the ugly, those craving power or influence but defeated by unfavourable circumstances. In co-operation with us, all these find a peculiar compensation. The sense of belonging to an influential, powerful organisation will give them a feeling of superiority over the handsome and prosperous people around them."* From an article by Ben Macintyre in *The Times*, June 30th 2010. Here we have the idea of the working of the Sycotic Miasm at the psychological level; the betrayal, death and destruction resulting from espionage are its Syphilitic aspect. No doubt we must distinguish between decisions taken as a result of psychological deficits and those taken as a result of the prosecution of war.

It can also be argued that the three categories are so general as to be more or less meaningless; a *reductio* almost *absurdum* of the complexities of disease. But in homoeopathy it is the individualisation of symptoms and the selection of the correct remedy from a Materia Medica which contains hundreds, potentially thousands, of anti-miasmatic remedies, which counts. It is how the miasm presents in the individual that is important; to repeat, *the character of the miasm* (the *wesen*) *is the same in each person but the symptoms produced by it can vary over a vast range*. It is this individualisation of symptoms which is the proposed basis for homoeopathic prescribing, and the remedy with the symptom-picture which matches the patient's symptoms is the one - the *simillimum*.

Two other miasms, Tuberculosis and Cancer, were added by later homoeopaths. Traditionally, Tuberculosis is seen as being predicated on Psora, and hence an alternative name for it in homoeopathic terminology is *Pseudo*-Psora. Cancer is said to be predicated on Sycosis, since this miasm covers the disorganized and uncontrolled reproduction of cells (i.e. excess). However, these two diseases and their ongoing miasmatic taint were eventually thought to be so important that they have come to merit separate major categories of their own:

TUBERCULOSIS (*DISSATISFACTION* and *EXHAUSTION*): Romantic longings, the desire to live at maximum intensity,[217] inexpressible yearnings for the unattainable,[218] feelings of burning up,

---

217. *'The light that burns twice as bright burns half as long. And you have burned so very very brightly, Roy. Look at you. You're the prodigal son. You're quite a prize!'* Eldon Tyrell to his replicant (android) creation, Roy, in the film *Blade Runner* (1980).

218 . *'This is the end – beautiful friend,*
This is the end, my only friend, the end
Of our elaborate plans, the end
Of everything that stands, the end
No safety or surprise, the end
I'll never look into your eyes again – the end
Can you picture what will be
So limitless and free
Desperately in need of some stranger's hand
In a desperate land
Lost in a Roman...wilderness of pain
All the children are insane –
All the children are insane
Waiting for the summer rain.'
– Jim Morrison, The Doors, 'The End' (1966). This was also used as the theme music to Francis Ford Coppola's *Apocalypse Now* (1978). The 19th Century was the era of Tubercular

'burning the candle at both ends', grudge-bearing, easily offended, many forms of respiratory complaints, chronic dry cough, bone and endocrine diseases, profuse night-sweats, excessive sexual desires etc. As a disease Tuberculosis was rampant, slow-developing and usually ended in death. It was introduced as a main miasm at the end of the 19th Century and its taint is widely indicated even today, some 50 years after effective drug treatment was introduced.

CANCER (ADAPTIVE FAILURE): Perfectionism, sympathetic and sensitive, conscientious with great sense of duty, easily offended, love for animals, nurturing. Ailments from domination and repression, especially in childhood; too much responsibility too early in life (e.g. children of alcoholic parents). Suppressed emotions, mild-mannered, yielding. Sensitive to reprimands. History of severe childhood diseases especially glandular fever, persistent sore throats. Multiple allergies. Difficulty falling asleep. Moles and naevi. Cancers of all types.

Note that an underlying theme of all the miasms is *compulsion*. The free will of the individual to respond has been compromised. He is *compelled* to make certain reactive or compensatory responses and is usually unaware of it; or logic cannot defeat emotional responses or programs, making him, for example, helpless in the face of neurotic fears. The strongly miasmatic person, neurotic or not, cannot reason with his personality traits any more than he can reason with his physical illnesses.

ACUTE MIASMS
These can be looked at from two angles, firstly as a presenting illness and secondly as after-effects or *sequelae* (*post-infective dyscrasia*). Thus in the first instance we find an acute infectious disease which takes the same general form from patient to patient, particularly in a specific

---

art. Many major artists succumbed to the disease e.g. Keats, Chopin, Paganini, Chekov, Schiller, Aubrey Beardsley, Schubert, Emily Bronte - it was a constant and ominous threat to the life of all. Thus the Romantic period may be considered in part a response to Tuberculosis, born of Tubercular miasmatic forces. Note that Schoenberg, the quintessential 20th Century composer, sought to impose order on his internal passionate feelings by inventing the rigid compositional method of the tone row (12-tone music). Thus Tubercular emotionalism gave way to Sycotic control. One may ask to what extent 20th Century compositional music recovered from this?

epidemic. In this category can be found diseases such as Influenza, Chicken Pox, Measles, Mumps, Whooping Cough, Glandular Fever, Cholera, Typhoid, Smallpox, Anthrax and so on. As noted, the miasmatic pattern may pollute the Earth's pranic field and via this route infiltrate the individual at the energetic level.

In the second instance we find a miasmatic inhibition, particularly of the Etheric Body and Morphic (Organ Counterpart) fields, which is a result or after-effect of the acute episode. In homoeopathy this is sometimes categorised as NBWS: 'never been well since'. A typical example is where the after-effects of some infectious disease such as Influenza or Glandular Fever (Infectious Mononucleosis) may linger for months, years, or even for life. The situation can be complicated by two further factors. The effects of an Acute episode may also be seen intergenerationally, so that a person may exhibit some symptomology resulting from, for example, Smallpox in a parent or grandparent, even though they personally have never had the disease.[219] In addition, the powerful effect of an Acute illness may be sufficient to activate, or entangle with, an underlying chronic (classical) miasmatic state, creating an even more complex situation.

ENVIRONMENTAL MIASMS - GURUDAS

During the 1980s Gurudas published a number of books, particularly on Gem and Flower essences. The books contain a great deal of channelled material, some of which relates to Miasms, Homeopathy and various associated topics. Gurudas introduced the concept of four 'new' miasms which can be related to pollution of various types and which might be described [by the present author] as 'environmental' in origin. These are denoted the RADIATION, PETROCHEMICAL, HEAVY METAL and STELLAR Miasms.[220] According to Hahnemann, miasms can be inherited or acquired, and Gurudas, in turn, states that the first three of these miasms, like the classical miasms, can also be inherited or acquired. Briefly,

---

219. See for example *Homoeopathic Links*, Volume 15, Winter 2002: *Variolinum, Vaccininum and Malandrinum – the powerful smallpox nosodes and their therapeutic use*, by Erika Scheiwiller-Muralt.

220. See Gurudas (1989) p. 84 - 91 (*Gem Elixirs and Vibrational Healing Volume I*); there are numerous references to these 'new' miasms (which are not, it seems, accepted by mainstream homoeopathy). I will not enter into a discussion of 'channelling' here; if the concepts have validity, the matter of their provenance can be considered later.

'the Radiation Miasm is associated with the massive increase in background radiation...it contributes to premature ageing, slower cell division, deterioration of the endocrine system, weakening of bone tissue, anaemia, arthritis, hair loss, allergies, bacterial inflammations (especially in the brain)... cancer...hardening of the arteries and the full spectrum of heart diseases....this miasm is mainly focused on the molecular level.'

Note that patients subjected to X-Ray and other imaging devices may also give readings for the presence of some form of Radiation at the energetic level and it may be necessary to take appropriate steps to attempt to neutralise this.

'the Petrochemical Miasm is caused by the major increase in petroleum and chemical-based products in society....some problems....include fluid retention, diabetes, hair loss, infertility, impotence, miscarriages....degenerative muscle diseases...metabolic imbalances that cause excessive storage of fatty tissue may occur. It is harder to resist stress and psychosis, especially classical schizophrenia and autism... overexposure to petrochemicals....may lead to schizophrenia and wildly erratic emotional behaviour patterns, especially those associated with allergic states.'

One may note the ever-increasing statistics for disturbances in the behaviour of children, the increase in autism and other syndromes such as ADD (Attention-Deficit Disorder). It should also be remembered that Hahnemann devoted considerable space to the strongest criticism of the methods of his contemporaries, notably concerning their excessive use of strong toxic medicines in so-called heroic doses, and the deleterious effects that resulted. In short, the Petrochemical Miasm may have its origins further back in time than Gurudas suggests.

'the Heavy Metal Miasm is cross-indexed with other Miasms. For instance, radioactive isotopes often latch on to heavy metals....the symptom picture of this developing Miasm includes allergies, excessive hair loss, excessive fluid retention, inability to assimilate calcium, susceptibility to viral inflammation...senility.'

In the past toxic metals such as lead were often used in domestic water pipes and even cosmetics; as another example from history,

'By the last years of the second century BC....huge new mines were sunk across central and south-western Spain. Measurements of lead in the ice of Greenland's glaciers, which show a staggering increase in concentration during this period, bear witness to the volumes of poisonous smoke they belched out. The ore being smelted was silver; it has been estimated that for every ton of silver extracted over ten thousand tons of rock had to be quarried. It has also been estimated that by the early first century BC, the Roman mint was using fifty tons of silver each year.'[221]

The dubious effects of Aluminium have long been noted in Radionics and the possible effects of dental amalgam, Gold and Mercury have been the subject of controversy for many years - and, in some people, said to be the toxic source of many symptoms, i.e. also, in a sense, a non-miasmatic source of chronic illness.

'the Stellar Miasm [stellar background radiation, or cosmic radiation]....constant low vitality....an overall sense of loss. The loss seems unconnected to the forces that bring an individual into existence, as if they are being told to go back to sleep, leave physical existence, or stop what they are doing. Such people will feel this as a general malaise....It is important to understand that stellar background radiation is an important energy that can transform people....'

In this account the Stellar Miasm is somewhat more existential in its effects. It is said to particularly affect the 5 higher chakras which are said to be located in the Subtle Bodies above the Crown Chakra.

ARTICULATED MIASM
We have the idea of an ongoing struggle between the Dynamis and the potentially destructive miasmatic forces. One or more miasms may be present in the individual but any serious effects are kept in check by the Dynamis. In short, the individual may be healthy or *vital* enough to resist the production of noticeable or unusual symptoms by the miasm, which in effect remains latent, inactive, or, at minimum, tolerated. There may be relatively mild but ongoing symptoms of some sort or other. However, when triggered by some powerful stressor to the Vital Force, such as a shock, trauma or serious infection (acute illness), the balance may then be disturbed in favour of the miasm, and the subsequent

---

221. Holland (2003), p. 43

development of a miasm-based illness. In order to differentiate this further:

'...the disease's essential esse (the dynamic, self-subsisting presence which is the disease) *is invariable. Miasms are collective diseases in that everyone who manifests the disease* (in whatever form) *has the same disease...the wesen* (nature) *of a miasm...always remains the same. This is true both of the acute miasms* (e.g. the measles) *whose disease manifestations are limited and fairly invariable, and the chronic miasms* (e.g. Psora) *whose disease manifestations...vary greatly; all miasms, no matter how variable or how fixed their disease manifestations, always remain the same as their wesen.'* [222]

In short, miasms may be thought as a collective 'property' of mankind and each one has the same fundamental characteristics regardless of the fact that individual humans differ widely; the Psoric miasm, if present, is therefore the same in me as it is in you. It is how *miasms are expressed in each personal case of illness* which may be completely different, producing symptoms in one person completely different to those produced in another.

The term *Articulated Miasm* has been introduced (by the author) to describe that combination of miasms and other Factors peculiar to an individual and which result in a pathological picture specific to that person.[223] The Articulated Miasm may be considered to arise when, at minimum, a group of 'latent' miasms have become activated and have combined together to create or be involved with a presenting chronic disease state. More typically, some combination of miasms has become entangled with a range of other inimical Factors such as the energy patterns of poisons, toxins, stressors, pathogens, and so forth, as might be found in any of the Subtle Bodies, Chakras, Nadis, Meridians, etc. These Factors can combine or entangle to create, from the Radionic point of view, an extremely complex energetic derangement of the Subtle

---

222. *The Organon* (op. cit.), Glossary, page 328
223. The word 'articulate' means to express, and therefore the *articulated* miasm is the particular expression of the range of Factors entangled with active miasms which combine to create the symptom-picture (or 'totality of symptoms') peculiar to the individual. Hahnemann and others following refer to the mixing of miasms, but here we take things a step further, in accordance with Radionic thinking. By way of comparison orthodox medicine has the concept of 'multifactorial disease.'

Anatomy, and this in its turn may underlie a wide range of chronic illnesses.

To a greater or lesser extent the Articulated Miasm can also be identified with the disease states described *and named* by orthodox medicine (e.g. Cancer, Ulcerative Colitis, Emphysema, Parkinson's disease, etc.) From the Radionic point of view these diseases suggest an underlying *typical* form of energetic disturbance to a *typical* set of Locations which manifest as the named disease. In this sense the total situation of a person with a chronic disease picture may be thought to include a range of energetic disturbances, some of which are the same in all persons suffering from that disease, and some of which are peculiar to that person. Orthodox medicine may describe a disease as having typical characteristics by which it may be identified, and in Radionics these are mirrored in equivalent disturbances to the counterpart fields and other more general fields such as those of Chakras, Nadis, Meridians, etc.

Therefore the Articulated Miasm can be viewed as having, potentially, three main components,

1. Centrally, an active miasm or number of miasms;
2. Any number of other Factors which become entangled with the miasms;
3. A specific form of energetic disturbance which characterizes a disease or range of diseases, as named by orthodox medicine.

The last component may well be the main presenting symptomology of which the patient complains, the others not being understood or recognised. *Nevertheless the presence of a named disease with a specific set of characteristics and symptoms should not be confused with the likely complexity of the underlying energetic difficulties. It is axiomatic that any therapeutic intervention at the energetic level should attempt to deal with the entire constellation of problems.*

As a point of practice it should be understood that in Homoeopathy a miasm is viewed as a general affliction of the Dynamis. No effort is made to study the composition of the Subtle Anatomy and the question of *where* in the Subtle Anatomy the miasm is acting. Homoeopathy uses the observation, evaluation and weighting (i.e. assessment of relative importance) of observed symptoms as its main guide to prescribing, and hence the presence and action of a miasm would be determined by reference to the nature of the symptoms observed. Therefore a key difference is that Homoeopathy studies the Dynamis by its external signs (the symptoms) whereas Radionics studies the Dynamis as part of the Subtle Anatomy, which is seen as a set of definable energy fields, the condition and quality of which can be analysed by radiesthesic methods. Again by way of contrast, in Radionics the presence (or absence) of a miasm in any particular Location can in principle be determined by analysis. For example, the Tubercular Miasm might be found affecting the Small Intestine, the Kidneys, the Joints, Connective Tissue, the Stem Cells, the Nadis, a Chakra; Syphilitic Miasm, the Nervous System, the Immune System, the Astral Body, and so on. A miasm may affect the Etheric Body as a generality as well as expressing in a particular Location, or set of Locations.[224]

It is possible that Hahnemann was aware in some form of the concept of a structured Subtle Anatomy and that he was also aware of esoteric concepts which he chose not to factor explicitly into his writings. He was clearly aware of the existence of what we now generally call stress. Compare for example §225 of *The Organon,*

> '...there are certainly a few emotional diseases that have not simply degenerated from somatic disease...with but little infirmity it develops outward from the emotional mind due to persistent worry, mortification, vexation, abuse, or repeated exposure to great fear or fright...emotional diseases of this kind often ruin the somatic state of health to a high degree.'

One may conclude that the emotional and mental symptoms described by Homoeopathy are primarily somatic in origin, i.e. they result from impacts to the Dynamis which may affect the nervous and endocrine systems in particular. If this is correct it then supports the idea that the Dynamis is most closely identified as the Etheric Body and related regions. As seen above, Hahnemann clearly differentiates between 'emotional diseases' resulting from impacts to the 'emotional mind', as opposed to emotional diseases which have 'degenerated from somatic disease.'

---

224. Nevertheless, as an early example of the recognition of a relationship between Homoeopathy and Radionics, Abrams noted that homoeopathic Mercury offset the reflex reaction to Syphilis in his test subject.

A RADIONIC VIEW OF THE MIASMS

Looking at the question from the standpoint of energy flow it is possible to propose a basis for the action of the miasms. The general picture is given in Table 4 below.

To begin with the problem of the nature of the classical miasms described by Hahnemann and his followers, Chapter 7 notes that the Etheric Body is built up from seven different primary energies, denoted the Etheric Pre-Physical. These seven primary energies combine in different ratios in each individual and *the Etheric Body is refreshed with them in an ongoing process.*[225] This means that the structure and quality of the Etheric Body is maintained by continual replacement or refreshing of its Etheric material. *Miasms in effect are disturbances to this refreshment process which create some form of ongoing and fundamental depletion in the structure of the Etheric Body.*[226] This means that the Etheric Body cannot function to its full or 'normal' potential and this is reflected in the condition of the Physical Body.

To take this a step further, it is also possible to correlate miasms with the seven Etheric Pre-Physical energies:

ETHERIC PRE- ENERGY	MIASM
1	NOT YET KNOWN OR IN MANIFESTATION
2	NOT YET KNOWN OR IN MANIFESTATION
3	PSORA
4	CANCER
5	SYPHILIS
6	TUBERCULOSIS
7	SYCOSIS

Table 4: Primary sphere of action of the Classical Miasms

This would also accord with Hahnemann's opinion that the *wesen* of each miasm is the same in every person. Each person with the Psoric

---

225. An analogy is the refreshment of the image on a television or computer screen, which typically takes place between 60 and 100 times a second (60 - 100Hz).

226. The author has noted many times in Radionic analysis that readings for miasms in various Locations can change quite rapidly, increasing or decreasing, as well as remaining static for long periods.

miasm would be deficient in Etheric Pre-Physical energy 3, each person with the Tubercular miasm would be deficient in Etheric Pre-Physical energy 6, and so on. A further and as yet not-answerable question is how these deficiencies may correlate with the known disease types and their ongoing effects, e.g. to what extent does the deficiency of energy 6 contribute to or correlate with the development of Tuberculosis? How do inherited deficiencies to energy 6 (Tubercular Miasm) contribute to the Tubercular miasmatic constitutional picture, which, of course, may not include any Tuberculosis as a primary illness in the individual? What determines the inheritance of miasms and how do they reflect in the genetic makeup of the individual? - and so on.

In turn Acute miasms may be thought to have their main affect on the Etheric Body proper. In this sense they are not as far back in the process of origination as the classical miasms and the result is more simply an inhibition of performance rather than a depletion of the underlying structure of the Etheric double. However, it may be reasoned that if the Etheric Body is already subject to miasmatic inhibition, then an Acute miasm might be more easily grafted onto it.

The Environmental Miasms are more particularly said (by Gurudas) to act at the genetic, molecular, cellular and metabolic levels; in Radionic terms, on the energetic counterparts of these physical microstructures. Here they would produce, as described above, an inhibition of some combination of the many processes needed to maintain the living organism at the relevant level. Finally, the Articulated miasm would be the combination of Factors described above, acting at many levels on the Dynamis and Vital Force:

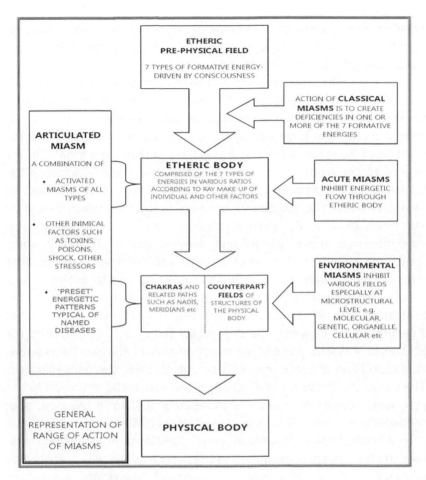

Figure 14: Range of action of Miasms

MIASMS IN THE HIGHER SUBTLE BODIES

While I suggest that the principal focus of action of miasmatic inhibition is upon the physical counterpart energy fields such as the Etheric Body, Radionic analysis indicates that certain of the miasms may manifest in the Astral, Mental, Atmic and Causal Bodies. Amongst these may be numbered most typically the five Classical miasms, the Stellar miasm, and, to some extent, the Acute miasms. Here they are present in the psychological, emotional and existential areas of the individual's life and their expression is more subjective, in the sense that although the individual will be driven to act and react in certain ways, there might be the possibility of defeating the miasm through action or experience; a life-event happens which is so powerful that it serves to dismantle the miasmatic delusions at this level. Freud describes neurosis as originating in the disruption of the sexual developmental stages of the child,[227] whereas Jung (who broke with Freud) sees neurosis as emerging from a frustration of the process of individuation, or self-realisation.

In the main sense, therefore, it may be proposed that miasmatic action at the psychic level equates with the Jungian idea and is a component of the inhibition of the impulse towards self-realisation. It may also be a component produced by the development of the self, and the frustration of its earlier efforts. If you believe perhaps in karma - i.e. the results of earlier actions - you may think that miasmatic inhibition is the accretion of karma presenting as an obstacle to the self which must be overcome. Its action would be as a blockage in the road which cannot be driven round or otherwise circumvented; it has to be removed by some means otherwise it will persist and demand *action*. This is in some respects like a neurosis, but which persists and demands *reaction*. Both psychic problems might be overcome by some experiential or therapeutic process. The difference is that the miasmatic forces may drive the individual towards self-actualisation, whereas the neurosis is a product of the circumstances in which the personality finds itself, and inhibits the individual in a typical pattern, i.e. a *congestion* of the psyche resulting from a repression of some kind. As a person ascends Maslow's Hierarchy of Needs, so the presence and action of the miasmatic inhibition in the higher Subtle Bodies may become more evident than in the past, and, consequently, a previously-unobserved object of Radionic attention.

It is also feasible that the action of the Miasms in the higher subtle bodies creates a range of symptoms in the psyche as typically described by psychology, such as depression, feelings of alienation, separation, loneliness, inferiority and so forth. Therefore correction of such symptoms might be better achieved by relief of the miasmatic inhibition than by attempts to address the psyche directly by any of a range of more direct therapeutic approaches.

---

227. See for example Freud (2006) p. 196 et. seq. (*The Wolfman*)

12: ANALYSIS

The objective of analysis is to discover the cause of the patient's symptoms, and, in turn, to find treatments which might counteract them. Obviously, the complexity of a patient's illness will tend to dictate the complexity of any analysis and possible therapeutic responses. In many cases there will be not be a quick or simple solution. Apart from the fact that the problems may be severe, persons very often seek Radionic treatment as a last resort, only after they have exhausted more conventional approaches. They may have had years of orthodox medicine which have not produced a result. They may have tried a range of complementary therapies which have also not produced much of a change. They may be desperate, and desperation can drive a person to places they would never have considered previously. The typical position, therefore, is that the case is probably quite difficult, possibly incurable, and it may be impossible to ameliorate the patient's situation to any great extent. There tend to be two outcomes. If the Radionic effort fails, Radionics will be dismissed as a failure. If, on the other hand, the Radionic effort succeeds to any extent, the Radionic intervention may well be ignored because few people like to admit that they had treatment by such seemingly arcane or weird methods. Therefore taking up Radionic practice is not for the person seeking the easy route, adulation, instant gratification, or substantial monetary rewards. In a certain sense you are on a hiding to nothing. There are of course persons who actively seek Radionic treatment, and they may well be grateful for your work if you have success with some difficult condition, but do not expect a visit from your local health centre to find out how it was done.

Hahnemann provides us with a succinct distillation of what the therapist needs to understand and do in order to work productively:

> 'To be a genuine practitioner of the medical art, a physician must:
> 1. clearly realize what is to be cured in diseases, that is, in each single case of disease.
> 2. clearly realise what is curative in medicines, that is, in each particular medicine.
> 3. be aware of how to adapt what is curative in medicines to what he has undoubtedly discerned to be diseased in the patient, according to clear principles .In this way recovery must result.

Adapting what is curative in medicines to what is diseased in patients requires that the physician be able to:

1. adapt the most appropriate medicine, according to its mode of action, to the case before him

2. prepare the medicine exactly as required

3. give the medicine in the exact amount required

4. properly time the repetition of the doses.

Finally, the physician must know the obstacles to recovery in each case and be aware of how to clear them away so that the restoration of health may be permanent.' [228]

In my view certain of Hahnemann's comments have a general validity and his central ideas as to what needs to be done can be applied to other therapeutic disciplines, such as Radionics. Clearly, the Radionic method is not the same as the Homoeopathic method but in the author's view the underlying concepts have a useful degree of correspondence. Part of the point is that although the approach may be different for each of the two disciplines, the therapeutic objective is substantially similar, perhaps identical. A further point is that homoeopathic remedies can be used to treat the patient, and synthesized, using Radionic methods. This will be explored further in Chapter 13.

It also can be argued that all energy, or vibrational, medicine must basically have the same objective because the objective - what needs to be done to help the patient - is substantially determined by Nature, not human preference. A disordered Subtle Anatomy is disordered in terms of reference to the ordered Subtle Anatomy, which latter is the result of evolution by Nature and natural process. Human ideas and concepts as to how to approach the problem vary greatly, as is evidenced by the plethora of alternative and complementary medical techniques, but to a good degree the objective is the same. There is only the question of which method, or perhaps combination of methods, have the best chance of achieving a substantial result.

Over the next few Chapters I will explore some of the techniques used in Radionic work and the reader may refer back to the quote above. To begin with we note that Hahnemann states '(a physician must) *clearly realize what is to be cured in diseases.*' Analysis is the heart of the matter. It is the means by which we apprehend the central problem, or group of

---

228. Organon of the Rational Medical Art, Aphorism 3. (*op. cit.*)

problems, which afflict the patient. A patient may exhibit a plethora of symptoms, which to the inexperienced or untrained observer are incomprehensible and overwhelming, without any central thread or pattern. As noted, the patient may have had any number of different therapies over any number of years. He may have got a little bit better, no better, a little bit worse, much worse, much better then back to square one, and so on. This situation is frequently met and it is the objective of the practitioner to go to the deepest level of understanding possible in order to find the causation, the common link or thread which has created the overall symptom picture. If these core symptoms are not addressed then the result will usually be more of the same.

SOME FUNDAMENTAL IDEAS

To begin with we should look at some underlying concepts. These are supplemental to earlier comments, such as those in Chapter 4, which also touches on methods of Analysis, construction of Charts, and so on.

1. *The presumption of normality.* That there are, for a given healthy patient of a certain age, typical characteristics which within an allowable range can be considered to be normal and an indication of good health. The presumption of normality serves as the basic objective backdrop against which tests can be made; as it were, a reference point or benchmark. There are, of course, some conceptual difficulties. When dealing with the paraphysical counterpart fields, definitions of normal physical functioning have been given quite clearly by orthodox medical science and it is reasonable to correlate these with the state of the corresponding fields. Where the psychological or emotional state is concerned, the situation is less obvious as the definition of 'normal' is far more subjective. The higher regions of the Subtle Anatomy, such as the Chakras, or Astral and Mental Bodies, are considered to be fields in their own right and their condition will reflect the state of the individual's psyche; but a 'normal' psychological state should not be confused with a conventional or conformist adaptation to societal norms. The creative individualist might be quite unconventional - perhaps not well-adapted to society - but this does not mean that he or she has innate psychological problems. Some may take a view that to certain extent society itself is sick. So it is the *condition* or *state* of the field and not the *contents* of the field which is the starting point at this level of investigation. If there is overstimulation or uncoordination of the Astral Body this may be the result of some other psychological Factor which produces, for example,

fear or anxiety. If a reading is obtained, then it is a test of the *condition* of the Astral Body produced by the Factor which is being made.

Identification of the specific nature of the stimulus - the *contents* - is a second step which may require considerable discretion if it is to be explored. The practitioner may inquire of the patient as to the cause, the actual underlying psychological or emotional problem; but a stressed or conflicted person may not want to reveal this as the matter might be too delicate, too inadmissible, too unacceptable, too embarrassing, and so on. It is also a fact that certain patients may reveal things about themselves to the practitioner which they have kept a close secret and by discussing them, achieve a certain degree of catharsis through this means.

2. (To reiterate) *Radionics studies and utilizes a model of the so-called Subtle Anatomy,* which has two main regions:

The first is that corresponding to the *psyche*, which has spiritual, intuitional, purposive, psychological, emotional and other components such as the subconscious and collective unconscious. These are thought to express themselves through fields such as the Causal Body, Mental Body, Astral Body, and so forth, as previously described.

The second is the *paraphysical body*, the counterpart fields - the Etheric Body and so forth - to those physical structures described by orthodox anatomy and physiology, for example, cells, tissues, organs, etc.

These various regions are referred to collectively as *LOCATIONS*.

3. *Sufficient trauma*. Similarly to the homoeopathic concept of disease outlined in the previous Chapter, in Radionics causes are thought to lie in derangements of, and disturbances to, the forces and energies - the fields - which underlie the physical form. As discussed in the previous Chapters, such disturbances may be caused by impacts of various kinds (for example, shock) and may occur at any point along a spectrum from origination to manifestation.[229] What is also important to bear in mind is that an impact coming from the exterior (manifestation) can also trigger, or exacerbate, a disturbance in the interior (origination). This gives us the idea, as discussed, that some disease or miasmatic state can be brought into play by events which do not appear to be directly connected to the problems which subsequently appear. This is a concept which gives an idea of a fractured, distributed or indirect chain of causation which is different from simple direct causation, such as, infective agent = illness. If

---

229. See Chapter 9.

the impact does not cause a disturbance to the underlying fields, or if the effect is fully counteracted by the fields and normal functioning resumes, then there are unlikely to be further consequences. The presumption is that whatever may be the origin of a disturbance, it was, or continues to be, so sufficiently strong as to cause, or have caused, an ongoing perturbation of the fields, which, in turn, produces symptoms. By way of example, concepts of feedback and feed forward might be considered as useful in describing the interaction between the fields. A psychological state induces an emotional reaction, circumstances aggravate the emotional reaction, this reinforces the psychological state, the whole disturbance is reflected in some derangement of the etheric body, perhaps laying the ground for some disease process to begin; the appearance of symptoms reinforces the emotional reaction, and so on.

The basic importance of this is as follows. When performing a Radionic analysis, many readings may be made which are essentially transient. The human system receives many inputs during daily life and tends to respond and react accordingly. You are late for the train for an important appointment. You make the train by 30 seconds but then it stands in the station for thirty minutes and you feel like exploding with rage at the outrageous injustices of the world. Your blood pressure goes up and you develop various stress-related symptoms. On the train journey you spill hot coffee on your hand. You eat a sandwich which doesn't agree with you. You finally get to the appointment and things do not go well. Your spouse calls you to find out what happened and you have an argument. There is a sudden change in the weather and you develop a mild sore throat. Finally you get back home, calm down, have a glass of wine, normal life resumes, and your sore throat goes away. This is a simple example, but many such transient reactions (which may be of relatively shorter or longer duration) may be picked up in Radionic analysis. Part of the operator's skill must lie in knowing the difference between what is trivial or temporary and what is relevant to the patient's illness. This last point needs proper understanding, because certain forms of trauma may have occurred for quite a short duration - for instance, birth shock - yet have effects which continue throughout the entire life of the individual. Thus what might seem to be trivial from some viewpoint is not in reality. Other events may have continued for long periods of time and of particular importance here would be childhood psychological or emotional trauma, since it is in childhood that we are most impressionable and have the least capacity to contextualise events. Severe acute illnesses, even of quite short duration, may also have effects which run throughout the individual's entire life. Tansley puts the situation quite trenchantly:

'What then are you tuning into when you seek to determine the state of a chakra? It isn't enough to mentally ask for an indication of over *or* under *or* normal *activity, your question has to consciously encompass the three tiers of petals or energy qualities. You can forget about the Bindu Point because your consciousness could not touch upon its vibratory rate in any event.*[230] *Further, unless your own chakras that you are working through are not in themselves acting at the Love and Will levels to any great extent, you are only going to pick up the surface activity of the chakra anyway....what I am attempting to illustrate and point out is that the capacity to penetrate and touch upon the activity of the chakra is dependent upon the state of unfoldment of your own chakras and your knowledge of the structure of the chakra....the lesson for us here as radionic practitioners is that anyone who analyses the states of the chakras must ask themselves is it enough to simply ask for the* over *or* under *or* normal *state, or is there more to it than that? Obviously there is far more to it, and our question must carry the intent and capacity to penetrate the chakra as deeply as possible so that we can obtain a meaningful reading, anything less and all you will register are the fluctuations of the surface aspects of the chakra activity which will tell you nothing of real value.*

What can be done to get accurate readings? First you have to have the ability to enter the chakra in depth and this must be accompanied by the intent to determine the FUNDAMENTAL STATE of the chakra under consideration. You may use that wording in your mental question but remember that it is useless without the ability to touch upon what you are seeking to know. Too many practitioners think that to wave a pendulum

---

230. Basically this is correct but the author's researches suggest that instruments can be made which increase the perceptual or intuitive range of the skilled practitioner, enabling a degree of access to the higher and more esoteric fields of manifestation, such as the Bindu point, Causal Body, and so on. But such an instrument does not automatically make you a Radionic maestro; you must know how to understand and interpret the information you might gain when using it. By analogy, you can see the night sky with the naked eye but to get into the detail you need a powerful telescope with a clear view (such as the Hubble). But even with such an instrument you need scientific training and experience to understand what you are looking at. Anyone can say 'that's a nice like looking galaxy!', but to know it is 2.5 million light years away (the Andromeda Galaxy) and will collide with the Milky Way in about 4.5 billion years (relates Wikipedia) requires somewhat more expertise.

and to get an answer to the question is all there is to it. I hope I have showed that there is far more to it than that, especially when the questions involve the chakras and subtle bodies, and even more so when dealing with ray energies. Some years ago I broached the idea of the FUNDAMENTAL STATE of the chakra with a leading instructor in radionics - who hadn't a clue what I was talking about; which leads me to wonder just how many practitioners are actually getting factual readings in respect to their chakra analysis work.'[231]

In general terms the practitioner should always have an honest, even ruthlessly honest, assessment of his or her own abilities. This does not mean you should creep timidly round the edge of the many difficult problems which patients bring. You try to do your best, and if you have some success, credit it to your account. But do not get carried away into egotistical reveries and fantasias of being a great healer, because the nature of the game is that the next case is likely to be tougher. Your invisible reward is self-development, and with that comes the development of one's abilities and faculties - the ability to perceive deeper into the reality of the patient's problems, and into the esoteric process of life itself.

4. *Deviation from normality can, in principle, be detected using radiesthesic techniques*, such as dowsing, and can be expressed as a percentage deviation from zero (0%). This is a qualitative, rather than quantitative, measurement. When doing this the practitioner queries the patient's fields on a location-by-location basis. In conjunction with a suitable chart and, very usually, a Radionic instrument,[232] a test is done to discover if there is any deviation from normality. If the pendulum indicates 0,[233] it can be presumed that the Location under study is functioning normally. Any indication of a number higher than 0 may indicate that there is a disturbance to the Location. That which causes such a disturbance is, in general, described as a *FACTOR*.

The percentage degree of deviation from zero is referred to as the *intensity* of the reading. Typically, *but not necessarily*, a lower reading is of

---

231. Tansley (1984) p. 54 - 55
232. A Radionic code for the Location under study would normally be used in the instrument, in order to increase the practitioner's focus and accuracy.
233. You could also use a scale where 100% is equivalent to full normal functioning and 0% is absolutely not.

less consequence than a higher reading. A contrary example might be where Infection reads 70% but Inflammation reads 90% in the same Location. Here if the Infection is presumed to be the cause of the strong Inflammatory response, it would obviously have a more primary importance in the chain of causation even though the intensity of the reading is lower.

It should also be mentioned, pursuant the discussion in 3) above, that the practitioner is unlikely ever to test a person who gives an entire set of readings at, or close to, zero. As noted, most of us have some irritation to the system or some disease potential which will give readings; the point is to discriminate between that which is a problem or has the potential to be a problem, and that which is not.

5. *It is necessary to distinguish between the concepts of Peak and Average readings.* 'Peak' means the reading at the worst point. This might be 90 [%]. 'Average' means the disturbance across the entire Location under study. This might be only 5 [%]. By way of example, a patient may display a point of infection in the Gastro-Intestinal Tract, which gives a reading of 90 although other parts of the Tract may be more or less unaffected. This may give a peak/average reading of, say, 90 / 5. The closer the average reading is to the peak, the more severe may be the problem. A peak/average reading of 90 / 40 may indicate that a Factor is impacting a greater, and possibly increasing, part of the Location. The diagram below illustrates this:

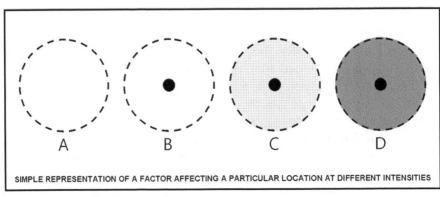

SIMPLE REPRESENTATION OF A FACTOR AFFECTING A PARTICULAR LOCATION AT DIFFERENT INTENSITIES

Figure 15:Factor affecting a Location

21st Century Radionics

In A there is no Factor impacting the Location, which is represented by a circle. [The dotted line indicates that the boundary of the field (the Location) is permeable, not sealed.]

In B, there is Peak Intensity at 90% but no average. The impact of the Factor is highly localized.

In C, there is Peak Intensity at 90% and an Average Intensity of around 30%. The impact of the Factor is both highly localized and somewhat regionalised.

In D, there is Peak Intensity at 90% and an Average Intensity of around 60%. The impact of the Factor is both highly localized and increasingly regionalised.

In practice, only Peak readings will be taken, since these will tend to bring out in sharper relief where problems may lie. As analysis continues, the practitioner can examine a Location of interest in more detail and make Peak/Average readings. Remember that 0% is considered to be Normal and 100% is the most extreme deviation from Normal. Although it is rare to see a deviation of 100%, it is possible. If, for example, a person has a broken bone where the bone is separated into two parts, then you could get a reading of *SKELETON:DAMAGE 100%*.

6. *The entire process is driven by the practitioner's intent, conditioned by expertise.* The method is to apply mentally-posed questions used in parallel with a radiesthesic device such as a pendulum, asking (for example) *'what is the peak percentage intensity of any Factor which may be impacting the Location under consideration?'* This of course does not need to be repeated like a mantra with every operation, although it helps while training. As the practitioner's skills develop, the mind will become habituated to the work and the subconscious will 'know' what to do with only a small prompt. In response to this question, the pendulum may swing and indicate 90%. This means that there is some problem (i.e. Factor or combination of Factors) inhibiting the normal functioning of the Gastro-Intestinal Tract in the patient. You are of course reading this problem at the energetic and informational level and it is creating a pendulum movement which indicates 90% on the scale.

A very wide range of questions can be asked and the skilled practitioner will usually be doing this in rapid succession, observing the pendulum response. For example, *'is the source of the problem in the paraphysical body?' 'is the source of the problem in the Astral Body?' '....in the Mental Body?' 'is there one central problem?' 'are there several* problems combining together to create the illness?' 'to what extent (%) can the problem be relieved by Radionic treatment?' 'to what extent is there a maintaining cause?' [for example problematic relational, social or economic circumstances which cannot be relieved by treatment]...and so on.

7. *Analysis identifies not only stressed Locations but also attempts to identify the nature of the stressors (Factors).* Factors and Locations can be displayed on suitable Charts and these, in combination with appropriate instruments, are used as an aid to the practitioner's focus and to enable greater precision in dowsing.

TAKING READINGS

The first step is to take some general readings using Charts, instrument and pendulum. To give a very simple example, you may find, and write down:

MENTAL BODY	16%
ASTRAL BODY	57%
ETHERIC BODY	89%
PHYSICAL-MORPHIC	90%
CHAKRAS	45%

It is more common to enter the readings into a pre-printed table. An example is given below in Fig. 16. Here the Locations are listed in the left hand column, percentages are listed in the intermediate columns, and in the right hand column, you can record the exact readings.[234] This creates a graph-like display. The usefulness of this method becomes more

LOCATION	0%	10%	20%	30%	40%	50%	60%	70%	80%	90%	100%	VALUE
MENTAL												16
ASTRAL												57
ETHERIC												89
PHYSICAL-MORPHIC												90
CHAKRAS												45

Figure 16:Example of Analysis graphic

---

234. These may be taken using the numerical scale in a two stage operation (i) ask for the first number (e.g. 8) and then (ii) the second number (9), hence, 89%. In short, the pendulum will point to first 8, then 9.

obvious when there are a large number of readings, since those that are high will be prominent and hence more readily-observed:

This example is of course a very basic set of readings. Use of a Chart such as that shown at the end of Chapter 4 (figure 10) would require a much larger set of entries in the table; forty-two Locations are listed in the outer sector, and many of these can, in turn, be deconstructed to reveal more detail. Figure 17 gives a hypothetical example of what might be found:

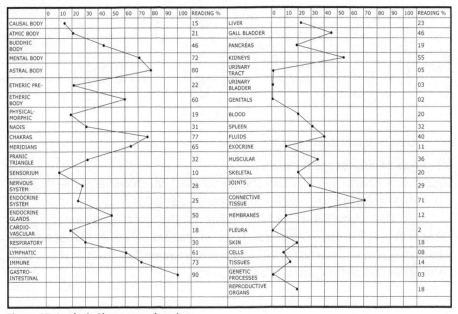

	0	10	20	30	40	50	60	70	80	90	100	READING %		0	10	20	30	40	50	60	70	80	90	100	READING %
CAUSAL BODY												15	LIVER												23
ATMIC BODY												21	GALL BLADDER												46
BUDDHIC BODY												46	PANCREAS												19
MENTAL BODY												72	KIDNEYS												55
ASTRAL BODY												80	URINARY TRACT												05
ETHERIC PRE-												22	URINARY BLADDER												03
ETHERIC BODY												60	GENITALS												02
PHYSICAL-MORPHIC												19	BLOOD												20
NADIS												31	SPLEEN												32
CHAKRAS												77	FLUIDS												40
MERIDIANS												65	EXOCRINE												11
PRANIC TRIANGLE												32	MUSCULAR												36
SENSORIUM												10	SKELETAL												20
NERVOUS SYSTEM												28	JOINTS												29
ENDOCRINE SYSTEM												25	CONNECTIVE TISSUE												71
ENDOCRINE GLANDS												50	MEMBRANES												12
CARDIO-VASCULAR												18	PLEURA												2
RESPIRATORY												30	SKIN												18
LYMPHATIC												61	CELLS												08
IMMUNE												73	TISSUES												14
GASTRO-INTESTINAL												90	GENETIC PROCESSES												03
													REPRODUCTIVE ORGANS												18

Figure 17:Analysis Sheet completed

SUBTRACTIVE ANALYSIS

A number of Factors may be affecting a particular Location. I will now give a simple method - Subtractive Analysis - which can be used to find out what these may be. Here we pose questions about what the state of a Location would be if a certain Factor was eliminated, i.e. the reading for the most prominent Factor is taken and then the investigation asks which other Factors might remain in play if a treatment was given to fully neutralise or remove it. Some simple diagrams will illustrate the method.

The table above indicates a reading of 90% for the patient's Gastro-Intestinal Tract, so the practitioner decides to investigate this

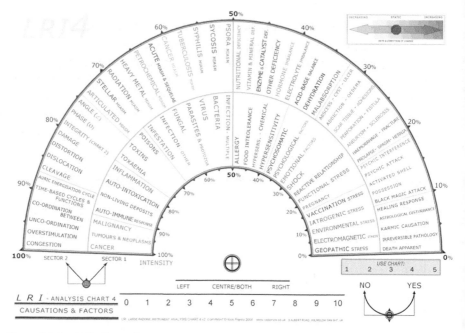

Figure 18: Analysis Chart - Factors

further. A Chart - see Fig. 18 - should be used which displays the range of possible Factors (for e.g. as listed in Chapters 9 to 11).[235]

The question is posed, *'what is the most prominent Factor impacting the Gastro-Intestinal Tract in patient X?'* and the pendulum indicates, Toxins, intensity, 90%. The 90% reading for Toxins agrees with the 90% reading for Gastro-Intestinal Tract.

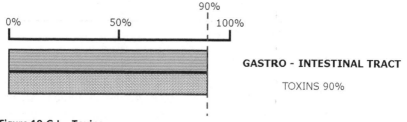

Figure 19:G.I. - Toxins

We then need to know if there is any other Factor affecting the G.I. Tract, so we can pose the question *'if all Toxins were eliminated from Gastro-Intestinal Tract, which Factor would then be most prominent and what would its value be?'* The pendulum responses might indicate the following:

---

[235]. This Chart is a part of the LRI instrument manufactured by the author.

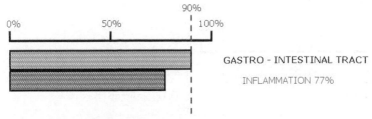

Figure 20:G.I. - Inflammation

Now we see that there is a degree of Inflammation at 77%. Note that it is equally possible that there could be another reading at 90%, parallel to that for Toxins - perhaps Inflammation. We repeat the question and discover the next Factor:

Here we observe a reading for Parasite Infection, 60%. In the next step we discover a degree of miasmatic presence:

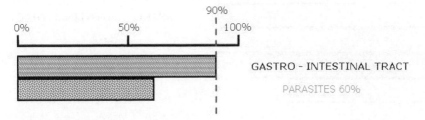

Figure 21:G.I. - Parasites

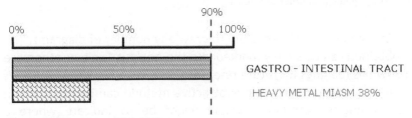

Figure 22:G.I. - Heavy Metal Miasm

There is a local presence of the Heavy Metal Miasm. Finally, a reading is obtained for Fungal Infection:

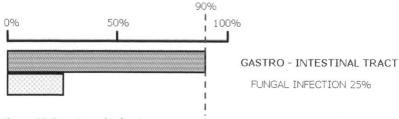

GASTRO - INTESTINAL TRACT

FUNGAL INFECTION 25%

Figure 23:G.I. - Fungal Infection

We can then ask if there are any other readings of significance and the answer, yes or no, will dictate whether the inquiry is complete. If complete, one can summarise the readings as follows:

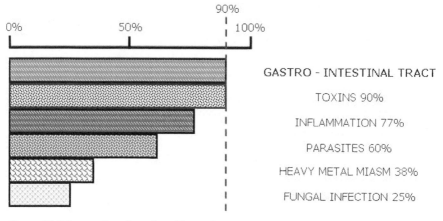

GASTRO - INTESTINAL TRACT

TOXINS 90%

INFLAMMATION 77%

PARASITES 60%

HEAVY METAL MIASM 38%

FUNGAL INFECTION 25%

Figure 24:G.I. - readings in order of intensity

Of course it is not necessary to draw any number of diagrams. The values obtained can be simply marked into the Analysis Table or otherwise noted down as readings for future reference.

It may apparent that the Subtractive method can be used from a number of angles. Another example might be to indicate where a particular Factor is most prominent. In this case we have taken an overall reading for Toxins at 90%. After establishing that the peak level of Toxins is found in the G.I. Tract we can then repeatedly pose the question, *'if all Toxins were eliminated from Gastro-Intestinal Tract, which Location would then be most impacted by Toxins (and what would its value be)?'* By doing this we establish that Liver 75%, Kidneys 49%, Lungs 37%, Joints 25% etc are affected by Toxins in that order.

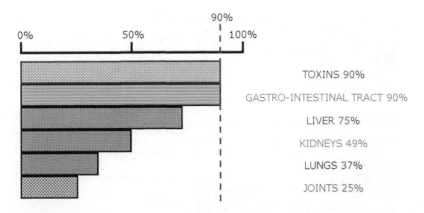

Figure 25: Toxins - Locations in order of intensity

TOXINS 90%
GASTRO-INTESTINAL TRACT 90%
LIVER 75%
KIDNEYS 49%
LUNGS 37%
JOINTS 25%

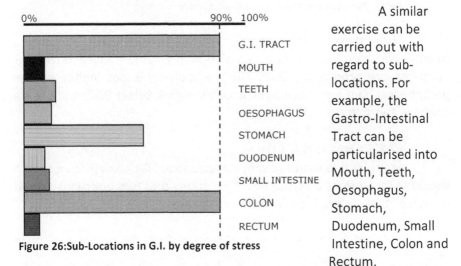

Figure 26:Sub-Locations in G.I. by degree of stress

G.I. TRACT
MOUTH
TEETH
OESOPHAGUS
STOMACH
DUODENUM
SMALL INTESTINE
COLON
RECTUM

A similar exercise can be carried out with regard to sub-locations. For example, the Gastro-Intestinal Tract can be particularised into Mouth, Teeth, Oesophagus, Stomach, Duodenum, Small Intestine, Colon and Rectum.

If the G.I. as whole reads 90%, we can use this method to establish which sub-locations are affected to what degree of intensity by any Factor, e.g. Colon 90%, Rectum 71%, Small Intestine 12%, Duodenum 9% etc. This exercise helps to localise the point where there is likely to be the greatest problem.

Finally, you could perform a similar exercise against the reading for Toxins. The reading for Toxins is 90% and you wish to know which sub-Locations of the Gastro-Intestinal Tract are worst-affected:

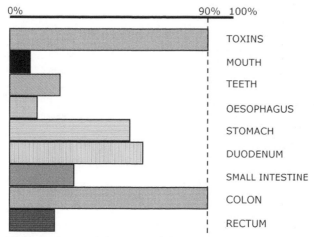

Fig 27: Toxins in sub-locations of the G.I. Tract

From these simple examples it can be seen that Subtractive Analysis can be used in various ways to help establish which Factors or Locations are prominent. Obviously the method is not limited to the paraphysical body and can also be used for higher Subtle Body and Chakra analysis, and so forth.

RAE'S ANALYSIS METHOD

Malcolm Rae wrote at some length about his analysis concepts in the book *Dimensions of Radionics*.[236] He states that two questions should be asked at the beginning of analysis, which are:

1. What is the *'Degree of deviation from functional perfection of....'*

In the section above *The presumption of normality* I have suggested that normality is contingent upon various situational factors such as the age of the patient. One could posit an ideal human who provides an 'absolute norm' against which we can test but we are unlikely to find one in reality, since everyone is to some extent in a degree of dynamic change. Therefore some latitude needs to built into our concept of a benchmark state because for many Locations, it may be difficult to

---

236. David V. Tansley (1992). Some of this is drawn from *Dimensions* and some from the *Instructions for using the Rae Magneto-Geometric Analyser*, published by Magneto-Geometric Applications.

21st Century Radionics

define what is 'perfect' or 'functionally perfect.' A man in his mid-fifties may have a 'functionally-perfect' musculoskeletal system but it is unlikely to be the same, or of the same efficiency, as that of a highly-trained athlete in his early twenties.

The second question is of a more esoteric nature and needs consideration because it proposes a limitation to treatment possibilities which is existential rather than technical, the latter meaning in the general sense of what may be possible with the techniques the practitioner has to hand:

2. What is the *'Degree of deviation from the patient's own soul ray influence that affects optimum functioning of...'*

Drawn from Bailey, this concept states that the individual's Soul is working through a specific Ray.[237] In effect, the life potential and experience of the individual are conditioned by the characteristics of the chosen Ray. The Soul influence sets the imperative for the life and quite often there may be a conflict between the Personality desires and the Soul's purpose. This could be put into the perspective of Jung's 'individuation' concept; as a person more closely aligns Soul and Personality, so he or she becomes individuated, in effect, self-realised. Neurotic problems in this psychological setting could presumably be seen as resulting from an inability to reconcile these two key aspects of the psyche.

If, therefore, the response to the second question is 0%, i.e. *there no deviation from the patient's own soul ray influence*, then Rae suggests that the difficulties which the patient is experiencing may to some great extent be a problem on their chosen path of life because they originate from within the sphere of the individual's own Soul Ray influence or their karma, so far as it can be determined. In short, the problem is self-generated because it is an experience which at some level the Soul needs in order to bring about the necessary progress of the individual. This therefore may pose a limit to Radionic treatment because the problem may not be resolved until the patient makes the necessary life adjustments; Radionics might help, but cannot interfere with what is, in effect, an aspect of the individual's sovereign will-to-be.

Clear distinction should be made between this and the many personality problems and conditioned responses which might masquerade

---

237. See Chapter 8 for basic discussion of the Rays

as a *'this is who I am'* attitude, which might be nothing more than a collection of ego defences, neurotic routines and subroutines, mind games and other dominance, interaction and survival mechanisms which are predominantly circumstantial in origin. The other side of this is the practitioner presuming to have the right to tell the patient what to do. You are not here to tell the patient how to live their life. If treatment works in such a way that the patient's psychological or emotional state changes to a sufficient degree, they themselves will, as a consequence, make the appropriate adjustments because the basis on which the original behaviour was predicated will have been weakened. If the patient asks your opinion, you can give it. You may see a person on a catastrophic course and want to intervene, but the possibility is that they already been told not to go there by their family or their friends and may not wish to be lectured further. Or they may value the opinion of a 'neutral' person - you. Most of the time, *'discretion is the better part of valour'*.[238] Your best possibility is to make a difference through the treatment they have requested, and, in time a relationship of trust may develop where your advice may be requested.

Taking this into account an approach to analysis suggested by Rae can be described. Figure 28 has been freely adapted by the author from Rae's work:[239]

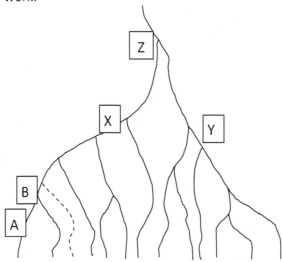

Fig 28: Rae's basic concept of the chain of causation

---

[238]. Falstaff, in Shakespeare's *Henry IV, Part One.*
[239]. See Tansley (1992) p. 86

Here an analogy is made between the patient's symptoms and a river delta. The multiple outlets at the base of the diagram present outlets to the sea, i.e. symptoms. The idea is to progressively trace back each symptom to its immediate prior cause until 'no detectable prior factor' can be established. Treating symptoms locally - say at 'A' - might only cause the problem to be driven back to some degree (i.e. suppression as earlier discussed) with the result that a new symptom appears at 'B'. It is therefore essential to try and reach the ultimate cause of the problems (at 'Z', which might be considered the primary level) because the presumption is that if the ultimate cause is treated and neutralised, a much better chance of resolving the lower-order symptoms is obtained. One may ask what would be the situation if 'Z' is removed; would, for example, the whole branch of symptoms along the line 'X'-'B'-'A' disappear? Would both branches ('X' and 'Y') fade away in time?

A problem not mentioned by Rae is that corresponding to what are described as 'layers' in Homoeopathy. In this instance no single remedy (*simillimum*) can be found which encompasses the totality of symptoms because a complex of interacting or interrelated problems exist at secondary levels. These create subsidiary symptom pictures which need to be treated before higher order problems can be addressed. The ultimate difficulty ('Z') might be of miasmatic origin but it may be necessary to deal with lower-order problems first, for example, at 'X' (say, Infection) and 'Y' (some psychological or emotional problem), because both are deeply-established in the individual and have - as it were - a 'life of their own'. There may simply be no one single level from which to work and several Factors may need to be responded to simultaneously. This in fact is one reason why I have been driven to propose the expanded model of the human system described in this book, because treating for example mainly through Chakras or mainly through paraphysical Locations does not give the range necessary to address the problems to which humans tend to be subject. Nevertheless, although method, system and knowledge can be taught and instilled in the practitioner's mind, no amount of training can ultimately substitute for a talent or aptitude for the work, reinforced by experience and a willingness to continue learning.

FURTHER REFLECTIONS

A number of important purposes are served by analysis in Radionics. Among these can be counted,

First, to develop the practitioner's conscious link with the patient. As Radionics is primarily a distant therapy, the practitioner may never meet the patient in person. Analysis develops the rapport between practitioner and patient. This, in turn, helps the practitioner to reach an understanding of the patient's problems, which are understood as deficits in the vibrational and energetic structures underlying the physical body. Of course, the patient will usually describe their symptoms and perhaps give copies of any medical reports etc. But as noted, the underlying problems may be entirely different to those recognized by conventional medical analysis or even, consciously, by the patient. As noted, the patient may well not be conscious of the existence of certain underlying Factors affecting him and it is part of the practitioner's art to try and discern these problems.

To clarify this, I will give some brief examples. A person may have suffered a strong psychological blow or impact in childhood which they were too young to remember. As noted, an example is birth shock, the result of a traumatic childbirth process. Or the mother herself may have been subjected to some kind of strong trauma, for example, may have been in a car accident while pregnant, thus experiencing impact shock which has also been transmitted to the unborn child. Such events can create lifelong patterns which inhibit the patient in some way. The patient may live in a house or area subject to strong geopathic stress which impacts, for instance, the patient's nervous system. The patient may have been subject to occult or psychic attack, or may, for example, have strongly jealous relatives who create a wave of psychic interference around the patient which blocks the normal progress of his life. The patient may have inherited or acquired miasmatic disease patterns which are a strong factor underlying his or her disease symptoms. The patient may have toxins leaching from dental amalgam, or undiscovered internal ulcerations or abscesses, or so-called chronic 'smouldering' infections such as Candida, which do not create a simple and easily identifiable disease condition but nevertheless degrade the immune system and may create a diverse set of seemingly disconnected symptoms. The patient may have food intolerances or hypersensitivity to certain foods, which do not create an observable allergic response but nevertheless create feelings of unwellness or lowered vitality. And so on.

Thus the analysis process itself serves as a means of tuning in to the patient, and it is often found that as the analysis proceeds the underlying 'picture' becomes clearer and clearer until the primary problems begin to stand out very markedly from the many secondary readings which can be made - 'secondary' meaning problems which are results or effects, rather than causes. As time goes on and skill develops, the ability to focus on the central problems because easier, and the need for complex and lengthy analysis is reduced because the mind is trained and knows what to do.

Second, to help the practitioner understand what treatment needs to be given and the means by which to give it. Treatments will be discussed in a later Chapter but suffice it to say that the most accurate possible identification of causes through rigorous analysis gives the best chance of selection of the most appropriate treatments.

Third, to provide a benchmark for the practitioner against which to judge the patient's progress. Primarily the practitioner will have made a set of readings corresponding to the intensity of the symptoms; of particular importance, to the intensity of those symptoms considered central or causal to the case. Thus an opening position is established. The readings can be re-checked as treatment proceeds and the practitioner may then observe which of the initial recorded values appear to have diminished - or, conversely, which have not. The patient of course will give his or her own report as to how they feel and if they think that the symptoms have ameliorated. In many cases, however, it will be impossible to get confirmation through orthodox tests; the symptoms being treated (for example Subtle Body problems) may be untestable by any standard method; or the practitioner may not have access to any medical testing facility unless he or she is a Doctor, and it is therefore impossible to get laboratory confirmation of a change in certain standard markers etc.

Fourth, for the development of the practitioner's own expertise and understanding. Beginners should not attempt complex cases without assistance from an experienced practitioner, but, nevertheless, each case analysed will reveal different aspects of illness, the inter-relationship between Locations and Factors, and how these develop into the Causations of illness, seen from the Radionic viewpoint of subtle energy analysis. Thus by stretching our abilities, pushing our limits and applying our minds, we find that they may, in fact, be expanded.

13: TREATMENT

The basic objective of treatment is to neutralise disturbances to the patient's energy field by applying appropriate energy patterns. To put it another way, vibrations are used to neutralise disturbed vibrations, in order to bring the disturbed field back into the normal range. Oschman, who studies scientific research underlying energy medicine, quotes Fröhlich, who indicates a clear relationship between vibrations (i.e. frequencies) and functioning:

'An assembly of cells, as in a tissue or organ, will have certain collective frequencies that regulate important processes, such as cell division. Normally these control frequencies will be very stable. If, for some reason, a cell shifts its frequency, entraining signals from neighboring cells will tend to reinstall the correct frequency. However, if a sufficient number of cells get out-of-step, the strength of the system's collective vibrations can decrease to the point where stability is lost. Loss of coherence can lead to disease or disorder.'

and himself adds *'While pathology may manifest as chemical imbalances, the underlying problem is electromagnetic. Hence balance can often be restored by providing the correct or 'healthy' frequency, and entraining the oscillations back to coherence.'* [240]

Information, seemingly, is a means by which it can be done. One can define Radionics as *an instrument-assisted, intention-driven means of directing energy via information for therapeutic purposes.*

---

240. Oschman (2000), p. 135. Oschman cites many formal studies which support the view that 'energy medicine works.' His basic focus is upon studies of electromagnetic phenomena in the body and how different types of complementary techniques interact with them. Herbert Fröhlich (1905 - 1991) was a physicist and Fellow of the Royal Society.

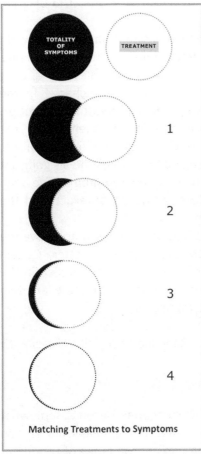

TOTALITY OF SYMPTOMS

TREATMENT

1

2

3

4

Matching Treatments to Symptoms

Figure 29: Matching treatments to symptoms

Physics states that there are waves and particles, but information appears to be the inviolable descriptor which orders the transition from waves to matter; one might propose that it is the third essential component of physical reality.[241] A proposition in this book is that the information which describes (for example) a substance, let us say the element Sulphur, is resident in the universal information field. It seems to me that the basis for Radionic action is that this information can be labelled with a descriptor - a Radionic code - which can then be used to evoke the pattern which describes Sulphur, and this pattern can then be entrained with the field of the patient. Therefore just as Sulphur in the physical universe can be isolated as a distinct substance, so its descriptive pattern in the informational universe can also be isolated in the form of information or, derived from that information, a pattern of energy or waveform. If there is a useful correspondence, the Sulphur pattern may counteract and normalise some of the vibrational disturbances in the patient's Subtle Anatomy. If the correspondence is poor, Sulphur will have little action on

241. As noted Herbert, *op. cit.*, gives various alternative and differing views about the production of reality and not all approaches agree with Schrödinger's equation (wave mechanics), which seems to be the most widely accepted option. Whichever interpretation is correct, it does not appear to abrogate the need for the *information*; and as I understand it the information acts as a constant in producing the physical reality which is familiar to us. See also Susskind (*op.cit.*), who argued for thirty years with Stephen Hawking over the fate of the information in a Black Hole - Hawking originally claimed that it would be destroyed, and Susskind concluded that if it really was destroyed then all of physics would have to be rewritten. In Susskind's account, Hawking retracted.

the patient and the treatment is likely to be unsuccessful. The diagram gives a basic idea.

The black circle represents the patient's symptoms, and the white circle represents a treatment or set of treatments which may neutralise the symptoms. In 1, the symptoms and the treatment have a poor relationship and there is unlikely to be any significant change in the patient. In 2, the correlation between symptoms and treatment is better, but not adequate. There might be short-term improvement in the symptoms, followed by a return to the original state. i.e. a more-or-less rapid relapse. In 3, the correlation is close and there might be a significant improvement in the patient, even though not all the symptoms have been covered. In 4, the correlation is very close, bordering on exact, and the chance of very good improvement is high.

Studying Jung we derive the idea that codes and symbols have the potential to be mediators between consciousness and matter. Certain means by which codes are developed in Radionics will be studied in the following Chapter, but initially it can be suggested that there are two fundamental types of code. These can be classed as:

1) Actions and concepts native to Radionics, centrally, *therapeutic commands*;
2) Presets

Inevitably the lines between the categories become somewhat blurred. There is a degree of crossover, but this simple classification should help the reader to understand the basis of the range of treatment possibilities, which is quite large.

ACTIONS AND CONCEPTS NATIVE TO RADIONICS
By 'native to Radionics' I mean actions which are exclusive to, or only found, in Radionics and which originate in the Radionic method. Of these, therapeutic commands occupy the central position. A therapeutic command is an instruction to the patient's subtle energy system to do something which is potentially beneficial for it, to guide it or induce it to revert to its normal range of function. The primary command may be said to be *Normalise*. The command may describe something which is done in the physical world, i.e. detoxification, but in Radionics *it has been encoded and is used as an action purely at the energetic and conceptual level*. A command is therefore an *intentional concept* or *concept driven by intention* which is used to try and achieve a certain therapeutic objective.

There are thousands of possible commands but a few examples can be given here:

Align
Antidote
Balance
Clarify
Clear
Co-ordinate
Co-ordinate digestive processes
Decongest
Delete
Desensitize
Detoxify
Eliminate
Eliminate addictive behaviour
Eliminate bacterial infection
Eliminate back pain - all forms of
Eliminate habitual patterns of stress
Eliminate heavy metals
Eliminate negative beliefs about the self
Eliminate poisons and toxins
Eliminate viral infection
Eradicate craving for alcohol
Free from possessing entity
Harmonise
Harmonise and restore complete structural and functional integrity to the seven major chakras and the endocrine glands they govern (Tansley)
Harmonise and restore complete structural and functional integrity to the spinal column and its ligamentous components (Tansley)
Induce
Induce beneficial fusion of causal body and personality imaged in the light of the soul's purpose
Neutralise
Normalise
Normalise acid-base balance
Occult attack - block and return
Offset and disperse the inimical effects of electromagnetic pollution to the chakras and subtle bodies (Tansley)

Optimalise
Protection against occult attack
Reduce
Reduce resistance to being healthy
Regain circadian rhythm
Rehydrate
Release
Remove
Render neutral all syphilitic, tubercular and cancerous taints (miasms) in the physical, etheric, astral and mental bodies and eject them from the living organism (Tansley)
Restore
Restore full integrity to all aspects of the human aura and to seal any tears or rents in the fabric of same, and prevent the leaching away of energy (Tansley)
Reverse all degenerative processes
Sedate
Stimulate
Tonify
Transmute negative thought forms[242]

A command usually consists of two parts, which are the proposed action (the instruction) and the target (a Location). Thus you could construct commands such as:

Eliminate poisons and toxins from colon
Normalise pancreatic functions
Co-ordinate (reduce uncoordination of) nervous system
Co-ordinate Heart and Brow Chakras
Eliminate bacterial infection from lungs

and so forth. In my experience *brevity, and the exact use of language to clearly and unambiguously specify the intention*, are centrally important. Vague, unspecific or unclear language, or lengthy, conditional

---

242. Some of these commands have been drawn from a list provided by MGA (Magneto-Geometric Applications), some have been created by the author, and some by David Tansley (where indicated). As will be explained in the following Chapter, defining a command is one thing, but coding it *efficiently* so that it may perform useful work is quite another.

and overwrought descriptions of the desired action may be absolutely useless.

Appendices 1 & 2 provide lists of Locations ,Appendix 3 a list of Factors and in Appendix 4, a partial list of some regions which may be disturbed by the problem of Integrity. One of the objectives of this book is to provide a basic framework for Radionic analysis, developed from the proposed model of the human system. The outline of this framework is found in the contents of these 4 Appendices. You will bear in mind that, to a high degree of correspondence, any Location could be affected by any of the Factors. By way of illustration I will give, drawing from this model, some sample Location-Factor combinations (i.e. disturbances to Locations by Factors). These are only a very few of the many combinations which are feasible:

Atmic Body - Psoric Miasm
Atmic Body - Cancer
Atmic Body - Damage
Buddhic Body - Congestion
Buddhic Body - Uncoordination
Buddhic Body - Co-ordination with Mental Body - Psychological
Causal Body - Stellar Miasm
Causal Body - Dislocation
Causal Body - Co-ordination with Mental Body
Mental Body - Congestion
Mental Body - Overstimulation
Mental Body - Heavy Metal Miasm
Astral Body - Cancer Miasm
Astral Body - Psychological Factors (stressors)
Astral Body - Possession
Astral Body - Occult Attack
Astral Body - Ulcer (i.e. feeling-toned image of the ulcer in the Astral Body)
Astral Body 6 - Cancer (i.e. emotional stressor possibly involved in development of cancer)[243]

---

243. Again you will note that I do not say that emotional stress causes cancer or ulcers directly, but prolonged emotional stress may disturb the paraphysical energetic system such that conditions for development of the pathology become more favourable. Hence the image of the oncoming disease may become present in various regions of the Subtle Anatomy.

Astral Body 5 - Syphilitic Miasm
Astral Body 5 - Tubercular Miasm
Astral Body 4 - Co-ordination with Brow Chakra
Astral Body 3 - Co-ordination with Heart Chakra
Astral Body 1 - Co-ordination with Throat Chakra
Crown Chakra - Co-ordination with Base Chakra
Soulseat Chakra - Cleavage
Soulseat Chakra - Sycotic Miasm
Throat Chakra - Allergy
Throat Chakra - Hypersensitivity
Throat Chakra - Tubercular Miasm
Heart Chakra - Damage
Heart Chakra - Distortion
Heart Chakra - Shock
Solar Plexus Chakra - Emotional stressors
Solar Plexus Chakra - Shock
Solar Plexus Chakra - Syphilitic Miasm
Sacral Chakra - Congestion
Sacral Chakra - Dislocation
Base Chakra - Activated Shell
Base Chakra - Psoric Miasm
Base Chakra - Petrochemical Miasm
Nadis - Distortion
Nadis - Petrochemical Miasm
Nadis - Co-ordination between
Nadis - Uncoordination
Etheric Body - Abscess, Allergy, Addiction, Articulated Miasm, Auto-Immune Response, Bacterial Infection, Cancer, Cleavage, Damage, Dislocation, Distortion, Inflammation, Infection, Malignancy, Prolapse, Sclerosis, Spasm, Sycotic Miasm, Tubercular Miasm, Tumours and Neoplasms, Ulcer, Viral Infection, etc etc
Meridians - Congestion
Meridians - Time-based Cycles and Functions
Meridians - Uncoordination
Meridians - Sycotic Miasm
Pranic Triangle - Petrochemical Miasm
Pranic Triangle - Overstimulation
Pranic Triangle - Uncoordination
Spleen Chakra - Congestion
Bone Marrow - Co-ordination with Lymphatic System

Lymphatic System - Infection
Lymphatic System - Heavy Metal Miasm
Lymphatic System - Malignancy
Lymphatic System - Poisons
Lymphatic System - Toxins
Pancreas - Enzyme & Catalyst Deficiency
Pancreas - Malignancy
Pancreas - Heavy Metal Miasm
Respiratory System - Congestion
Respiratory System - Fungal Infection
Respiratory System - Tubercular Miasm
Respiratory System - Viral Infection

Obviously many more such combinations are feasible - well into the thousands - and each can, in principle, be radiesthesically tested as a percentage deviation from normal functioning. To analyse the patient using such an approach would be heroic but impractical, since the number of readings to be taken would be enormous. The large range of Location-Factor disturbances is needed at the onset because the potential range of sources of human illness is large and requires a large palette from which to begin work. The essence of the matter is to discover what is central to the patient's symptom-picture. This may well boil down to a just few critical Location-Factor combinations out of the possible range. Nevertheless, a large proportion of the patient's symptoms may have their origin in them. To look at it another way, the practitioner seeks to discover which Locations, if normalised, would result in the greatest reduction in the patient's symptoms. This is the essence of the analytical endeavour; the practitioner needs the technical skill to be able to make good readings but the process of analysis should not be confused with the process of taking measurements.

The possibility of each such combination suggests that a counteracting therapeutic command can be created. For example, referring to the above list,

Astral Body 4 - Co-ordination with Brow Chakra suggests the command *Co-ordinate Astral Body Layer 4 and Brow Chakra;*

Crown Chakra - Co-ordination with Base Chakra suggests the command *Co-ordinate Crown and Base Chakras;*

Solar Plexus Chakra - Shock suggests the command *Eliminate Shock from the Solar Plexus Chakra;*

Etheric Body - Sycotic Miasm suggest the command *Eliminate Sycotic Miasm from the Etheric Body*;

Meridians - Congestion suggests the command *Eliminate Congestion from the Meridians*;

Respiratory System - Viral Infection suggests the command *Eliminate Viral Infection from the Respiratory System*

and so forth. This leads to the possibility that a large 'library' of standard commands could be created which could form the backbone of a Radionic therapeutic response. These could be used to counter problems identified in analysis.[244]

As a further step it might also be possible to draw up a table of Locations vs. Factors as a matrix - perhaps, in fact, a (very large) 3-dimensional matrix. With much research it might be possible to determine certain typical trends or pathways of energetic disturbance which lie behind the observed and defining symptoms of the different diseases and pathologies described by orthodox medical science.

PRESETS

Presets are codes that evoke the energy patterns of objects and concepts which already exist. These may be denoted *sources*. A preset is therefore a descriptor of a source existing in the universal field. Sulphur, the element mentioned above, is a *source* and a code used to describe its vibrational pattern is a *preset*.

By comparison a command is something has to be created and coded by the practitioner, or, more usually, by *a* Radionic practitioner for others to use.[245] So, essentially, and without getting lost in the detail, there are two main lines of coding: in the first, the *creation of codes which evoke a therapeutic command*; in the second, the *creation of codes which describe sources - energy patterns resident in Nature*.

In principle any source can be encoded and used in Radionics, although in practice there are many considerations; for example, a source may be useful in fact but if the coding is not sufficiently detailed, it may of little use in treatment. Sulphur may be the remedy which will alleviate the

---

244. The author has been engaged in this since 2002.

245. Some practitioners (such as the author) specialise in the production of Radionic codes and these may be available in the form of Rate books, which are lists of suitable Rates for use on appropriate instruments, or in other formats, such as pre-printed cards, according to the coding method employed.

patient's symptoms but if the code being used has insufficient accuracy, it may be such a poor representation of Sulphur that it cannot evoke the information field adequately.[246]

Two central problems in the creation of such codes are:

1) in creating *commands*, how accurately can you describe and how well can you depict your intention and anchor it in the universal information field? and

2) in creating *presets*, how accurately can you depict the energy pattern of the source pre-existent in the field?

It seems to follow that if action 1) is done properly, a new 'object' has been placed in the universal field which becomes, in effect, a *new* source. In doing so you have, feasibly, somewhat modified reality because you have modified the all-encompassing universal field which underlies it. If action 2) is done properly, you have generated a new access to some of the information which underlies physical reality and therefore, potentially, a new therapeutic possibility. Thus the action of conscious intent has the potential to change objective reality in some degree.

Examples of sources which have been encoded for use in Radionics include:

Acupuncture points
Allergens
Amino acids
Bacteria
Chemicals and drugs
Crystals, Gems, Minerals and Elements
Diseases
Emotions
Enzymes
Flower remedies and flower essences
Frequencies and Waveforms
Fungi
Gem essences
Herb remedies

---

246. As a simple example, sending a letter to 'Nick Franks - England' is unlikely to reach me because the address contains insufficient information for the Royal Mail to be able to find me; but there is, nevertheless, a simulacrum of accuracy in it because I live in England and not some other country.

Homoeopathic remedies
Hormones
I-Ching Hexagrams
Meridians
Parasites
Phenomena of Nature
Plant remedies
Psychological states
Subtle and paraphysical anatomy
Thought patterns and thought forms
Viruses
Vitamins[247]

Obviously many of these categories can include hundreds if not thousands of sources, which indicates the very large potential range of presets which can be created and used in Radionic treatments. To give but one example, the range of remedies in the homoeopathic *Materia Medica* is well into the thousands.

A code may combine not only a concept native to Radionics - for example, the command *eliminate* - but also a preset, i.e. the command evokes an action which is intended to bring about some type of useful change in a target, which is some object pre-existing in the field. To give a simple example, you might have:

Eliminate	2299644227
Poisons & Toxins	99449.10.1674448
Liver	4877480.10.10.77422009

and you might create a command string for 'Eliminate Poisons & Toxins from Liver' as:

229964422799449.10.16744484877480.10.10.77422009,

which is a sequential combination of all three codes. In this case *Eliminate* is the command and *Poisons*, *Toxins* and *Liver* are the sources used as a target for the intended action. Combining the command and the sources into a single action creates a new instruction (vibrational entity) tailored to a specific task; consequently, you could treat the whole string as a unity and make the new code:

---

247. I have hardly touched upon categories relating to veterinary, agricultural, or horticultural sources in the above list.

Liver - Poisons & Toxins (to Eliminate)   9944449.10.1248

By way of another example, you might have:
Eliminate   2299644227
Anxiety   10.10.10.10.4220099448
Solar Plexus Chakra   4422.10.144994

and you might create a command string for 'Eliminate Anxiety from Solar Plexus Chakra' as:
229964422710.10.10.10.42200994484422.10.144994
which, once again, is a sequential combination of all three codes. In this second example *Eliminate* is the command and *Anxiety* and *Solar Plexus Chakra* are the sources used as a target. Coding the whole string as a unity would give you:

Anxiety - Solar Plexus Chakra (to Eliminate)
498989949.10.1248811448[248]

The 'unity' rate might be said to encapsulate the intention more exactly than the sequential combination and is therefore more efficient as a code.

The reader may reasonably ask what is to stop someone attempting to develop destructive commands with which to attack other people. The basic answer is nothing; but human intent for good or evil is not restricted to any particular area of human activity. Nuclear energy can be used to generate electricity to power homes or as a weapon of extreme violence with which to kill people by the hundred thousand. Television, film and other media can be used as a means of mass education or for the dissemination of propaganda to achieve many objectives, such as the

---

248. These codes have been developed by the author. I will give some basic ideas how to do this in the next Chapter. At this point you may have asked 'why not use plain English' (or French, Latin, Mandarin, Spanish, Swahili, Russian? - i.e. other languages (which are in themselves codes). The simple answer is that it is possible to do so, but does not work as efficiently in practice. Symbols, numbers, etc, appear to be much closer to meaning at a higher order of coherence than language. You frame the intention in your native language but you seek to reach a more 'universal' depiction of that intention by creating a code. Similar comments may perhaps apply to mathematics. You might be able to describe an equation at length in ordinary language but it would probably be difficult, laborious, even impossible to 'solve' the equation by describing what the mathematics does using words.

prosecution of war, bloodshed, hatred and terror. More specifically, humans have been waging psychic war on each other through many methods, including witchcraft and sorcery, for millennia and certainly well before the development of Radionics. But the primary point is that the Radionic objective is to *work with Nature*, to restore to normality that which Nature has evolved, the normal functioning of which has been disturbed; *the whole activity is thus aligned with the normal process of life*. The action of the destructive intent would be to *work against Nature*, to subvert the normal order of things. Since Nature is the force behind the whole Universe, he who attempts to pervert its course plays against the corrective power of the natural order and may well excite energies which rebound upon him with severe consequences. *This*, then, is what is to stop you. Furthermore, as I shall mention in Chapter 14, there appears to be a natural barrier to the human psyche in the creation (for example) of Radionic codes beyond a certain level of complexity, and it is very difficult to breach this barrier; more so, I suspect, if the intent is to work against Nature.

USEFUL PRESETS

Some of the main categories of preset which the author has found to be of use in Radionics will now be described briefly.

HOMOEOPATHY

Homoeopathy appears to be of very great use because of the potential wide range of action of many homoeopathic remedies. Radionic commands might be particularly useful in treating specific problem areas but systemic symptoms - for example, the range of symptoms which accompany some form of acute illness, such as fever, chill, malaise, inflammation, aches and pains, loss of appetite, perspiration, and so forth - might be better covered by a homoeopathic remedy. Here you could use one or more commands together as specifics and a homoeopathic remedy as a general and the two types of treatment will reinforce each other's action, i.e. they are synergistic. To give a simple example, you might combine commands such as '*Eliminate Bacterial Infection from Respiratory Tract*', '*Eliminate Inflammation from Respiratory Tract*' and '*Eliminate Inflammation from Bronchi*' with an appropriate homoeopathic remedy, which might be, for example, *Kalium Carbonicum*.

Note of course the difference between the two methods. In practice, a homoeopath, using repertorisation - the recording, categorisation and evaluation of symptoms - would establish that the patient's symptoms correlate well with the Materia Medica for a particular remedy, let us say Kalium Carbonicum, and give the patient a tablet imprinted with that remedy. By way of comparison, the Radionic practitioner, *using radiesthesic means*, would establish that the two commands and Kalium Carbonicum are the most suitable remedies for the patient and 'send' the same remedy to him by evoking it with appropriate Radionic codes used on a suitable instrument - no tablet or physical carrier material of any kind whatsoever involved.[249]

In order to understand something about the wide range of action of homoeopathic remedies I will give the symptom picture of a commonly-used remedy. There is the idea that the remedy describes a 'type' of person, or 'state' that a person can get into:

'PHOSPHORICUM ACID (Phos. Ac.) - *This remedy is useful for mental and physical debility, especially in rapidly-growing young people. It is used after acute diseases, grief, severe emotional upsets, fatigue, and loss of body fluids. The patient is apathetic, indifferent, listless and suffers from impaired memory and intellectual slowness.*

Main medical uses: Ailments from loss of body fluids; Debility; Diarrhoea, chronic; Excessive urination; Grief-induced ailments; Hair loss (Alopecia); Headache; Heartburn; Impotence; Indigestion

[REPERTORY] *Major symptoms* [usually grouped by bodily region]:
HEAD: Four types of headache can occur: one feels like pressure on top of the head; another feels as if the temples are being pressed together; a third comes on after coitus, and the fourth is due to eye strain. Baldness and premature greying.
EYES: Sunken and surrounded by blue rings.
MOUTH: Dry, cracked lips. The gums bleed. The tongue is swollen, dry and may be bitten during sleep.
CHEST: Weak feelings in the chest from talking and coughing, with pressure behind the breastbone affecting breathing. Dry, tickling cough. Palpitations in fast-growing children and after grief.
STOMACH: Craving for juicy drinks and cold milk. Sour food and drink lead to nausea and discomfort.

---

249. The Radionic commands would also be selected radiesthesically. 'Pure' Homoeopaths use homoeopathically-prepared (potentised) remedies more or less exclusively and do not use Radionic techniques.

ABDOMEN: Distension and fermentation, with loud rumblings and an ache around the navel.

STOOL: White, watery, involuntary, painless diarrhoea with much wind. The loss does not tire the patient.

URINE: Frequent, profuse urination, especially at night. The urine appears milky.

GENITALIA: Loss of virility. Partial impotence. Scrotal eczema.

LIMBS: The arms and legs feel weak. Cramps in the upper arm, and wrists, with scraping pain in the bones at night. Itching between the fingers and in joint folds.

[MODALITIES] *BETTER*: for keeping warm; for sleep. *WORSE*: from exertion; from being talked to; after sexual excesses.' [250]

From the above it can be seen that Phosphoricum Acidum is, centrally, an acute remedy for states of exhaustion and debility, where the energetic resources and processes of the body have become depleted and the vitality has been dragged down. You might find, for example, *'the patient is apathetic, indifferent, listless and suffers from impaired memory and intellectual slowness'* in any number of illnesses, particularly chronic illness, but the background leading to the deteriorated mental state may be quite different to that typifying *Phos. Ac.* [251]

You may ask how a single remedy can have such a wide range of action. One way of looking at it is that in Homoeopathy *all the symptoms produced by a substance are of interest and will be recorded as a possible guide to the homoeopathic use of that substance.* The concept is the opposite of that used in orthodox medicine. In orthodox medicine the causal chain tends to be much less complex with the idea of cause and effect being directly linked, for example insult (e.g. an infection) = identifiable illness. The result tends to be the search for a drug which can be inserted into the chain to eliminate the cause and therefore the effect.

---

250. Rose (1992) p. 283. Phosphoric Acid as a chemical has a wide range of uses and is for instance part of the formula of several brands of cola. This is an outline of the remedy picture and those who consult the homoeopathic literature can find further information about it. Note that it is common practice in Homoeopathy to refer to remedies by their Latin names, which are often abbreviated.

251. For example, the remedy *Conium Maculatum* (Poison Hemlock) could have this type of mental picture but this occurs after a slow process of degeneration which might initially be hard to recognize because of its subtle and gradual onset. *Conium* might therefore be a remedy suitable for the aging patient

Other actions produced by the drug on the body are usually regarded as undesirable and are denoted *side effects*.

In homoeopathy all the symptoms produced by the action of drug are of interest. Consequently the resulting picture may show a diffuse or indirect relationship between cause and effect; you may look at the description of *Phos. Ac.* and ask yourself how baldness is linked to dry and cracked lips or headache after coitus. The answer is the depletion of the *Dynamis*. The patient has been worn down or is worn out and this weakness has a range of effects on the Subtle Anatomy which produce a set of typical, if wide-ranging, symptoms such as those noted above.

Returning to the question of *side-effects*, these are the unwanted effects of a drug and they may have a considerable, and even harmful, action on the body.[252] For example, SSRIs (selective serotonin reuptake inhibitors, a class of antidepressant drug):

'Side effects include dose-related gastrointestinal effects (diarrhoea, nausea and vomiting, dyspepsia, abdominal pain, constipation, and loss of appetite) and weight loss; headache, restlessness, nervousness, and anxiety may also occur. Other possible side effects are dry mouth, palpitation, tremor, confusion, dizziness, low blood pressure, mania, convulsions, interference with sexual function, sweating, and movement disorders. Allergic reactions....should be reported to a doctor.'[253]

From the above description the range of symptoms which might be produced by such a drug extend far beyond the desired effect. The objective is to treat depression but in the process of so doing any number of side-effects might occur; the list is quite diverse and comparatively you could ask the question as to how nervousness, anxiety, confusion, mania and low blood pressure could be produced by a drug which is intended to combat depression. From the homoeopathic point of view all these symptoms are of interest because they are all products of the action of the drug. Consequently if a homoeopathic version of an SSRI was made, it could be found that it has a counteracting effect on some combination of symptoms such as, *'diarrhoea, nausea and vomiting with anxiety,*

---

252. *'Side-effect - an unwanted effect produced by a drug in addition to its desired therapeutic effects. Side-effects are often undesirable and may be harmful.'* Oxford (1994)
253. Oxford (2000) p. 565

restlessness, convulsion, and mania' and therefore might be found to be homoeopathic to various forms of acute illness.[254]

As a brief comment on the different approaches, in homoeopathy the study of potentised substances is generally known as 'proving' and is the attempt to understand the entire symptom picture of the remedy and discover the common threads which point to its possible use. It is important to know that the primary method of conducting a proving is to give the *homoeopathic version* of a substance (*'there's nothing in there'*[255]) to a group of persons (provers); some will receive the remedy and some will receive a placebo, but no-one will know whether they have received the remedy or not.[256] Over a period of time they will record their reactions and at the end of the process, the homoeopath conducting the proving will evaluate the results, assessing the value of *all the recorded symptoms* to the remedy picture.[257]

In contrast, orthodox medical drug trials select a group of patients with the same illness - for example, arthritis. The *physical drug* is given to some members of the group and a placebo to the others, who are acting as a control group. The idea is that the effects of the drug on the arthritis may be compared with the placebo, which is presumed to have no medical effect, i.e. a randomized controlled trial. In short, homoeopathic remedies have their effect at the energetic level (on the Dynamis) whereas the effects of physical drugs are principally on the biochemical processes of the body, but both are assessed by similar testing methods.

A possible problem with this form of testing is that people also have healing responses to placebos, which leads to the idea that belief itself has extraordinary power; at some point you feel ill and display symptoms and at some later point you are given a pill which *you believe* will make you better, and you do indeed recover or experience a

---

254. A simple example is the homoeopathic remedy *Coffea Cruda* (unroasted coffee beans). Everyone knows that coffee acts as a stimulant or pick-me-up; but in homoeopathic form *Coffea* is a potential remedy for insomnia, where there is *overactivity* (i.e. overstimulation) of the mind and nervous system.

255. Homoeopathic remedies are prepared by a combined process of dilution and shaking ('succussion') and beyond Avogadro's number, approximately equivalent to potency 12C, there can be no further molecules of the original substance present. It particularly beyond this point that critics of homoeopathy reject claims that it has any therapeutic value.

256. In short a random, placebo-controlled double-blind trial - the so-called 'gold standard' of drug testing. As far as I am aware this procedure was adopted in homoeopathy long before its use in conventional drug testing.

257. See the work of Jeremy Sherr as an expert present-day prover - www.dynamis.edu

mitigation of symptoms.[258] It seems that the power of the mind, or the mental attitude, must not be underestimated in any therapeutic endeavour.

GEMS, MINERALS AND CRYSTALS (GEM REMEDIES)

The therapeutic action, spiritual properties and purported esoteric characteristics of these compounds have been written about extensively and two detailed sources are Gurudas[259] and Melody[260]. The essence of the matter appears to be the highly-ordered atomic structure and regular vibrational frequency of crystals. According to Wikipedia,

> *'A crystal structure is the orderly geometric spatial arrangement of atoms in the internal structure of a mineral. There are 14 basic crystal lattice arrangements of atoms in three dimensions, and these are referred to as the 14 "Bravais lattices". Each of these lattices can be classified into one of the seven crystal systems, and all crystal structures currently recognized fit in one Bravais lattice and one crystal system. This crystal structure is based on a regular internal atomic or ionic arrangement that is often expressed in the geometric form that the crystal takes.... Crystal structure greatly influences a mineral's physical properties. For example, though diamond and graphite have the same composition (both are pure carbon), graphite is very soft, while diamond is the hardest of all known minerals. This happens because the carbon atoms in graphite are arranged into sheets which can slide easily past each other, while the carbon atoms in diamond form a strong, interlocking three-dimensional network.'[261]*

Because of the ordered nature of crystals and their constant vibration, the therapeutic action of gemstones is considered, basically, to be restorative and can be likened to that of an attractor in a phase space, to use the terminology of chaos theory. If Radionic commands and homoeopathic presets can be said, basically, to counteract negative or

---

258. The author has treated various persons with Radionics and tries to avoid 'suggestion' by not telling the patient exactly when the treatment was started.
259. Gurudas (1985) (1986)
260. Melody (1995)
261. Wikipedia, entry on Mineral (2011)

disturbed vibrational patterns,[262] then gem remedies act by resonance to restore the vibrational pattern to its normal range. Gurudas writes:

'....the properties and faculties of gemstones are....a direct correlation within the individual....based on sympathetic molecular structure. Gemstones stimulate healing within the body physical, based on the principles of resonancy or harmony and vibration. All things are in a constant state of vibration and in a constant system of harmonics and resonancy, according to the point of stability within the ethers. These harmonics generate fields of an electro-magnetic and electrical nature, but above all, the fields within the ethers are activated....Crystalline structures contain a stable element or proper pattern of molecular activity that may act as a proper frequency to amplify the vibration of other life forms....Many times gemstones have a specific resonancy or harmonic with specific points of the anatomy to which their healing properties are attributed. There are certain mineral properties that have an exact point of harmonics with various organs in the body physical. Examination even upon chemical levels would....reveal specific sympathetic areas of minerals and substances that are critical to the functioning of various organs of the body physical on the cellular and anatomical level....Real healing extends from the biomolecular to the cellular level, and eventually to the anatomical level, where it is brought into harmony with other levels of the body physical....Therefore, the resonancy that is crystallized within the pattern of the gemstone has empathy when it is transferred to the unstable biomolecular level of the body physical. This unstable pattern in the body physical is especially strong during the disease state. On the transference of that vibration, a specific pitch and resonancy may stabilize the molecular activity within the anatomy and then may extend to the biomolecular level, then to the level of biochemistry within the cellular structure, particularly upon the genetic level.'[263]

---

262. The idea being that of *phase cancellation* i.e. the Factor has a typical waveform and the treatment has a similar but phase-reversed waveform; when you add the two waves together, they cancel out. There are many other concepts which can be taken from wave mechanics, such as interference, intermodulation, resonance etc which may describe the action of Radionic treatments. Whether the process is actual, virtual or a combination of the two requires much further investigation but - referring back to Chapter 7 - I suggest that it is a process which begins at the conceptual level and ends at the physical level.

263. Gurudas (1985) p. 2 - 3. This quote is from channelled material contained within the book and the language is a little bit arcane. Most people know of quartz clocks; the regular vibration of quartz crystals is used for accurate timekeeping in clocks, computers, and

In short the regular vibration of the gem acts as a fixed reference point which may be used, by resonance, to try and stabilise the disturbed vibrations of the body at various levels. These include the subtle anatomy and especially chakras; Gurudas states:

'The ruby, when applied to the area of the heart chakra or the heart meridian, brings into focus within the individual patterns concerning any distress within the parental image of the father and aids the individual in knowledge of his or her ability to give or receive love....Study the patterns of individual chakras because these are the main power points for the application of gemstones to be....received and evenly distributed throughout the body physical. There is a concentration of intelligent energy and thought forms within the chakras.'[264]

Thus gems and crystals, on account of their structure, have a particularly stable vibrational presence. One possible analogy is that of the vibrating tuning fork. If held near a piano with the damper pedal off, the strings will begin to resonate in sympathy. Similarly the patient, whose fields have been disturbed, will be entrained by the vibrational patterns of the crystal. If the selected crystal bears an appropriate relationship to the patient's problem, and if this is entrainment is strong enough, the patient's system may be induced to return to a more typical or normal vibrational frequency.[265] In Radionics, the energetic image of the crystal is normally used in coded form, although it is possible, with certain instruments, to use a physical crystal placed in the instrument as a direct source of treatment.

FLOWER ESSENCES
Originally introduced by Dr Edward Bach (1886 - 1936) as a system of 38 remedies, the flower essences are intended to counter negative

---

other digital devices by providing a fixed frequency against which time can be referenced. Also refer back to the quote from Oschmann at the beginning of this Chapter.
264 . Gurudas, *ibid.*, p. 4
265. It may be added that this brings us, in the present day, full circle back to the original ideas of Abrams and Drown. Their approach was to find the vibration of the healthy organ or other body structure when functioning normally and feed it back into the patient in the hope that physiological processes would normalised and would thus be induced to replace unhealthy cells with healthy ones.

emotional conditions in the individual. Bach's view was that such conditions underlie all diseases and if they could be effectively relieved, a healing transformation would be achieved. Although Bach considered his system of remedies complete, since his time a considerable number of additional flower essences have been introduced using species from various continents. Flower essences may be considered to work principally on the Astral Body and, as a secondary effect, on the effects of disturbed emotions on the Chakras. Each essence is considered to have a typical range of action, for e.g. Bach:

Agrimony - mental torture behind a cheerful face
Beech - intolerance
Centaury - the inability to say 'no'
Holly - hatred, envy and jealousy
Olive - exhaustion following mental or physical effort[266]

Or Australian Bush Flower essences:

Billy Goat Plum - (*negative condition*) shame, inability to accept the physical self, physical loathing; (*positive outcome*) sexual pleasure and enjoyment, acceptance of self and one's physical body, open-mindedness;
Red Grevillea - (*negative condition*) feeling stuck, oversensitive, affected by criticism and unpleasant people, too reliant on others; (*positive outcome*) boldness, strength to leave unpleasant situations, indifference to the judgment of others
Waratah - (*negative condition*) despair, hopelessness, inability to respond to a crisis; (*positive outcome*) courage, tenacity, adaptability, strong faith, enhancement of survival skills.[267]

As with crystals, in Radionics the energetic image of the flower is normally used in coded form, although again it is possible - with certain instruments - to use the actual essence in the instrument directly as a source of treatment. Flower essences are made by various techniques which involve the use of the actual petals and other components of the flower and in the case of rare or endangered species, the use of a

266. Source: www.bachcentre.com
267. Source: www.ausflowers.com.au

properly-constituted Radionic code could, in principle, achieve the same results without use of the actual plant.[268]

HERBS AND OTHER MEDICINAL PLANTS

Herbs and plants have been used in medicine since time immemorial and continue to be so used to the present day in many folk and local traditions, Ayurvedic and Traditional Chinese Medicine (TCM) being typical examples. Furthermore many medical drugs have been extracted from herbs, the objective being to separate what are regarded as the pharmacologically-active constituents of the plant from the whole biological form.[269]

Medicinal plants have been used to deal with a large range of illnesses and each is considered to have certain properties e.g. adaptogenic, antibiotic, antispasmodic, antiviral, carminative, diuretic, emetic, febrifuge, laxative, sedative, stimulant, vermifuge, etc. These are described in various Materia Medicas. However herbs and plants are used in material form (tinctures, dried leaf etc) and the effect on the body is principally at the physiological level. Employing them in Radionic form means, in effect, converting them to the energetic level and the usage may be different to that found for the plant in its material form.

COLOURS

See Chapter 4 for the basic information and in particular comments about the work of Dr. Bhattacharyya. Different colours or combinations of colours are said by Bhattacharyya to be typically deficient in certain diseases, an example being Green in Cancer. Radionic treatment with colours is therefore used to entrain the individual with the spectrum of colours predominantly absent from their subtle energy system and thereby induce a rebalancing or restoration of the system. In addition to single colours it should be noted that many colour combinations are possible, such as Red - Orange - Violet; Infra-Red - Red - Ultra-Violet; Orange - Blue - Yellow; Lemon - Yellow - Green - Infra-Red; and so on.

---

268. A code, or copying from a small original sample, might be relevant in therapeutic uses of body parts of animals hunted to near extinction.
269. e.g. Atropine from Belladonna; Vincristine from Madagascar Periwinkle.

ALLOTROPES[270]

In Chapter 11 I write that *'To a greater or lesser extent* the Articulated Miasm can also be identified with the disease states described *and named* by orthodox medicine (e.g. Cancer, Ulcerative Colitis, Emphysema, Parkinson's disease, etc.) From the Radionic point of view these diseases suggest an underlying *typical* form of energetic disturbance to a *typical* set of Locations which manifest as the named disease.' The idea is that a treatment or set of complementary treatments which attempt to neutralise the complex of energetic disturbances which characterise a named disease could be developed. These disturbances would be typical within a certain range and, within that range, more or less unchanging in all cases of that disease. Here you could have Influenza Allotropes, Bronchitis Allotropes, Ulceration Allotropes, and so forth. The symptoms the individual displays, which might be wide ranging according to the underlying situation and background of the patient, may also require treatment with a remedy having a broader scope of action, such as a Homoeopathic remedy. In principal an Allotrope could be used in combination with Homeopathic and other remedies.

ISOMORPHS[271]

A range of treatments which might be used to counteract the energetic presence of pathogens. The general concept has been discussed in Chapter 9, section 5 *Invasion*.

EMOTIONAL AND PSYCHOLOGICAL STATES

There are many negative emotional and psychological states such as anger, fear, anxiety, self-consciousness, feeling of inferiority (inferiority complex), loneliness, addiction, suicidal tendencies, naivety, paranoid delusions (persecution complex), shame, timidity, guilt, intolerance, hatred, greed, religious fanaticism, victim mentality, and so on - to name but a few. An individual might experience any of these fleetingly during the course of life but if the personality structure is sufficiently stable a condition of psychological balance will reassert itself. When these reactions become fixed, static or standard personality responses they

---

270. 'Allotropy: The existence of elements in two or more different forms' Oxford (2005). Diamond and graphite are allotropes of the element carbon. Hence, in this application, different forms of the same basic disease.
271. 'Biology: different in ancestry, but having the same form or appearance.' (www.dictionary.com)

21st Century Radionics

acquire the character of complexes, possession, obsession, neurosis and other non-negotiable mental and emotional states. In this sense they are habits or conditioned reactions, and given an appropriate trigger the individual will tend to default to the same response and the pattern cannot generally be changed by logic or reasoned argument. The same is possible for a group of people or even an entire society, racism, intolerance, and religious fanaticism being just three examples. There is a tendency for every experience to reinforce the existing beliefs or prejudices and thus a strong thought form is created which dominates some aspect of the individual's personality. To repeat Jung:

'Everyone knows nowadays that people "have complexes". What is not so well-known....is that complexes can have us.' [272]

and Saraydarian:

'Obsession is etheric, astral or mental inhibition....Obsession on the etheric level is a mechanical habit which is the result of some distortion in the nervous and the corresponding etheric body. Emotional obsession is an emotion caught in the astral plane which controls other emotions....In the mental plane, obsession is an inhibited, trapped thoughtform, with or without entities attached to it.' [273]

In Radionics we are interested, potentially, in trying to dissolve the vibrational pattern which characteristically underlies the psychological reaction or emotional state which is experienced by the patient. The thoughtform or emotional habitual response becomes, as it were, a stationary wave[274] in the mental or astral body and is a congestion or barrier to the free flow of mental or emotional energy in the psyche. One may say that the individual is 'stuck'. A possible therapeutic method is to create codes which are specifically intended to neutralise or weaken the pattern of response. Examples might be to counteract fear or specific fears, such as fear of cancer, fear of death, fear of spiders; or anxiety, timidity, lack of self-confidence; or religious, racial or sexual intolerance; inhibition by past negative experiences, and so on. Many such codes can

---

272. See Chapter 6
273. See Chapter 10
274. 'A form of wave in which the profile of the wave does not move through the medium but remains stationary....[it] results when a travelling wave is reflected back along its own path .' Oxford (2005). Sometimes referred to as a standing wave.

be created and may have uses in an individual's treatment where there is a strong psychological or emotional problem, particularly where the origin of the pathology lies in the subtle fields (for example, Hahnemann's 'diseases spun by the soul') and not as a product of some physical pathology or other somatic impingement. Also note earlier comments about the possible action of the miasms in the higher fields of the subtle anatomy.

USING RADIONIC CODES IN COMBINATION

The essence of the matter is the synergistic effect of the remedies, which, when combined, may bring about a more rapid or permanent correction of the energetic disturbance than a single remedy or a number of remedies used in sequence. If each remedy can be characterised as a waveform, then waveforms can be mixed with more or less harmonious results according to a) the compatibility of the remedies with each other, and the b) the compatibility of the combination with the patient. An example everyone knows is the symphony orchestra; each instrument produces its own characteristic waveform and the whole orchestra playing together produces a combined waveform which will be more or less harmonious according to factors such as the skill of the composer and the ability of the players. As described in Chapter 3, the compatibility of remedies (as remedy codes) can be checked with each other and with the patient using radiesthesic means. The combined codes can also be checked against the patient's witness so that the potential degree of correction of the disturbance can be observed.

14: INSTRUMENTS AND CODES

The use of codes which evoke the intended therapeutic action, in combination with compatible instruments, is at the heart of Radionics. This is the central focus of the art. It is this which defines it, makes it different to other therapeutic approaches, and, via the means of the practitioner's radiesthesic faculty, assists investigations into the inner side of reality. It is the study of how to build instruments and create codes which leads us there, because it is the problem of how these artefacts can be constructed so that they perform effectively which leads to questions as to the nature of Nature.

Now some Radionic practitioners will maintain that they do not use or need instruments and can rely on the projections of their own mind, which is to say, their own focused intention projected to the patient by some internal method, such as concentration. As an aid to concentration, this intention might also be summarized in some type of written statement as to the therapeutic objective. There is probably nothing wrong in doing this. The technique is used in various systems, such as the creation and use of affirmations or prayers. But it must be questioned whether it is Radionics. The point is that if we are to have some form of satisfactory definition of Radionics, we need concepts which not only *allow* it to be defined but also allow it to be readily demarcated from other therapies. Otherwise, as noted, everything tends to disappear into a fanciful mush of incoherence where everything becomes anything you want, and *this* is neither scientific, logical or desirable. Such confusion is good neither for the patient nor for the practitioner.

It could, for example, be proposed that the therapist projects his or her intention to the patient in all forms of healing, and in these other techniques no Radionic-like methods are involved nor is this referred to as Radionics. Some may use mentally-held symbols, some may use prayer, mantrams or visualisation, some may invoke God or gods, saints, ancestral spirits, the spirit world, and so on. There is a panoply of approaches and it is not for me to say which are good, correct, useful or useless because extraordinary things happen in this life and what may seem to some to be the most arcane, weird or even offensively ridiculous of methods (doubtless there are those would be more than happy to include Radionics this latter category) may bring results. But the first point is that in an attempt to assess the efficacy of any therapy, it is also necessary to know what it is and what it is not. The second point is that there are any number of healers and therapists, some with orthodox medical qualifications, who have treated a wide range of problems in a large sample of people across all races and nationalities, and in general it is clear to the patient that one approach is not the same as another.

If appropriate differentiations are not made there will be tendency to lump all therapeutic approaches together as a target for science and sceptics. In general, are we to call *all* complementary medical therapists liars or fantasists because their methods cannot satisfy a random, double-blind, placebo-controlled test or agree with the present-day, accepted, scientific best estimate of what is real and what is not? Several centuries ago such healers might have been accused of witchcraft and burned, and several centuries later they are medical frauds, perhaps because no method which agrees with scientific convenience is apparent.[275] But it is at the fringes, margins or extremes of experience that the dominant paradigms or beliefs about the nature of reality are challenged or even break down and so we should observe carefully as we may learn new things. This has certainly applied in the development of physics. At the microscopic scale, the determinism of Newtonian or 'classical' physics has been totally undermined by quantum mechanics and relativity, the phenomena of which were initially observed at the boundaries of 'normal' reality. For all the proclaimed precision and repeatability of modern science, quantum indeterminacy and randomness, and the breakdown of the real[276], appear to sit at the centre of it. This seems to be the heart of the problem: how does one thing - the quantum world - become experienced as something entirely different - everyday reality?

One the central contentions of this book is that Radionics is not some vague 'healing' activity but a focused and rather precise method aimed at repairing and restoring the relationship between consciousness, the paraphysical form, and the fields which underlie them. With regard to instruments, nothing can replace the skill, experience and, ultimately, wisdom of the practitioner, such as it may be, but my contention is that the higher the calibre of the tools, the better and more consistent will tend to be the result. In short one may say that although tools cannot substitute for ingenuity and ingenuity may get the job done despite the

---

275. I am not, however, recommending a therapeutic free-for-all in which 'anything goes'. There must be an appropriate degree of rigor. However, again, see Oschmann (*op. cit.*) for a discussion of the science behind 'energy' therapies.
276. For example, as the speed of light is approached, if we stick, for instance, with the predictions of relativity.

shortcomings of the tools, any properly-designed tool which makes the job easier must be welcome.

Radionics is concerned with waves and vibrations and their interaction with conscious intent and whatever is achieved is, in my very considered opinion, clearly facilitated by using codes and instruments. There might be the occasional therapist who has almost-superhuman or perhaps preternatural abilities and can literally 'will' or 'image' some other person back to health. You yourself might get up some morning and in a supercharged state perform some extraordinary healing on some other person, but most of the time you will not be able to do this, one reason being that the demands made on *your* energetic system by such a performance are usually large and tend to be unsustainable over long periods.[277] Hence my argument that a regularised and consistent system must be available for, and useable by, persons of more normal talents. Such a system is being proposed in this book.

FUNCTION AND CHARACTER OF INSTRUMENTS

Many designs of Radionic instrument have been constructed over the last century but in general it may be said that instruments have four principal functions:

1) To assist the practitioner in analysing the patient by enhancing radiesthesic accuracy, thereby allowing a higher degree of mental focus and penetration into the subtle anatomy and related fields;

2) To give treatment;

3) To protect the practitioner from the patient's energetic state, acting, as it were, as a kind of firewall;

4) To enable the synthesis of remedies from codes, or copying the vibrational patterns of existing materials, into carrier materials such as water or *sac lac.*

Practitioners may, if they want, avoid the use of instruments and be content to pass their hours projecting their intent to patients by simple means and also claim to be practising Radionics and not, say, visualisation. Having by now treated enough patients with severe disease states, I am sure that the work was difficult enough to do *with* instruments, let alone

---

277. For example, advanced Qigong practitioners are said to be skilled at transferring or projecting substantial amounts of Qi energy to their patients but no doubt they compensate this by assiduous Qi Gong practice in order to replenish their reserves.

without them. Radionic work may link the practitioner intimately with the patient's energy field and if that is full of derangements and disturbances, there is the risk of a backwash. I have heard practitioners who do not use instruments complain of constant debility and exhaustion. Repeat this with any number of patients, coupled with attrition of the practitioner's vitality through (probably) overwork and any number of other external factors, and the risk of depletion and illness stands to be multiplied greatly. This risk is possibly greatest in the enthusiastic, idealistic but inexperienced practitioner; but people can, and do, take risks with themselves at any age. No instrument will protect against such perils completely because the practitioner is *involved and connected*, but a well-designed instrument should certainly help by creating some form of strong barrier. Instruments, in effect, act as a sample-and-hold device for intention configured into specific therapeutic actions. Both code and instrument, to the degree that they are well-constructed, allow those actions to be accurately and consistently projected to the patient, and over long periods of time, if necessary. In short the well-designed instrument carries the burden for the well-intentioned practitioner.

Radionics instruments have been subject to much ridicule from orthodoxy, and the author has had enough involvement with high-quality electronics and skilled electronic engineers to be able to confirm that many instruments do not accommodate accepted rules of electronics design. But on closer examination it can also be found that certain Radionic instruments were granted patents, for example, the Drown and de la Warr cameras, and the T. Galen Heironymus eloptic instrument.[278] Radionic software certainly runs on standard mass-produced computer technology and the software itself must conform to the requirements of the operating system or it will not work *as software*, irrespective of any therapeutic effects it may (or may not) have.

Readers will doubtless be familiar with the idea that there are sacred sites and buildings, places which have a certain special resonance which is often identified as a focus of spiritual energy. The radiesthetist Blanche Merz, in *Points of Cosmic Energy*[279], describes visits to sacred buildings in many parts of the world and attempts to establish a value for

---

278. When a patent is granted the technical scrutiny of the Patent Office must be satisfied. For a description of Heironymus and his activities see for example Chapter 16 of Laurie (2009).

279. Merz (1988). The concepts of sacred geometry, and related principles such as Feng Shui, which may be applied to the design and construction of buildings and the confinement of spaces, have existed for millennia.

their energetic presence, using the pendulum in connection with the Bovis scale, originally proposed by the eponymous French dowser. The range of the scale is from 0 to 10000 and is intended to *'measure the intensity and vibrational quality of subtle energy radiation'*. Considering a human being, the point at 6500 is neutral, values moving lower being described as Depleting (tending towards illness) and values moving higher being described as Energising (tending towards greater wellbeing).[280] The value of 10000 is presumed to be the maximum amount of such energy a healthy person can absorb, any excess being thrown off (mainly through the aura). Merz describes various locations which have a reading higher than 10000 Bovis units. In her analysis of energy points in Chartres Cathedral, for instance, the highest value of those tested, at 18000, is to be found at the centre of the labyrinth.

Having spent a great deal of time studying and designing Radionic instruments it seems not altogether unreasonable to describe them in a similar fashion. Although not all designs are of equal quality (some are rather poor), they could, nevertheless, be considered 'sacred' objects - not that there's anything holy about a Radionic instrument - so, therefore, 'sacred' from the point of view that their energetic presence should well exceed the normal range, as do the properties of the buildings of antiquity and the Middle Ages studied by Merz. They should, if properly designed, possess a concentration of energy - a 'power point' - which enhances access to the 'higher' dimensions. By way of comparison it is easy enough for the dowser to test all sorts of manufactured objects e.g. computers, cameras, mobile phones, televisions etc for coherence at the etheric level. Typically this can be found to be about 20 - 30% (zero being etheric incoherence). Obviously such objects have a high degree of functionality and design logic at the material level and there is no 'etheric engineering' considered, involved or required.[281] But the concept of coherence cannot therefore be dismissed as an irrelevance, since it is a central characteristic of a major scientific and industrial product - the laser. Ordinary light

---

280. There is a discussion of Bovis and his work in Chapter 9 (Medical Radiesthesia) of Sahni (1992). The Bovis Biometer dowsing scale can be purchased from www.emeraldinnovations.co.uk.

281. This suggests, for example, that computers and calculators, being, potentially, etherically rather incoherent, are not good platforms on which to make Radionic instruments - the convenience of the data handling and processing capabilities notwithstanding. Such tests can be done using a metre rule technique such as that described in Chapter 3. The author first heard the term 'etheric engineering' in a lecture by Dr Peter Moscow (1945 - 2011).

consists of waveforms which are incoherent i.e., not all marching in step. In a laser this is changed - the wavefronts are brought into step and the result is that you can have a beam of light which will cut through metals if powerful enough. Coherence in the physics of light is perhaps not the same thing as etheric coherence (at minimum the etheric field as understood in Radionics is not considered by science to exist), but the idea of what might be called *presence resulting from coherence* is certainly there.

Most instruments are adjustable in some way, which allows me to suggest that if well-designed they are 3-dimensional energetically-coherent symbols which may be appropriately varied or *tuned* - i.e. by using codes - to clarify (using analysis techniques), amplify, and project the user's therapeutic intention. To be more precise, instruments are (or should be) coherent resonating nodes which exist simultaneously in the physical and supra-physical dimensions i.e. they have a force-presence sufficiently powerful to interrupt the higher-dimensional fields when appropriately tuned. The wave coherence of the instrument at the etheric level is the all-important factor and this originates in the means of construction at the physical level. The rules and techniques governing etheric engineering, although not yet well-defined, are clearly different from those governing normal electronics and related disciplines. Therefore an etherically-engineered design may have aspects which seem nonsensical from the electronic viewpoint, but the reverse may also be said to be true - electronically well-engineered products may be poorly designed from the etheric viewpoint.

Looking at the problem from another angle, *codes* originate in the fields which constitute the higher dimensions of reality. In order to entrain these fields, they must be adequately described and 'crystallised' into 'physical' mnemonics - i.e. the codes themselves. These codes must, in turn, interface correctly with the instrument in order to properly entrain the fields the codes are intended to represent. The tuning of the instrument is achieved through the coding function in connection with the operator's consciousness and conscious intent. This, in its entirety, should accurately impact the totality of the patient's state at the pre-conscious (*pre-physical/conceptual domain of formative forces*) level.

In other words, if correctly selected and if acceptable to the patient (hence, the requirement for the patient's consent to treatment) this should produce a degree of re-ordering or re-alignment of the patient's *subconscious* reality constructs i.e. the Subtle Anatomy. If the changes are appropriate they may then propagate into the various subtle and para-physical fields substanding the physical body and may ultimate in the reduction or elimination of perceived symptoms and organic pathology and related afflicts (e.g. infection). The success of the action will depend upon the accuracy of analysis and consequent selection of treatments by the practitioner, these, clearly, mediated by the calibre of the code and the instrument itself, and the combination of the two.

The process described above can be deconstructed into a number of steps:

- (as described in Chapter 12) Radionic treatments consist of commands and sources (presets) described by codes;
- codes must be correctly constructed if they are to evoke the underlying fields usefully;
- the code must also be designed such that it interfaces correctly with the instrument;
- code and instrument must combine to create a good interface with the universal information field;
- the presence of the patient's witness in the instrument identifies the energetic image of the patient in the universal information field;
- code, instrument and witness then combine to link or entrain the patient with the field described by the treatment code;
- this entrainment may have a corrective effect on disturbances to the patient's Subtle Anatomy. This process is 'invisible' to the patient's normal conscious state (i.e. what might be described as everyday consciousness or 'physical brain' consciousness) and may be considered to be in the unconscious or subconscious domain;[282]
- the correction may be transferred into the paraphysical fields underlying the structure of the body, or into the structure of the psyche, the basic intention being to relieve physical, psychological or emotional suffering.[283]

---

282. For example when you use a computer you see images or text, internet content, etc. You are unaware of the binary processes being used in the computer's electronics to generate what is on the screen nor, basically, do you need to be. Your lack of awareness of them, however, does not mean they are not there.

283. To give a simple analogy, the process could be compared to that of playing music to someone from a CD. Your intention is to play a certain piece, for instance Mozart's 40th Symphony. This music has been recorded in digital form then captured on the CD. Thus the title of the CD is the 'code' which labels the recording, and the recording itself comprises the music originally composed by Mozart, the interpretation of the conductor, the sound of the orchestra, the ambience of the hall, etc, all recorded and digitized by the audio

The sense of health and wellbeing is probably in a direct relationship with the degree of energetic coherence found in the individual, at both the paraphysical and psychic levels. Information and energy flow in an ordered, co-ordinated and organised manner throughout the system. As a person becomes ill, there is a reduction in this coherence. If the reduction continues, incoherence can turn into chaos, which means the increasing predominance of arbitrary and disorganised energy and information, and energetic and informational flows and exchanges, in (at minimum) the Subtle Anatomy. Thus the central objective of design is to create an instrument which is so sufficiently coherent as to be able to counteract energetic disintegration by providing a fixed reference point, 'tuned' by the treatment codes, which evoke the information that may help re-order disordered parts of the patient's field. Or in other words,

'....put simply, an extremely ill person is in effect being overwhelmed by a chaotic and disintegrative force which will eventually break down the Physical-Etheric Body and the morphogenetic field counterparts to the Physical Body organs, tissues, cells and systems and ..... If we are to successfully deal with severe physical pathology, we have to address these dense fields directly and with a powerful combative organisational and integrative therapeutic force....in this context disease can be considered to be entropic, producing chaos and disorder, and health

---

reproduction process, i.e. from the consciousness and inspiration of Mozart (intangible) to the sound that fills the room (tangible). What you *hear* as the music of Mozart has been deconstructed in the recording process to the level of chunks of information which *of themselves* bear no direct relationship to the musical experience but are nevertheless a code which describes the music. With appropriate equipment you can see how digitized music looks in binary form - strings of 0s and 1s. In the middle sits the CD player, speakers and amplifier, which are the playback or *transduction* system. The player contains circuitry which converts the numbers back into electrical waves which are then amplified and translated by the speakers into sound. Thus your intention is play Mozart; the title identifies the music (the information field); the CD is a 'capture' of the information in the field; the equipment is the transducer; the press of the button actualizes your intention; and the air is the medium through which the sound reaches the listener's ears. As we are aware, not all orchestras, conductors, recording and playback equipment or even listeners are equal; but regardless of the interpretation and performance, Mozart's composition - equivalent to the source in the universal field - remains at all times the same. Malcolm Rae in Tansley (1992) p. 70 - 71 gives a similar sort of example, except that in the intervening years we have gone from analogue to digital technology.

can be typified as morphic (structured). Thus, to re-iterate, energetic insults to the vital system must be met with a more powerful counteracting force.[284]

CODES

The origin of Radionic codes has been briefly discussed in Chapter 2 where Abrams' work was described. The codes he found originated in a purely physical system, in which the patient and the subject (the healthy person used as a reference point in the testing process) were all linked by wires. There was in the beginning no 'distant' aspect to the process. The circuit itself was tuned using a sample or specimen of the disease and if the patient was in resonance with the specimen, there would be a reaction in the test subject. Because certain different disease specimens produced an identical muscle reaction in the subject, it was necessary to find a means by which one disease could be differentiated from another. This was done by placing a variable resistance (rheostat) in the circuit. Codes were, initially, resistance values (in Ohms) recorded from the settings of a rheostat placed in the circuit and were, therefore, in effect, measurable electrical phenomena.

It is only later, in the work of Ruth Drown (1892 - 1962), that the process of code creation was moved closer to the mental and intuitional arena. Here the dowser, using the stick pad or, later, the pendulum, would adjust the instrument knob by knob until it came into resonance with either a sample of the substance or the *idea* or *concept* of the substance held in the dowser's mind (recall that Figure 7 in Chapter 4 illustrates a basic instrument). As each knob was turned it would be set to one of the numbers 0 - 9 when the 'stick' or, latterly, pendulum rotation, was found. Thus all the knobs on the instrument would be adjusted until the entire instrument came into balance, indicated by a pendulum rotation. The numbers to which the knobs were set would then be noted down and could be used repeatedly to describe the command or source being coded.

Having examined many codes created from Ruth Drown's time onward I have noted that a good number, particularly so-called Base 10 Rates, appear to be quite incomplete representations of the 'energy pattern' stated to be described by the Rate. There are complex reasons for this, but the principal point seems to be the extent to which the code is a projection or characterisation based on the code maker's perception as

---

284. From the author's "Genesis of the ANT part 3." *Radionic Journal* **50**(1): 22-30.

opposed to an objective depiction of the 'absolute', which is to say, an apprehension of the image of the proposed treatment or remedy *in Nature*. Thus the extent to which the code maker can mentally penetrate the higher dimensions of Nature and capture and describe the necessary information will determine the efficiency of the resulting code. Let us say the coding of a given remedy requires representation of its image at several levels, for example, Atmic, Causal, Mental, Astral and Etheric. If, perceptually, you cannot penetrate beyond the Astral level, or your responsiveness is primarily Astral, then your comprehension of the remedy image will tend to be incomplete. The resulting code will not necessarily be unusable, but will perhaps lack the necessary depth and detail that a first-quality code should possess and therefore will not have the required depth of therapeutic action in some cases.

For the esoterically-inclined, see again Fortune, *op. cit.*, and particularly, Chapter XX *Tiphareth, the Sixth Sephirah* where the problem of the extension of human consciousness into the higher dimensions is discussed. How to extend this *reach* is a central part of the problem for the would-be Radionic code maker. Many codes which may have been quite effective when developed may lose their effectiveness over time. *Over the longer period and in short, what is made by man may fade with man but what is made by Nature, from the human point of view, tends towards permanence.*[285] One may consider - in the Radionic context - that the essential point is the extent to which the human mind and the 'consciousness' of Nature can come into alignment, and the closer the alignment, the better the chance of creating the highest calibre of codes - to get closer to *reality*. This is no sundry endeavour; it seems the greatest minds of physics have been trying to do something similar for several hundred years.[286]

Figure 30 indicates what might be called a 'complexity' curve. The idea is that the higher up the curve you go, the more closely you describe all the attributes of the source you are trying to code. This curve is not linear but more generally exponential, to suggest that detail is added disproportionately; beyond a certain point it becomes progressively more

---

285. Correctly-made Rae (Magneto-Geometric) cards appear to have maintained their viability, which suggests that they do indeed represent some characteristic of Nature. Ultimately, we are told, even the works of Nature, which may have lasted billions of years, will be determined by entropy.

286. Herbert, *op. cit.*, p.177, quotes Einstein: '*I want to know how God created this world. I am not interested in this or that phenomenon, in the spectrum of this or that element. I want to know His thoughts, the rest are details.*'

difficult to approach completion, since each degree of increase requires the inclusion of a greater amount of information. This might be somewhat compared to the idea of a fractal, where a detailed pattern might contain a large or, potentially, infinite number of additional detailed patterns.

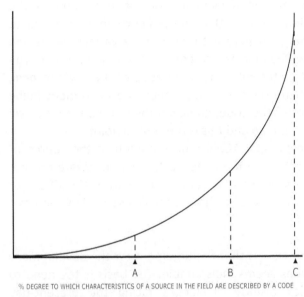

% DEGREE TO WHICH CHARACTERISTICS OF A SOURCE IN THE FIELD ARE DESCRIBED BY A CODE

Figure 30: Complexity curve

The first position, *A*, is around 25%. Certain people (known to and including the author) have done experiments attempting to program a remedy into water by holding a vial in their hand and 'thinking' or 'visualizing' the image of a homoeopathic or other remedy into the water.

There is also an idea that you can write the name of a homoeopathic remedy and a potency value on a piece of paper (e.g. Sulphur 30C), stand it under a small glass of water, and after a certain amount time, again, the remedy image will be programmed into the water. It seems to be possible to program water using such methods and it seems equally possible that many people possess the faculty to be able to do it but at around 25% the result is *weak* - slightly useable and will fade fast.[287] [288] This does not necessarily preclude, however, that some persons might have the ability to print extremely complex patterns into water using their mind only.

B represents the *optimum* viability typically found in standard Base 10 Radionic rates, at best approximately 70%, although many are not

---

287. But see also *The Paper Doctor: A Vibrational Medicine Cabinet* by Don Gerrard - if you can find a copy.

288. Another criticism of homoeopathy involves the idea that since the human body contains a large amount of water, we would be susceptible to being programmed by any amount of stray information. But I argue against this because any such information and the consequent programming would be too weak to have any substantial effect and would be easily deprogrammed by bodily processes.

as good. This is, nevertheless, a great improvement and is workable to a certain degree. To put it crudely, if the efficiency of a code is 70% but the 'depth' of the energetic disturbance is 85%, the code cannot provide sufficient information to fully neutralise the disturbance. Even so, it might provide enough support to the individual - or the projection of the intention of the practitioner - such that the patient can be induced to throw off the illness. The point here is that there are various forces and factors in play and the Radionic treatment is only one of them. The practitioner, on account of the intensity and desire of their *will to heal*, may succeed in spite of the paucity of the codes and instrument being used. My point is that better the code, however, the more effective it will be in carrying the treatment load and *this* is the central point.

C represents the target - 100% representation of the source or command intention described by the code. As far as I am aware no pre-existing codes reach this target. From experience it is extremely difficult to achieve and necessitates the use of techniques which go far beyond basic Radiesthesia.

Consequently, my view is that the argument for the development of a better calibre of codes seems indisputable. The basis is the need to respond to the complex disease challenges facing the present-day practitioner. This has clearly been understood for some time, by some. Rae, for example, began with Base 10 rates, proceeded to Base 44 Rates, and finally developed Magneto-Geometry. Rae gives a description of the development of Magneto-Geometry in *Dimensions of Radionics*:[289]

'The alternative method, which I have called Magneto-geometric potency preparation, came about in the following manner:-

Radiesthetists frequently use a 100cm rule, along which to measure the "potency energy" of a sample of a remedy. With the sample located at the "zero" end of the rule, they move the pendulum along the rule from left to right, noting the point at which the pendulum swings exactly at right angles to the rule. This point indicates a relative potency of energy.

It occurred to me that the point of balance thus detected is, in fact, the boundary between the remedy's local energy field and a component of the earth's magnetic field....this lead to a series of measurements being

---

289. Tansley (1992), section 2, Radionic Instrumentation. My concept of the design of instruments is, in very many respects, quite different to that proposed by Rae.

made in respect of several different remedies, using the remedy vial as the central point, and finding the balance point along the rule, with it pointing in turn to each of the Cardinal and half Cardinal points of the compass. The results of these measurements were then plotted on polar graph paper, and the adjacent points joined by straight lines to form a geometric pattern related to each remedy. Each point was found to be solely related to one remedy.[290]

At the end of the process, Rae developed his characteristic Magneto-Geometric cards, three examples of which are shown here (at full size):

COMMAND: ELIMINATE POISONS

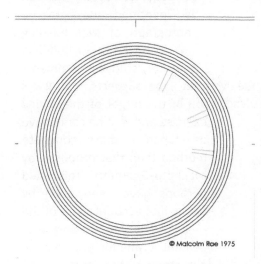

© Malcolm Rae 1975

In each case the outer configuration of seven rings is the same. According to Rae, up to 6 points may be found on the circumference of the circle and these are indicated by the radial lines projecting inwards towards the centre. If a pendulum is held over any point of intersection between the innermost ring and a radial, it should rotate if the card has been properly constructed. Similarly, the pendulum should also rotate over the whole card.

---

290. Tansley (1992), p. 90 - 93. Note that use of the rule was also described in Chapter 3 of this book.

SULPHUR

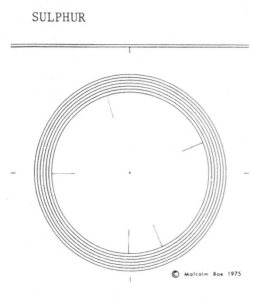

© Malcolm Rae 1975

Now as noted, any code might be properly constructed and reasonably workable even if it is only a partial representation of the source. By analogy, a photograph of the first three floors of a skyscraper does not tell us a great deal about the whole building, even though the photograph might, technically and artistically, be perfectly satisfactory and can be identified as being a photograph of *that* building and not some other building. However, studying comments by no less an authority than Abbé Mermet, one suspects that Rae's method did not offer a complete description of the target of the coding exercise and that he could have developed a more complete method than that proposed by Magneto-Geometry. This could perhaps have been done by taking into account more of the - as it were - magneto-geometric phenomena feasibly detectable by the dowser.

THYROID GLAND

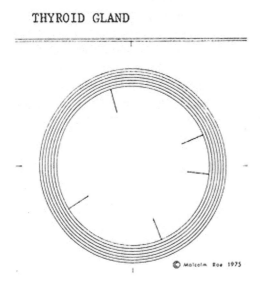

© Malcolm Rae 1975

Figure 31: three MGA remedy cards

According to the Abbé:

'....one will find the constituent elements listed below which will be indicated by the pendulum:
1. Magnetic surfaces and lines of force
2. Fundamental Ray
3. Mental Ray
4. Solar ray and artificial rays
5. Witness rays
6. Vertical column
7. Radiesthesic images
8. Numerical figures and direction of rotation
9. Spirals
10. Pendular designs
11. Variations in weight [of pendulum]
12. Fading'[291]

This suggests a level of complexity which far exceeds that offered by the six radials of standard Magneto-Geometry. Or one may turn to an article by the late Mike Hallas (1943 - 2000), published in the December 1985 issue of the Radionic Quarterly. Commenting on the researches of one John Claydon, he states that Claydon discovered six qualities of a remedy which need to be taken into account in any remedy 'simulation' process:

1) Potency Value
2) Intensity Value
3) Information density
4) Polarity
5) Acceleration Factor
6) Erasure Factor

and comments *'this may be subject at a later stage to change or further discoveries.'* Point 3 'Information density' is of clear interest; Hallas notes that *'there is a degree of complexity of the actual wave form or interference pattern, from the patterns emitted by a substance, the energy*

---

291. Mermet , *op. cit.*, p 42. This book was certainly available in English in Rae's time, although I have no idea if he read it. For more information the reader should study Mermet's book as there is too much detail to cover here.

field of a substance or a crude drug. This contains all the necessary information about the substance.' He contends that **'any simplification of this data - as we may do with a geometric card - can, if it is not prepared carefully, result in only an outline of the remedy or substance.'** [Emphasis mine - NF]. This appears to be a clear reference to Magneto-Geometric cards and some potential limitations to the encoding method.

The author uses a number of techniques in the development of codes, and one of them is the creation of radials. Three examples of homoeopathic remedy cards are shown below (at full size), these being Campanula Rotundifolia, Causticum, and Thorium Oxydatum.

CAMPANULA ROTUNDIFOLIA
HOMOEOPATHIC 10.4.2012.
© copyright Nick Franks 2012

THORIUM OXYDATUM
HOMOEOPATHIC 19.4.2012.
© copyright Nick Franks 2012

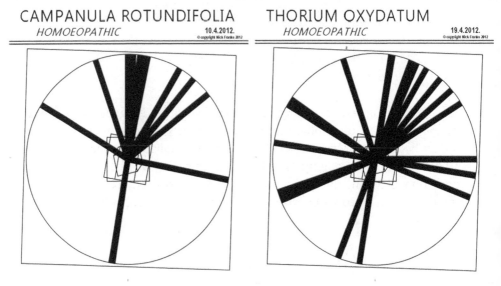

Figure 32: Three homoeopathic remedies made by the author using a radial method

The radials are nominally arrayed around 360 degrees of arc emanating from a central point. Some radials are pitched at hundreds, or even thousands of degrees of arc, and have been reduced to conform with the 360 degrees nominally available. Thus you might imagine in fact concentric spirals superimposed one over the other with various lines raying out from the central point at different levels of the respective spiral. For practical purposes, the diagrams show three dimensions collapsed into two. In the case of Causticum, 18 radials have been used even though only 16 are visible; this is because several are overlaid.

Deconstructing this somewhat further, radials are found as follows:

21st Century Radionics

Physical-Morphic Level	2
Etheric Level	6
Astral Level	3
Astral Layer 2	1
Astral Layer 4	1
Astral Layer 5	1
Astral Layer 6	1
Astral Layer 7	1
Mental Level	1
Buddhic Level	1

This gives a more complete picture of the 'image' of the remedy at various levels of reality and, therefore, should give a more accurate representation for use in treatments and in remedy simulation. Colour plates in the book give other examples of coding techniques, some of which employ shapes and alpha-numeric texts.[292]

---

292. Note that radial cards developed by the author are only suitable for use in the author's instruments. MGA cards, can, however, be used in the author's instruments.

15: REMEDY SIMULATION AND THE RADIONIC MODEL

'I think it is safe to say that no one understands quantum mechanics. Do not keep saying to yourself, if you can possibly avoid it, "But how can it be like that?" because you will go "down the drain" into a blind alley from which nobody has yet escaped. Nobody knows how it can be like that.'

Richard Feynmann (1918 - 1988), Physics Nobelist

In the previous Chapter the 'complexity curve' was discussed. Some further ideas about the qualities and characteristics of this complexity can be gained by placing the curve against the backdrop of the consciousness-driven model of reality used in Radionics. In order to do this it is first necessary to examine another action unique to Radionics, which is the synthesis of 'energy' remedies such as homoeopathic treatments. This, in principal, is another approach to making vibrational medicines, which, when done correctly can equal or perhaps exceed the standards obtained by other methods.

REMEDY SYNTHESIS

In short, this is an important and unique function of appropriately-designed Radionic instruments. Essentially, the energy pattern evoked by *any* Radionic code can 'printed' into a suitable carrier material. These carrier materials can then be ingested orally or even used topically, in the same way that a homoeopathic remedy may be taken by mouth or applied in a suitable ointment. Carrier materials may also be used as a 'store' for treatments and may be used later in appropriate instruments for distant treatment. It should go without saying that the calibre of remedy obtained depends on the quality of the instrument and the code; but the principle applies across Radionics.

Tansley informs us that Ruth Drown discovered that homoeopathic remedies could be synthesized in a Radionic instrument.[293] Basically, this is done by using a quantity of carrier material in the well, such as sac lac (*saccharum lactis*, sugar of milk) or distilled water, instead of the patient's witness. In this configuration, the instrument transfers the

---

293. Tansley (1992), p. 88 and there follows an extensive discussion of Rae's approach to the problem.

information to the field of the carrier material instead of the field of the patient. Refer, for example, back to the instrument illustrated in Chapter 4. This instrument is set up using the Rate for the remedy Ferrum Phosphoricum. To synthesize Ferrum Phosphoricum you would place the carrier material in the well for a certain amount time, maintaining the settings on the instrument. The programming of the material, when complete, will be indicated by a rotation of the pendulum. It is also usually possible to establish a fixed amount of time per quantity and type of carrier material for each instrument type.

As noted, synthesis is not limited to homoeopathic remedies and it seems that in principle *any* Radionic code - such as, for example, any of the commands or presets listed in Chapter 13 - can be programmed into a suitable carrier material. On this basis, you could, for example, program the vibrational pattern of a thought form, emotion, Location, flower essence, etc., into water.

REMEDY COPYING

A further aspect of the synthesis process is remedy copying. Copies can be made either of an existing vibrational remedy or some form of physical material, for example, a crystal or, feasibly, any other physical substance, such as an allergen or foodstuff. Usually the copying instrument has a separate input well, the source material being placed in the input, and the carrier material in the output, well. When making a copy, codes are not used and the instrument is used, basically, to connect the two wells in an efficient manner such that an accurate transfer of the pattern of the source material into the carrier is made. In some operations a potency setting might also be used, for example, starting with a sample of an allergen such as a pollen, you might make a copy at 30C, i.e. 'Pollen 30C' being the end product.

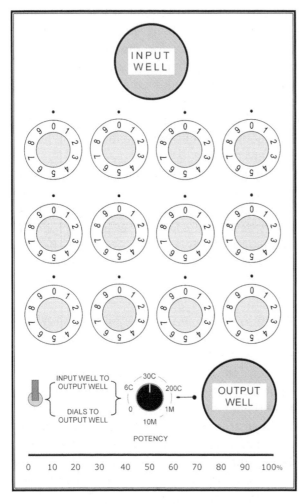

Figure 33: simple Radionic instrument with two wells

A revised basic instrument is shown to the left, an input well having been added above the dials and a selector switch and potency range control beneath them and to the left of the output well. The selector switch allows the user to choose between copying mode ('input well to output well') or Rate mode ('dials to output well'). The potency control is a continuous rotary knob which allows potencies over the range 0 to 10M to be selected.[294] The drawing shows the knob set at 30C, so, in principal, the energy pattern of a source material placed in the input well would be transferred to a carrier material in the output well at the potency 30C. *It should also be borne in mind that quality or calibre of any such energy transfer will be constrained by the quality of the instrument being used.* If the source material is of a better energetic quality than the copying instrument, the copy will not be as good.

As a point of practice it should be noted that when giving treatment, the practitioner should check whether instrument-given or oral versions of the treatment are more suitable. An advantage of instrument-

---

294. Some instruments manufactured by the author allow potency to be synthesized up to 100MMM.

21st Century Radionics

given treatments is that settings such as potency can be varied during the course of the treatment.

POTENCY, AND REMEDY MANUFACTURE

I will discuss remedy manufacture only in the context of homoeopathy, although similar techniques can be used in the preparation of other vibrational remedies, such as gem or flower essences.

In Homoeopathy the matter of potency, and potency selection in prescribing, is of great importance and much discussed. Equally, Radionic distant treatment may well be given at a potency setting, potency value selection typically being made with the pendulum. Thus to select potency the homoeopath uses an experiential method and the Radionic practitioner, a radiesthesic technique. The question as to what potency actually *is* has preoccupied me for a number of years and it is through a brief discussion of the methods used in preparing homoeopathic potencies that we might be able to discern something useful.

The homoeopathic manufacturing process begins with a mother tincture. This, in the case of, for example, botanical specimens, is prepared by making a solution of the required parts of the plant in alcohol. The parts could be the root, stems, leaves, or the entire plant, as required. In the case of metals and chemicals, the tincture is prepared by triturating (grinding) the substance with sugar of milk (*saccharum lactis*). The idea, presumably, is to transfer the vibrational characteristics of the metal to the sac lac, which may then be dissolved in water to make a mother tincture. The tincture, whatever the source material may be, is the starting point in the manufacturing process.

Potentising involves both dilution and succussion (forceful shaking). The usual cry of rage or derision from the sceptics is that '*there is nothing in there*' and '*how can it get more powerful if there is less of it?*',[295] and certainly one must presume that simply diluting the base material literally out of existence will in fact not produce much of a viable remedy. It appears to be the combination of the two processes according to a

---

295. In this country (the UK) there is an ongoing stampede of scientists and medical authorities competing to denigrate homoeopathy; it is almost as if one is trying to outdo the other in the contest to pull it down - 'placebo' etc. But in all of this uproar never and not once do I recall hearing a discussion by the detractors about success in veterinary homeopathy - the treatment of animals with homoeopathic remedies. Does any reader think that animals know if they are being given medicines, or placebos, or any medicine at all?

definite method which gets the result, that is, dilution *in conjunction with* succussion.

DILUTION RATIOS

Three potency ranges are in common use in Homoeopathy, these being denoted X,[296] C and LM. These terms refer to the dilution ratio used at each new stage in the manufacturing process.

This ratio is 1:9 for X potencies; 1:99 for C (Centesimal) potencies; and 1:50,000 for LM potencies. This means that in each step of the manufacturing process, 1 part of the existing potency is diluted with 9, 99 or 50,000 parts of Distilled Water (*Aqua Destillata*), respectively, according to the potency scale being manufactured.

Considering the manufacture of Centesimal scale remedies, therefore, 1C is 1:99. Here 1 part of the original tincture is diluted with 99 parts water.

2C is 1:99 of 1C, which means that 1 part of the 1C tincture is diluted with 99 parts water.

3C is then 1:99 of 2C, and so on - it is not hard to see that the degree of dilution at, for instance, 200C is absolutely enormous.

In terms of succussion, we see that at each dilution step X and C potencies are both then given 10 forceful shakes while LM potency is given 100 shakes.[297]

SYNTHESIS

In the case of remedy synthesis using Radionic methods, a code evokes the energy pattern of the remedy. Using the code in the instrument and treating the carrier material placed in the well for the appropriate period of time will, in principle, produce the required result - a

---

296. Usually referred to as D potencies in Europe, for 'Decimal'.

297. I have much simplified this for the sake of brevity. It is not entirely, uniformly, or simply true that homoeopathic medicines become more powerful as they become more rarefied. The essence of the matter is that potency needs to be matched to the patient, which is to say that the result will be optimized when the potency is most closely matched to the patient's state. Too high or too low a potency may be ineffectual. It is also suggested that some remedies have an optimum potency at which they may be used, higher or lower than which they become less effective. Potentising technique is a large subject in itself. I have drawn these few comments from detailed information given by Gaier (1991) and the reader should study in particular pages 431 - 468. The reader should also consult the source, which is Hahnemann's *Organon of the Medical Art* (1842). Succussion is mostly done by machines nowadays.

version of a remedy produced not by mechanical methods but by evoking the energy pattern from the information field. Since the claim is that it is possible to produce a viable homoeopathic remedy using Radionics then comparatively, it seems reasonable to propose that a) the code has to replace the mother tincture as the source for the energy pattern and b) the action of the instrument on the carrier material has to replace the process of dilution and shaking.

Since not all homoeopathic pharmacies appear to manufacture a product of comparable or standardised quality, establishing a benchmark is not quite as simple as it might first appear. I have heard homoeopaths comment that some pharmacies produce a better product than others, which suggests that the manufacturing process is not uniform. One may also ask, for example, if Hahnemann's method is an absolutely lossless procedure guaranteed to transfer a complete picture of the energy pattern of the source material, or whether the transfer is variable from substance to substance. In such a case the amount of trituration needed for one source might be quite different to that needed for another, e.g. depending upon factors such as the hardness or underlying energetic coherence of the source material.

We note from the homoeopathic process that dilution is followed by succussion. The following additional idea can be proposed. Dilution increases the number of water molecules in the solute, with the result that the combined etheric field has grown larger; i.e. not only living organisms but *also materials such as water* have an etheric field. The simple position is that the more material there is, the larger the etheric field. Thus ten drops of water have a certain size of etheric field, and a litre of water has a proportionally larger one. The process of succussion - shaking - may act to *order* the molecules in the water and, consequently, its etheric field, i.e. making the field more coherent. But at each dilution step, more water is added, which therefore means that a quantity of new 'incoherent' molecules is added; the size of the field is increased, but the coherence of the field is potentially reduced. Therefore we may think that dilution increases the size of the field but decreases order, while the subsequent vigorous shaking then helps re-align all the molecules and therefore reorders the etheric field, restoring a new measure of coherence to it. This new larger field, *less material* through dilution but *more coherent* through shaking, is the new potency. As can be seen from the dilution ratios described above, the quantity of 'new' water molecules, particularly in the case of the LM potency, can be quite substantial and, consequently, the number of successions required to produce ordering is greater.

The circuitry of the Radionic instrument essentially works to bring the etheric field of the carrier material into energetic coherence, the limit of course being the limit in coherence of the instrument. From observations I have made using my own instruments[298], it takes a relatively short time to reach, say, 50% completion and further percentage increases seem to take somewhat proportionally longer, as if the process was, again, 'fractal' in nature, with more and more detail being added until the limit of resolution is reached.[299] The carrier material is entrained by the field of the instrument and, by analogy, the transfer of a specific pattern or characteristics from the mother tincture in the homoeopathic process is replaced by the specific pattern evoked by the Radionic code. Again by analogy, the variable circuitry of the instrument replaces the dilution process in homoeopathy by moderating or modulating the coherence field to emulate the desired potency, so that when you program 10MM, you get it.

It should be noted that in many instruments once the charging process has been commenced, no changes can be made to the settings. Changing the potency control settings, for instance, may cause the instrument to 'start again' and the new potency will be written over the previous potency, in much the same way that the magnetic data storage process overwrites existing data with new data. Other instruments may allow a certain amount of 'layering' of patterns in the carrier material, with the possibility of printing several patterns over each other. Subject to further investigation, the more coherent an instrument, the more likely it is that erasure of previously-stored patterns will occur.

---

298. Other designers have a different view, e.g. that remedy synthesis takes a fixed amount of time regardless of quantity of material etc.

299. Some may say 'but this instrument, that instrument, some other instrument, takes 10 seconds, 8 minutes, 10 minutes...' etc. I have given the analogy of the digital photograph previously. A 1-megapixel camera will give you *basically* the same image as 21-megapixel camera, but as you start to enlarge the image, coherence will rapidly drop away and you will soon see that the 1 megapixel image is a meaningless jumble of pixels. With vastly more enlargement the same will happen to the 21 megapixel image, but you will definitely be able to enlarge it much further before it starts to fall apart. Therefore the granularity and resolution at 21 megapixels is far greater, and while for practical purposes there may be satisfactory limits there may be no limit to resolution in nature unless there is something to be found equivalent to (or which is?) Planck's constant - at the etheric level....??

SPIRIT AND SUBSTANCE

Hahnemann states:

'For its own special purposes, the homoeopathic medical art develops to a formerly unheard of degree the internal, spirit-like medicinal powers of crude substances. It does so by means of a procedure which belongs exclusively to it....whereby those substances become altogether more than ever - indeed, immeasurably - penetratingly effective and helpful, even those substances which, in their crude state do not manifest the least medicinal power in the human body....this procedure develops the latent dynamic powers of the substance which were previously unnoticeable, as if slumbering.'[300]

The modern Radionic researcher might take a different view and turn Hahnemann's statement on its head, proposing, rather, that the potentisation process *frees* the 'spirit-like' qualities of matter from the *limitations and confines of substance* and in doing so allows its archetypal qualities and formative forces, i.e., that which is condensed and precipitated into the world of matter and emerges as material, to be better observed, understood more clearly, and wielded more usefully in the therapeutic art. It is the process of *removal of the confining substance* which reveals its inner nature; this nature does not 'develop' autonomously as a consequence of the potentisation process but pre-exists the observable material and is confined by it in the physical world. The material Universe is governed by the laws of physics and chemistry but it is also the end result of the process of condensation of the formative fields and forces into physical form.[301] As a (not inconsiderable) aside I

---

300. Hahnemann (1842) §269

301. Not that I am criticizing Hahnemann. The magnitude of his achievement is unquestionable. There is also the question of how formative forces are involved in the appearance of strictly man-made substances, such as the tens of thousands of chemical compounds which have been developed over the last 150 years. These substances have not occurred in nature and therefore no specific pre-existing field would be available. But the *components* of such fields exist in nature and the laws of physics and chemistry (presumably) pre-existed the development of the chemicals, so we may start to surmise that new formative fields can at least partially be brought into existence as a result of human invention, but on the base of that which Nature has already created, such as the elements, the laws of physics and chemistry, etc. Whether humans can create *entirely new* fields and forces not previously existing in Nature and thus *precipitate entirely new forms beyond the range of its laws* (as far as they are known and understood) is also a question which might be considered. Sheldrake generally has much to say on this topic.

think it therefore follows that how 'archetypal qualities and formative forces' (or however they might be described) are understood must be an essential prerequisite for the design of effective Radionic codes.

Homoeopathic potentising starts with the actual physical material and the potentisation process removes it step by step, revealing the underlying energy pattern. This separates the material from its energetic qualities, retaining and clarifying the presence of the latter. If the Radionic concept of many layers of formative force and energy substanding physical reality is correct, what must most probably remain as a result of the homoeopathic process is a 'key' programmed into the potentised material, e.g. water, *sac lac*, and *this* links it to these underlying paraphysical and formative fields and forces. This key may be a frequency[302], there may be some kind of polymerisation of the water molecules, a 'memory of water' [303], or any combination of such effects. It is the external fields which water 'remembers'.

Whatever character or quality may be imparted to the water by the potentisation process, from the Radionic viewpoint the logical conclusion is that its central function is to provide a *link* to the underlying fields - the same fields which are described by Radionic codes. In the main, therefore, I suggest that the potentised remedy - the 'water' - does not itself bring about the therapeutic action. I suggest that the remedy is a link to the underlying information fields and patterns and the act of taking the homoeopathic dose entrains the related fields with those of the Dynamis of the patient in the same, or comparable, way, that a Radionic code and

---

302. See for example the work of Dr Jacques Benveniste (1935 - 2004), and Dr Cyril Smith (currently alive).

303. '....criticisms centred around the vanishingly small number of solute molecules present in a solution after it has been repeatedly diluted are beside the point, since advocates of homeopathic remedies attribute their effects not to molecules present in the water, but to modifications of the water's structure. Simple-minded analysis may suggest that water, being a fluid, cannot have a structure of the kind that such a picture would demand. But cases such as that of liquid crystals, which while flowing like an ordinary fluid can maintain an ordered structure over macroscopic distances, show the limitations of such ways of thinking. There have not, to the best of my knowledge, been any refutations of homeopathy that remain valid after this particular point is taken into account. A related topic is the phenomenon, claimed by Jacques Benveniste's colleague Yolène Thomas and by others to be well established experimentally, known as the "memory of water". If valid, this would be of greater significance than homeopathy itself, and it attests to the limited vision of the modern scientific community that, far from hastening to test such claims, the only response has been to dismiss them out of hand.' Professor Brian D. Josephson (Nobelist in Physics) www.tcm.phy.cam.ac.uk/~bdj10/water.memory/ns/homeopathy.html

instrument combination also entrains the patient with the fields evoked by the codes. Thus the physical material is progressively removed but the energetic imprint or pattern remains linked to the carrier material and, broadly speaking, becomes progressively more clearly defined and expanded in scope as potency is increased. In general terms, therefore, the means of action of a Homoeopathic remedy may be little different from the action of the equivalent Radionically-synthesized remedy. Granted indeed that there may be wide quality differences, between for example, the products of different homoeopathic pharmacies, or between the products of Radionic methods; but there is nothing in my experience that suggests to me that Hahnemann's method is necessarily the *ne plus ultra* or only way of going about the matter.

To further expand this point, the situation is not that the higher the potency, the more powerful a homoeopathic remedy becomes. I think that the broad rule for prescribing must be that the higher the potency, the more closely must the remedy fit the patient's symptom picture, or *totality of symptoms* - it must be a *simillimum*, not a *similar*. This totality typically includes mental and emotional symptoms. A similar can be used at low potency (say 30C or lower) for localised symptoms or first aid - to give simple examples, *Arnica* for bruises, *Rhus Toxicodendron* for sprains. The same remedies might be less effective or ineffective at higher potencies (typically 200C, 1M, etc) because the patient's overall symptom picture may be entirely different on the mental and emotional levels. The remedy is a similar at low potency but not a simillimum at high potency; here it does not have an appropriate degree of antidotal correspondence to the full range of disturbances to the patient's energy field.

TRANSITION FROM CONSCIOUSNESS TO MATTER
If the 'higher' fields of consciousness and formative forces do not exist, it is difficult to think that Radionics has any possible source, sphere or range of action except perhaps for some limited effects at the electromagnetic level. I find it hard to see how Radionic instruments could produce a simulacrum of a homoeopathic or any other remedy given that the only components of the process are the code, the instrument, and the carrier material, none of the original substance being present as a basis for preparation. Although one may propose, furthermore, that the actual difference between Homoeopathic and Radionic methods of preparing remedies - and therefore the remedies themselves - is to a great extent one of technique, it is clear that in the case of the former, the process starts with the material and proceeds to the immaterial, whereas in with

the latter, the process begins with the immaterial and, in fact, concludes with the immaterial.

Looking at the situation overall, we can represent homoeopathic potency as follows:

At point A we find the limit of dilution, Avogadro's Limit[304]. *This is the point beyond which no further molecules of the original material can be found in the diluate.* We are in the realm of the purely energetic. In potency terms, it is around 12C. At lower dilutions, some molecules of the

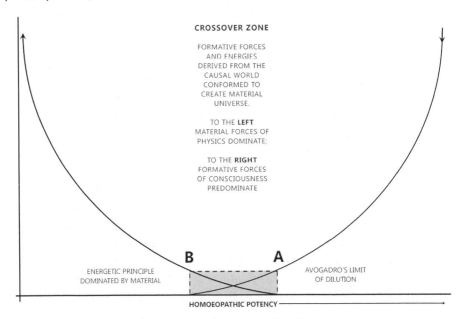

Figure 34:crossover zone between consciousness and matter

original material may remain and there is always the possibility of some degree of pharmacological action taking place when the remedy is ingested by a patient. Beyond this point, i.e., 13C and up, any therapeutic properties which the water may possess must result purely from changes to its energetic state as result of the potentisation process.

At point B we find, basically, the opposite situation: we have entered the realm of matter governed by the known laws of Physics. Here

---

304. After Count Amedeo Avogadro (1776 - 1856). It should be borne in mind that Avogadro's Limit has nothing to do with Homoeopathic action or any of the phenomena it describes. What I am doing is developing a thesis from two observations, i.e. that there is a limit to dilution, and that in Homoeopathy, regardless of dilution, there appears to be a form of medicinal action remaining in the carrier material.

the energetic principle has been greatly reduced or, it may be thought, thoroughly subsumed to known physical reactions. Basically, substances which, when potentised, begin to act homoeopathically to the right of B, act only chemically, or, we might say, materially, to the left of it.

Between B and A lies what might be termed the crossover zone, where potency and matter are to some degree both present. One might also say that this is the zone where formative forces precipitate into matter, or where the consciousness of Nature produces matter out of waveforms. If 'reality' consisted only of matter governed by deterministic laws, one might think that the Universe would be nothing much more than a mechanism little capable of development or evolution, let alone producing life. One could easily see how, in such a rigid Universe, the idea, imago or even actuality of a creator God would be needed, literally, a *deus ex machina*[305], performing miracles. But miracles are not the order of battle of these days; science finds for evolution. In that case we are obliged to ask whether the materialistic hypotheses have sufficient explanatory power. The paradox is that it is scientific materialism, denying the existence of God, which might most *need* a creator God in order to be viable as an explanation for the emergence and development of a complex Universe which contains us.

It should be noted, equally, that the synthesis of remedies by Radionic means cannot synthesize actual physical matter - atoms, molecules, compounds etc. Any Radionically-produced remedy, however low the potency, will not contain any of the 'original' material. Clearly one might observe that Radionic synthesis of matter 'out of the ether' would be a phenomenon of abnormal significance. Nevertheless, the proposal is that this is done by Nature on an ongoing basis across the Universe. If this process can be understood in full then we have the key to manifestation.

This depiction of the remedy-making process can be put into context by adding more detail to the diagram (below). It should be noted that although I have separated out the various levels, this is only for the purposes of explanation. All levels are, essentially, present at the same time and in the same 'space', and so within this context the comments by Dion Fortune recorded at the top of Chapter 6 should be borne in mind.

---

305. 'a person or thing (as in fiction or drama) that appears or is introduced suddenly and unexpectedly and provides a contrived solution to an apparently insoluble difficulty' Merriam-Webster Dictionary www.merriam-webster.com/dictionary/

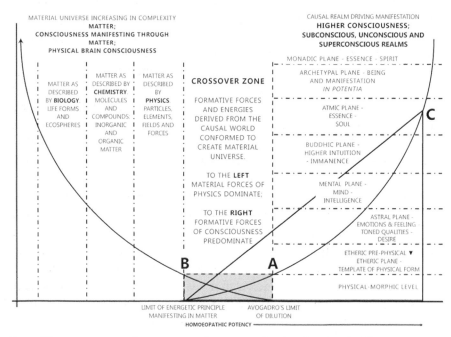

Figure 35: crossover zone between consciousness and matter in more detail

To the *right* of A are shown the planes of consciousness alluded to in Chapter 5. This is a somewhat modified model of the planes of consciousness proposed by Bailey. These planes may also comprise, in totality or to a certain degree, the fields of the subconscious, superconscious, unconscious and collective unconscious experienced by humanity. They constitute what might be termed the *subjective* side of reality. The highest point is the Monadic plane. The lowest, or most dense, point is the Physical-Morphic paraphysical level. These are arranged in a horizontal stack suggesting movement, basically, from ideation towards matter, which might be termed *involution*. Point C indicates the probable upper limit of homoeopathic potency; Radionic codes may be able to depict forces and energies at an even higher level of conceptualisation.

To the *left* of B is found what may be termed the *objective* side of reality, basically, the three levels of the material universe as described by science, for simplicity, physics, chemistry and biology. This is also the world of ordinary objects and everyday experience, the everyday physical or macroscopic world where cause and effect are most clearly linked; time flows in only one direction, entropy rules, and so forth. These levels are

21st Century Radionics

arranged in three parallel vertical stacks, where the fields, particles and fundamental forces of physics precede the appearance of complex matter, which in turn precedes the appearance of life forms and the ecosphere. This developmental process is termed *evolution* 'Normal' human consciousness, emerging from the physical brain, is said to be one of the results of this evolutionary process.

The 'complexity curve' referred to earlier can be related to the right-hand side of the diagram. When creating Radionic codes, it needs to be understood how the command or source is structured across the various planes. As described, a substance may have an energetic presence on several planes, such as the Physical-Morphic, Etheric, Astral and Mental, but it should not be assumed that all commands or sources have an identical presence in all planes. It is this implicit complexity which is partially at the root of the problem of making codes which are more effective; a 'one size fits all' approach is not sufficiently comprehensive.

It is the existence of the crossover zone, with its continually moving and shifting but nevertheless real, if subtle, boundaries that allows us to contact and explore the underlying subjective character of reality. In Jungian psychology, for example, this makes itself known through the unconscious, and in Physics, perhaps, this makes itself apparent through quantum and other phenomena, and in Radionics, provides the doorway through which the practitioner may seek to pass in order to do his work.

16: RADIONICS IN THE CONTEXT OF THE PRESENT AGE

"Have you not heard of that madman who lit a lantern in the bright morning hours, ran to the market place, and cried incessantly: "I seek God! I seek God!"- As many of those who did not believe in God were standing around just then, he provoked much laughter. Has he got lost? asked one. Did he lose his way like a child? asked another. Or is he hiding? Is he afraid of us? Has he gone on a voyage? emigrated? - Thus they yelled and laughed.

The madman jumped into their midst and pierced them with his eyes. "Whither is God?" he cried; "I will tell you. We have killed him - you and I. All of us are his murderers. But how did we do this? How could we drink up the sea? Who gave us the sponge to wipe away the entire horizon? What were we doing when we unchained this earth from its sun?....Are we not straying, as through an infinite nothing?....Do we hear nothing as yet of the noise of the gravediggers who are burying God? Do we smell nothing as yet of the divine decomposition? Gods, too, decompose. God is dead. God remains dead. And we have killed him.

"How shall we comfort ourselves, the murderers of all murderers? What was holiest and mightiest of all that the world has yet owned has bled to death under our knives: who will wipe this blood off us? What water is there for us to clean ourselves? What festivals of atonement, what sacred games shall we have to invent? Is not the greatness of this deed too great for us? Must we ourselves not become gods simply to appear worthy of it? There has never been a greater deed; and whoever is born after us - for the sake of this deed he will belong to a higher history than all history hitherto."

Friedrich Nietzsche, *THE GAY SCIENCE* (1882)

Once more, but in a new and cold and penetrating light, I watched all the lives of stars and worlds, and of the galactic communities, and of myself, up to the moment wherein now I stood, confronted by the infinity that men call God, and conceive according to their human cravings.

Olaf Stapledon, *STAR MAKER* (1937)

IDEAS

A proposition in this book is that the material Universe, measurable by scientific means, and life itself, originate in a non-material realm which is primarily governed by consciousness. This realm cannot be directly apprehended, contained, manipulated, quantified, controlled or distrained by science or the scientific method. It can, however, be queried using many and various introspective means and one of them is

Radiesthesia; another is Jung's 'active imagination', another is intuition. For example, Einstein:

'The really great steps forward in the knowledge of nature were made in a way almost directly opposite to induction. The intuitive understanding of what is essential in a large complex of facts leads the scientist to the construction of one or several hypothetical fundamental laws. From the fundamental law (system of axioms) he draws the consequences, as much as possible in a completely deductive way. These consequences....can be compared with experience and so provide a criterion for the fundamental law....Every expert knows that the greatest steps forward in the knowledge of nature, for example, Newton's theory of gravitation, thermodynamics, kinetic theory of gases, modern electrodynamics, etc., were all born this way....Therefore the researcher always starts from the facts, whose connection is the basic task of his work. He does not, however, reach his theoretical system in a methodical and inductive way, rather, he clings to the facts by intuitive selection among the thinkable theories based on the axioms.' [306]

This realm includes, at minimum, not only the essence or source of consciousness but also its subjective components. In the model used in this book - others exist or could doubtless be constructed - these components are described as planes of energy or planes of existence, each of which has certain general characteristics. It also said to substand the external objective phenomena of physical reality, which are to some variable and unknowable extent a projection, or perhaps mirror, of the unmanifest. This realm also underlies the normal human consciousness, the origin of which is attributed by science to the nervous system only; and therefore the whole concept stands pretty much opposed to materialistic thinking. In the Radionic model presented here, human consciousness and its phenomena would seem to a varying extent to be both local (produced by the brain in response to inputs from the sensory system, resulting in feelings, sensations, emotions etc) and non-local (emanating from the unconscious and the non-physical self), and the borderline between the two is permeable and ever-changing.

---

306. Quoted in Kostro (2000) p. 108 - 109. I do not know if Einstein accepted any concept of an extra-physical realm of consciousness, but he certainly uses the word *intuition*, and what then is that and where does it originate?

Because of its subjective aspect, this realm cannot be confined by laws (such as those described by physics) which it underlies. Science strives to define objective and immutable laws which describe physical reality and to prove the accuracy of those laws through testable predictions as to how matter will behave. This has shown to be a valid, and world-changing line of enquiry. One result of this law-defining activity appears to be the idea that all physical phenomena have a limit, threshold or boundary, the speed of light being a very well-known example, or Planck's Constant, another.

By way of contrast the Universe as a totality is thought to be infinite, and that which is infinite can by definition have no boundary. From this type of idea one can perhaps estimate why objectivity must be subsumed to subjectivity. To put it another way, that which must, presumably, include all possibilities and probabilities cannot be described by laws and theorems which limit its range of action. Bohm tells us:

'Evidently, the notion of formative cause is relevant to the view of undivided wholeness in flowing movement, which has been seen to be implied in modern developments in physics, notably relativity theory and quantum theory. Thus....each relatively autonomous and stable structure (e.g. an atomic particle) is to be understood not as something independently and permanently existent but rather as a product that has been formed in the whole flowing movement and that will ultimately dissolve back into this movement....Nevertheless, in most of the work that is being done in physics today the notions of formative and final cause are not regarded as having primary significance. Rather, law is still generally conceived as a self-determined system of efficient causes, operating in an ultimate set of material constituents of the universe (e.g. elementary particles subject to forces of interaction between them). These constituents are not regarded as formed in an overall process, and thus they are not considered to be anything like organs adapted to their place and function in the whole....Rather, they tend to be conceived as separately existent mechanical elements of a fixed nature.*

The prevailing trend in modern physics is much against any sort of view giving primacy to formative activity in undivided wholeness of flowing movement. Indeed, those aspects of relativity and quantum theory which do suggest the need for such a view tend to be de-emphasized and hardly noticed by most physicists....When it comes to the informal language and mode of thought in physics, which infuses the imagination and provokes the sense of what is real and substantial, most physicists still speak and *think, with an utter conviction of truth, in terms of the traditional atomistic notion that the universe is constituted of elementary particles which are the 'basic building blocks' out of which everything is made. In other sciences, such as biology, the strength of this conviction is even greater, because among workers in these fields there is little awareness of the revolutionary character of development in modern physics. For example, modern molecular biologists generally believe that the whole of mind and life can ultimately be understood in more or less mechanical terms, through some extension of the work that has been done on the structure and function of DNA molecules. A similar trend has already begun to dominate in psychology. Thus we arrive at the very odd result that in the study of life and mind, which are just the fields in which formative cause acting in undivided and unbroken flowing movement is most evident to experience and observation, there is now the strongest belief in the fragmentary atomistic approach to reality....*To be confused about what is different and what is not, is to be confused about everything. *Thus, it is not an accident that our fragmentary form of thought is leading to such a widespread range of crises, social, political, economic, ecological, psychological, etc. Such a mode of thought implies unending development of chaotic and meaningless conflict, in which the energies of all tend to be lost by movements that are antagonistic or else at cross-purposes.*

Evidently, it is important and indeed extremely urgent to clear up this deep and pervasive kind of confusion that penetrates the whole of our lives....Nor will it be useful to try and impose some fixed kind of integrating or unifying 'holistic' principle on our self-world view, for....any form of fixed self-world view implies that we are no longer treating our theories as insights or ways of looking but, rather, as 'absolutely true knowledge of things as they really are.'[307]

Bohm stands against both reductionism and holism and thereby offers a critique of present-day science. On the one hand against reductionism - phenomena should be understood not as things in isolation, as unconnected events, but as part of a dynamic, interrelated and ongoing process. The consequence of reductionism in human thought is endemic disorder which, it might be thought, is becoming critical at both local and planetary levels. On the other, against holism - a static holistic world view also militates against an evolutionary dynamic. In the way of things such a world view would eventually break down in the face of

---

307. Bohm (1995) p. 14 - 17

actual events, since its explanatory boundaries would be breached. So it seems that a new type of model is required, one which explains things within an interconnected context of process and development, an evolutionary and adaptive dynamic.

This appears to be the mode of thought underlying Radionics. The attempt is to understand the patient within the context of his or her life experience, this including both knowables - the traumatic events and symptoms experienced by the patient - and those much harder to discern with the external eye, such as miasmatic forces and other hidden antagonists, such as repressed trauma. A key point is not *'To be confused about what is different and what is not'*, which in the therapeutic context I interpret as being able to discern *where* in the exposition of the self that is a human being the problem occurs. Put another way, to what extent is a symptom or illness a local or exterior event - originating, perhaps, in an epidemic - or to what extent is it an outgrowth of the individual's life experience and process of self-development? To what extent is it a personal reflection of the collective crisis? What is different in this patient that makes him or her an individual to be treated as such?

The non-material realm or source can also be thought of as presenting itself to us as a universal information field, ever-present, holographic, limitlessly vast in the amount of information it can hold. A principle of Radiesthesia is that it is a method by which we can explore this information field and bring aspects of it into our 'ordinary' conscious mind. According as to how our individual perceptual mechanisms have been programmed and constructed - or perhaps, to put it another way, according as to how well both our intellectual and intuitive faculties are developed and free from programming, bias and preconception - so will be our ability to conform information gleaned from the field into understandable and useable concepts. A closed mind may well find nothing in the radiesthesic method and dismiss it. An unprepared mind may be able to draw certain information from the field, but be unable to grasp it in any significant or useful way. But these actions are not different from what has taken place throughout the entire history of the development of the human mind. One may think, for example, that the potential for all the technology we have developed has already existed for thousands of years or even 'forever', but it is only now that the ability to materialise it has emerged. Why now and not then? Perhaps generations a millennium or so in the future will look back at this age and ask a similar question: the technology *we have now* - why couldn't *they* figure it out? Why couldn't they see it? [308]

Information is not the same, however, as consciousness. Information is descriptive content. Consciousness implies awareness, action, reaction and interaction - life. Information is 'dead' - for example digital data stored on magnetic media, or the words of this page - without the demands of the living consciousness which gives it context and meaning, or creates it.

It can be proposed that the primary original source of consciousness, the prototypical essence, has at least three archetypal characteristics. The first is *the will-to-be*, resulting in the second, which is *an awareness of self and that there can be a not-self* (that which is not it), and the third is *harmony and balance* - or at least, striving towards harmony and balance. The result of the third is process governed by laws. From this prototypical essence comes the material Universe, the projection of primary consciousness into form, something which is *of* it but *not it*. Here one might also conflate monism ('all is one') with dualism ('all is two').[309] These primary characteristics can be considered typical, in varying degrees of sophistication, of all forms of life, beginning with the smallest microorganism.

For present purposes I propose a hierarchy of origination which includes *information* as a central component of Nature.[310] In this model, it

---

308. Of course there are many 'obvious' reasons 'why not' - sociological, economic, technological, epistemological, etc - but here I am not interested in what is obvious. I am interested in what is not obvious.

309. May I remind you of the quote from Lao Tzu in Chapter 8. The ancient sage knew, but did not quantify: '*The way begets one; one begets two; two begets three; three begets the myriad creatures. The myriad creatures carry on their backs the* yin *and embrace in their arms the* yang *and are the blending of the generative forces of the two.*' Apart from a few natural numbers, there are no electron volts or calculus in this apprehension of the totality; is it thereby less valid? One may add that there could be Laws which govern the workings of the Universe, of which the Laws of Physics might simply be a subset, and which are completely different in character to those presently discerned by science.

310. Also refer back to Chapter 7. The present Chapter (or any other in this book) is not intended to be a definitive and absolutist description of how things come into existence. I am trying to explain Radionics, not provide a master key to the Universe. The problem is that to attempt to explain Radionics - to attempt to answer the prototypical question '*but how can it possibly work?*' - it seems necessary to posit some kind of theory or principle of action, the implications of which reach right back to the problem of cosmogenesis, in the sense that the way I perceive things to be now must be a product of what must have been then, since one thing grows out of another. To qualify this I think that any attempt at a theory of 'everything' must be at best partial, simply because we do not know what

is a means by which consciousness imposes order on the two other primaries of physical Nature, energy and matter. Information is neither energy nor matter, but is nevertheless is a force, driven by consciousness, controlled by Laws, which imposes order on process. At the end of the previous Chapter I discussed a model of what might be called the hierarchy of emergence, which moves from consciousness to matter. Entwined in the stages of emergence are layers of information. It may be this information which describes, for example, the waveforms underlying physical matter, and which, amongst other things, the Radionic code endeavours to capture and use for analytical and corrective purposes. In the Radionic model it is disturbance to the flow of energy which causes distress to the fields underlying form, and it is the correction of these disturbances which, one may think, may allow the normal functioning of the fields to be reasserted.

Some summary concepts are:

The primary consciousness, the prototypical essence, acts through archetypal forms and characteristics;

Matter is the projection of consciousness into form;

Consciousness cannot manifest directly into form and requires intermediary and progressively denser vehicles (planes) through which formative forces are organised;

Information is an irreducible basic constituent of Nature, along with energy and matter;

'everything' includes; obviously I am throwing 'consciousness' in all its aspects into the cauldron of 'everything'. Things at the margin of knowledge (and not only the margin) tend to degenerate into speculation, mysticism, or stupidity. We human observers are currently limited to one location in the Universe and most of what we can see out there happened in the distant past. An absolutely fundamental assumption of science is that the laws of physics apply equally at all points across the cosmos (the *cosmological principle* - the Universe is homogenous and isotropic. See Coles (1999) p. 147 et. seq.) and this assumption does seem reasonable, but the fact remains that no-one has yet been into deep galactic or intergalactic space to find out, nor have we met (as far as I know) any beings from other planets or regions of the cosmos which can present us with comparative notes.

Information, fields and form are in a continuous state of dynamic interaction;

No matter can pre-exist or exist without consciousness, acting with intent, organizing it at some very fundamental level. This may occur by setting the general conditions or Laws of Nature within which both living and material forces must work. This does not mean that all matter, material actions and living beings are controlled or manipulated directly by a superior consciousness or 'God'. This does not mean that the primary or source consciousness can necessarily or even possibly be understood or interpreted in terms of ordinary human thought. Mirrors of its actions may perhaps be found, however, in concepts proposed by science, such as:

the will-to-be - the survival instinct, or the so-called 'selfish gene';

the *awareness of self and not* self - which is the central concept of the science of immunology[311];

the striving towards harmony and balance - for example, the orthodox medical concept of homoeostasis, and the *Gaia* hypothesis[312].

Qi (Prana) is the limitless universal energy underlying the life force.

EVOLUTION

A central dogma of our age, around which there is much ideological and theoretical struggle, is neo-Darwinism. To accept evolution as the process of development of species from primitive beginnings is not the same thing as to accept neo-Darwinism. As a theory of evolution neo-Darwinism has two central constituents: random genetic mutation (natural selection), and survival of the fittest. A random mutation causes a change in the genetic structure of an organism; if that change enhances its chances of survival by giving it an advantage over its competitors, then the organism will prosper to their detriment, and the mutation will become an evolutionary step. If it provides no advantage, it will be defunct. The

---

311. That the body can distinguish between self (that which is it) and not-self (that which is not it) and acts against that which is not-self, for example, a pathogenic microorganism.
312. Developed by James Lovelock and Lynn Margulis. 'The Gaia hypothesis proposes that all organisms and their inorganic surroundings on Earth are closely integrated to form a single and self-regulating complex system, maintaining the conditions for life on the planet. The scientific investigation of the Gaia hypothesis focuses on observing how the biosphere and the evolution of life forms contribute to the stability of global temperature, ocean salinity, oxygen in the atmosphere and other factors of habitability in a preferred homeostasis.' (Wikipedia)

organism will continue to exist but, presumably, if chance does not endow it with characteristics which work to its advantage in an evolving environment, then in the long term it will become extinct. The influence of environment, habit, and the possibility of inheritance of acquired characteristics are ruled out of the process of genetic modification. Neo-Darwinism is also, basically, value-free. There is no such thing, intrinsically, as a positive, negative, or purposeful aspect to evolution; any outcome will do. Nothing is either good, bad or necessary; there is only what exists and persists. There is only the reductionist position that *what survives wins*. The biologist Rupert Sheldrake writes:

> *'Very little is actually known or can ever be known about the details of evolution in the past. Nor is evolution readily observable in the present. Even on a timescale measured in millions of years, the origin of new species is rare, and of genera, families and orders rarer still. The evolutionary changes that have been observed mainly involve the development of new varieties or races within established species....with such scanty direct evidence, and with so little possibility of experimental tests, any interpretation of the mechanism of evolution is bound to be speculative: unconstrained by detailed facts, it will largely consist of an elaboration of its initial assumptions about the nature of inheritance and the sources of heritable variation.*
>
> *The orthodox interpretation is provided by the neo-Darwinian theory, which differs from the original Darwinian theory in two major respects: first, it denies the inheritance of habits, which Darwin accepted; it asserts that heredity is essentially genetic. Second, it assumes that the ultimate source of heritable variability is random mutations of the genetic material.'*[313]

The idea of randomness as a central actor in science has been fiercely contested; Einstein himself is credited with saying *'I cannot believe that God plays dice with the Universe.'*[314] To get an idea of what it might take to enable a new and complex animal to emerge through natural selection alone:

> *'....an important part of the adaptation of the giraffe would have been protogiraffes' copying one another in stretching towards higher*

---

313. Sheldrake (2009) p. 169 - 170.
314. This with reference to the randomness at the heart of Quantum Mechanics. Quoted in Herbert, *op. cit.*, p. 199 and in many other books.

leaves, and this would promote the selective process favouring longer-necked mutants. This still leaves a lot for natural selection to explain. The protogiraffe not only had to lengthen neck vertebrae (fixed at seven in mammals) but to make many concurrent modifications: the head, difficult to sustain atop the long neck, became relatively smaller; the circulatory system had to develop pressure to send blood higher; valves were needed to prevent overpressure when the animal lowered its head to drink; big lungs were necessary to compensate for breathing through a tube 10 feet long; many muscles, tendons, and bones had to be modified harmoniously; the forelegs were lengthened with corresponding restructuring of the frame; and many reflexes had to be reshaped. All these things had to be accomplished in step, and they must have been done rapidly because no record has been found of most of the transition. That it could have come about by synchronized random mutations strains the definition of random. The most critical question, however, is how the original impetus to giraffeness - and a million other adaptations - got started and acquired sufficient utility to have selective value.' [315]

This is from Chapter 11, *Positive Adaptation*, in which Wesson deals at length with adaptive strategies and the possibility of acquisition and inheritance of new characteristics. I suggest that one major factor appears to be stress on the organism, notably environmental stress, whether coming from the ecosphere of Nature or, by way of contemporary example, the introduction of 'unnatural' agents such as antibiotics, which, as everyone knows by now, have - at enormous speed - lead to the development of resistant and potentially untreatable strains of bacteria, which use a wide range of evolutionary and adaptive strategies to counter the threat we pose to them.

One may also think that neo-Darwinist evolution would have to have an absolutely enormous number of throws of the dice in order to achieve even part of the synchronicity of mutation that Wesson suggests is needed to produce a complex result. Given that each mutation needs to be translated into a generation (of the animal) and then, presumably, tested in the environment on a pass/fail basis, with the best will in the world one might conclude that there is actually *not enough* evolutionary-

---

315. Wesson (1997) p. 226. Not to mention the question of how instincts and drives came into existence, or the ability of birds to migrate thousands of miles, etc etc

scale time[316] to produce significant evolutionary steps by randomness alone. This notwithstanding, one can allow that, amongst many other factors, serendipity might indeed be a significant contributor to the evolutionary process.

In Radionics we propose the existence of the Etheric Body and related fields which substand the physical form. These fields are considered to act as an energetic and informational template for the physical structure, this including the DNA and genetic material. The complexity of the physical form is reflected in the hierarchical, nested nature of the subfields of the Etheric Body. Just as larger structures such as organs are composed of smaller structures such as cells, so each of these are thought to have their exact mirror in the structure of the fields in the Etheric Body. Since all of these fields also sit within the environment of all the formative fields underlying Nature, it might be thought that an evolutionary step may commence with action and response on the energetic and informational level and then translate into the physical form. What might be considered is that there is a cumulative effect at the informational and probabilistic levels which reflects in complexity and complex relationships between organism, environment and genetic structure by multifarious and diverse processes. It also may allow the possibility of reaction, adaptation and other responses being translated into rapid evolutionary and perhaps co-ordinated changes at any or all levels[317], including the psyche. As noted, the Radionic practitioner may also be able to discern compound disturbances to these relationships in

---

316. 'That protists [single-celled organisms] required at least 500 million years to achieve multicellular differentiation shows that it must have been difficult to work out.' Wesson, op. cit., p. 228. 'Work out' is the expression he uses - but neo-Darwinist evolution is to take place by random process without any objective other than survival. How is becoming *more complex* a better result (survival strategy?) than remaining less complex?

317. I commend the reader to Chapter 8 of Wesson (*op. cit.*) *'Dynamics of Evolution'*, where he goes at it hammer and tongs. Monumentally, 'The basis of life is a tangled complexity.' (p. 141) There is emphasis on the idea of attractors. 'The genome may be regarded as a set of integrated information complexes, for which one may borrow a term....from chaos theory: attractors. In mathematical terms, an attractor is a multidimensional phase space; it is a set of permitted states of a system.' (p. 144) One also needs to note the ideas of Georges Cuvier (1769 - 1832), who established that extinction of species was a fact, and proposed that catastrophic events had taken place in the earth's past. The extinction of the dinosaurs by asteroid impact is a modern version of such an event, and must be considered another, and rather abrupt, determinant of the evolutionary process.

the etheric and other fields of seriously ill persons, particularly those suffering from chronic degenerative diseases.

Rupert Sheldrake has discussed the problem of form at length:

'It is not immediately obvious that form presents any problem at all. The world around us is full of forms; we recognize them in every act of perception. But we easily forget that there is a vast gulf between this aspect of our experience....and the quantitative factors with which physics concerns itself....if a bunch of flowers is thrown into a furnace and reduced to ashes, the total amount of matter and energy remains the same, but the form of the flowers simply disappears....(If) the mere description of any but the simplest static forms presents a mathematical problem of appalling complexity, the description of the change of form - of morphogenesis - is even more difficult.'[318]

'Time after time, when atoms come into existence, electrons fill the same orbitals around the nuclei; atoms repeatedly combine to give the same molecular forms; again and again molecules combine into the same patterns; seeds of a given species give rise year after year to plants of the same appearance; generation after generation, spiders spin the same type of web. Forms come into being repeatedly, and each time each form is more or less the same as previous versions....This constancy and repetition would present no problem if changeless physical laws or principles uniquely determined all forms. This assumption is implicit in the conventional theory of the causation of form. These fundamental physical principles are taken to be temporally prior to the actual forms of things: theoretically, the way in which a newly synthesized chemical will crystallise should be calculable before its crystals appear for the first time; likewise, the effects of a given mutation in the DNA of an animal or plant on the form of the organism should be predictable in advance. But such calculations have never been made; this comfortable assumption is untested....by contrast, according to the hypothesis of formative causation [Sheldrake's theory], the known laws of physics do not uniquely determine the forms of complex chemical and biological systems. These laws permit a range of possibilities between which formative causes select. The repeated association of the same type of morphogenetic field with a given type of physico-chemical system explains the constancy and repetition of forms. But then what determines the form of the morphogenetic field?

---

318. Sheldrake, *op.cit.*, p. 73 -74

One possible answer is that morphogenetic fields are eternal. They are simply given, and not explicable in terms of anything else. Thus even before this planet appeared, there already existed in a latent state the morphogenetic fields of all the chemicals, crystals, animals and plants that have ever occurred on the Earth, or that will ever come into being in the future.

This answer is essentially Platonic....It differs from conventional physical theory in that these forms would not be predictable in terms of energetic causation; but it agrees with it in taking for granted that behind all empirical phenomena lie pre-existing principles of order.

The other possible answer is radically different. Chemical and biological forms are repeated not because they are determined by changeless laws or eternal forms, but because of a causal influence from previous similar forms. *This influence would require an action across space* and time *unlike any known type of physical action.*

In this case, what determines the form on the first occasion? No scientific answer can be given: the question concerns unique and energetically indeterminate events that, ex hypothesi, *once they have happened are unrepeatable because they themselves influence all subsequent events.'*[319]

COSMOGENESIS

Bearing the above in mind, we can take a very brief look at the problem from another angle. The origin and development of the Universe, according to astrophysics, is conventionally described by what is known as the Standard Model. The primary origination event is commonly known as the Big Bang. All of the matter in the Universe - all of everything - is concentrated into an utterly minute point - a singularity, where it exists as undifferentiated plasma possessing an absolutely and utterly stupendous amount of energy. There are no particles, atoms, matter, molecules or known structures; there is only energy concentrated into an infinitely small space.

According to Einstein, space and time, or spacetime, are the four basic dimensional properties of the physical Universe. As a consequence, one must presume that before the Big Bang there is no space and no time because nothing exists. The singularity is presumably not floating 'somewhere' in a full size but totally empty Universe. Space and time do not expand into, as it were, a colossal empty space waiting to be filled

---

319. Ibid, p. 115 -117

with the stuff of the stars and galaxies. *Empty* in the sense that there is no gravity, no other forces, no particles, no vacuum, no zero point field - no *anything*. But it is also *not empty*, in the sense that there is nothing for the emptiness *to be in*. Since there is no time, the question 'what happened before the Big Bang' is irrelevant. It can be asked, but there is no flow or framework of time for it to occur in because time is a property of a Universe which has not yet come into existence. Then, 'at some point' - if such an expression can be used - and for no known reason, the singularity explodes and the Universe begins; the titanic explosion is followed by a brief but massive expansion (inflation), time and space come into being and primary particles condense from the primal energy, all under the control of the laws of physics.[320]

Nevertheless, this does not stop the reasonable enquirer from asking numerous questions about this problem[321], such as, how did the singularity itself come about; was there anything before the singularity; and where were the Laws of Physics - as we understand them (and bearing in mind Pagels' comments at the top of Chapter 7) - before the beginning? At a point where there was no material for them to apply to, were they waiting, in a latent state, *in potentia*, for some situation in which they could be brought into play? In which case *where* is the latent state - in some proto-informational virtual continuum which is external to the singularity? If everything is 'in' the singularity then how can anything not be in it, even if it is the Laws of Physics? Or are the Laws of Physics subsections of some overarching Law, which first allows the Cosmos to originate and then provides its various components - the known Laws which produce the varied phenomena of the material Universe? Or did the Laws of Physics begin come into existence at the moment of the Big Bang, implying that they are not eternal and immutable, but the results of process? In this case, perhaps the Laws of Physics come into being as a

---

320. This model is of course being put to the test; one new approach to origination is M-Theory, although the primary problem still remains: where did the Branes come from? Two pieces of evidence which point to the Big Bang, thought to have occurred about 14 billion years ago are, first, the Cosmic Microwave Background, which is microwave radiation, detectable everywhere in the Universe, and, second, the discovery that the Universe is expanding in every direction, and the conclusion, therefore, that it must be expanding from some point. Presumably if you 'ran the movie backwards' the location of the singularity could be identified?

321. Sheldrake quotes the late Terence McKenna (1946 - 2000): '*Modern science is based on the principle: "Give us one free miracle and we'll explain the rest."* The one free miracle is the appearance of all the mass and energy in the universe and all the laws that govern it in a single instant from nothing' (*op. cit.*, p 3)

result of interaction of the 'primal stuff' and through repetition, the *'habits of Nature'* as Sheldrake calls them, acquire inviolable characteristics. Perhaps there were many Big Bangs which initially failed because a viable or sustainable balance between the initial forces did not occur and so Nature kept trying until the 'right stuff' emerged? To have developed the Standard Model is a triumph of observation and deduction; but that does not mean the inquiry is over and the mystery is solved.

EVOLUTIONARY UNIVERSE

Bearing points like this in mind, for present purposes I propose that the Universe develops from beginnings where there are absolute primitives of all that exist or can exist. They are at one and the same time absolutely primitive and, because they possess the *potential* for all things, simultaneously utterly sophisticated. They are the nodes or ultimate *attractors* around which reality forms. They may be utterly unknowable in themselves (as Jung describes the archetypes) but through their action in producing the cosmos may be identified as the source of all phenomena. Feasibly, by interpretation and observation, we may find their reflection in us. Through our ability to perceive them working in Nature we might develop concepts of what they may be. This in turn may have some scientific applications, for example, in that the form and qualities of possible extraterrestrial life might be predicted. Such a source might underlie all manifestations of the Universe, in the sense that the present Universe might be one in a series, or one of many in parallel, or even one in a hierarchy of Universes. However many there are, they have to begin or have their origin somewhere or with something, or even with *no thing*.

In this book I have considered a range of concepts which Radionics might use. Some of these are proposed to be qualities conditioning the character of the entirety of manifestation, such as the Rays. Other concepts include a structure of the subjective realms of consciousness - the Planes; and the proposal that the objective, material world originates in the realm of consciousness which acts through formative forces. Furthermore I suggest that the physical bodies of living beings, including humans, have their exact counterpart in a living energy field. This field, denoted the Etheric Plane, is the focal point of all the formative forces and energies of consciousness proposed by esoteric science. The function of the etheric body is to produce and condition the living physical body via the multiple focal points of the Chakra system. The living material being is only the immediate manifestation of all the underlying processes which combine to bring about the human. The human form provides a physical vehicle through which the nascent essence of consciousness which *is* each human being may continue its evolution. Evolution as basically understood by science is part of this process, but in humans at least, an acceleration of evolution may be possible, as the higher self of each progressively starts to act on the personality. Dion Fortune states:

'The esotericist does not limit himself by declaring the Unknown to be the Unknowable, for he is above all things an evolutionist, and knows that that which we cannot compass to-day we may achieve in the to-morrow of cosmic time. He knows, too, that evolutionary time is an individual matter upon the inner planes, and is measured, not regulated, by the revolution of the earth upon its axis.'[322]

To reiterate, Radionics is not here to prove or disprove any particular philosophical, scientific or metaphysical proposition. It is here to be applied, first and foremost, in the healing endeavour, in the sincere effort to relieve suffering and lift the human spirit. But, because of its nature, methodology, concepts and means of action, it calls into question ideas which are conventionally accepted about the world. As a result, it also becomes a means of research and inquiry through which anyone who wishes to exercise mind and intuition may venture forth into the little-known empire of the inmost reality.

---

322. Fortune, op. cit., § 9, p 33

APPENDIX 1: SUBTLE BODY LOCATIONS FOR THE PURPOSE OF RADIONIC ANALYSIS

As described the Human Subtle Energy field can be subdivided into a number of Locations for the purpose of analysis. The separation of the fields into discrete units should not delude the reader that they *are* discrete entities, factually and actually separate from each other as if they were unrelated objects on a table or specimens of unrelated materials in test tubes. This outline is an aid to comprehension; the human system should be understood as an integrated system, with a definite direction of causality driving it.

Appendix 1 gives the Locations in the Subtle Bodies proper and Appendix 2 gives the Locations in the Paraphysical Counterparts to the Physical organism.

Appendix 1 shows 13 main Locations (left column) and 31 subdivisions (centre column). For the present, Etheric Pre-Physical is treated as one Location; likewise the 39 Bindu points, the 14 External and 39 Internal Meridians, and the 12 Rays. There are, of course, more than 39 Bindu points but these are the ones central to the treatment effort.

In addition the Morphic Fields of the Etheric Body are treated as an integral, since all the Morphic Fields of the entire system may be affected together, to a greater or lesser extent, by some disturbing Factor. It is more typical in treatment to deal with individual Physical-Morphic fields (e.g. Gastro-Intestinal Tract) although in some cases a more-or-less systemic disturbance of the Morphic Fields may demand a therapeutic response. In a further appendix the Morphic Fields are broken down into various general subdivisions corresponding to the Physical Body structures they energise.

The right-hand column, Quality, serves as a basic reminder as to the Function of the Locations and their Subdivisions:

LOCATION	SUBDIVISION	QUALITY
ATMIC BODY		SOUL QUALITY
BUDDHIC BODY		HIGHER INTUITION
CAUSAL BODY		HIGHER EGO; HIGHER PURPOSE;
MENTAL BODY	MENTAL - INTELLECTUAL; MENTAL - PSYCHOLOGICAL	MIND; INTELLECTUAL, RATIONAL AND PSYCHOLOGICAL PROCESSES
ASTRAL BODY	ASTRAL BODY 7 ASTRAL BODY 6 ASTRAL BODY 5 ASTRAL BODY 4 ASTRAL BODY 3 ASTRAL BODY 2 ASTRAL BODY 1 ASTRAL BODY CORE TO 8; ASTRAL BODY, 8 TO CORE	EMOTIONS, FEELINGS, SENSATIONS; EMOTIONAL QUALITY & FEELING-SENSATION (FEELING-TONED) QUALITY OF BOTH LIVING HUMANS, OTHER ORGANISMS & OBJECTS
ETHERIC BODY	ETHERIC PRE-PHYSICAL (7 STAGES); ETHERIC BODY; MORPHIC FIELDS	ORGANIZATION & ENERGIZATION OF THE PHYSICAL FORM, MEDIATED THROUGH THE CHAKRAS
CHAKRAS	CROWN:	SUMMATION OF THE INDIVIDUAL, SEAT OF HIGHEST AWARENESS;
	SOUL SEAT:	INTEGRATION OF TRANSPERSONAL SELF WITH PERSONALITY ASPECT;
	BROW:	PERSONALITY;
	ALTA MAJOR:	TIMING & CO-ORDINATION OF PHYSICAL PROCESSES; AUTONOMIC PROCESSES

	THROAT:	CREATIVE EXPRESSION OF SELF;
	HEART:	COMPASSION & SELFLESS LOVE;
	SOLAR PLEXUS:	GROUP INTERCONNECTEDNESS &INTERCONNECTION WITH NATURE; DESIRES &INSTINCTS;
	SACRAL:	PHYSICAL CREATIVE PROCESS; REPRODUCTION;
	BASE:	WILL-TO-BE; SELF & SELF-PRESERVATION
SPLEEN CHAKRA	PRANIC TRIANGLE	RECEPTION & DISTRIBUTION OF PRANIC ENERGIES
BINDU POINTS	1 - 39	TRANSDUCTION OF ORGANIZATIONAL FORCES & ENERGIES VIA CHAKRAS
NADIS		INTEGRATION OF CHAKRA ENERGY WITH PHYSICAL FORMS AND SYSTEMS
MERIDIANS	EXTERNAL MERIDIANS 1 - 14; COLLATERAL MERIDIANS; INTERIOR MERIDIANS 1 - 39; INTERIOR COLLATERAL MERIDIANS	TIME, TIDES & QUALITIES OF ENERGIES AFFECTING ORGANS & SUBSTRUCTURES OF PHYSICAL BODY
AURA	AURIC ENERGISATION CYCLE	PRESENCE & CHARISMA
RAYS	1 - 12	FUNDAMENTAL QUALITIES UNDERLYING MANIFESTATION

APPENDIX 2: PARAPHYSICAL BODY LOCATIONS FOR THE PURPOSE OF RADIONIC ANALYSIS

The Morphic Fields of the Etheric Body may be considered to be regions of an integral, the *Physical-Morphic Body*. Thus there is a cascade of nested fields. The Etheric Body 'contains' the Physical-Morphic Body; and this, in turn, 'contains' the counterpart fields of the physical anatomy.

In this Appendix 2 the Physical-Morphic Body is broken down into various general subdivisions corresponding to the Physical Body structures. These may be denoted the *structural counterpart fields*, or (as applicable) *organ counterpart fields*. It is more typical in analysis and treatment to deal with individual counterpart fields (e.g. Gastro-Intestinal Tract), but in some cases a more-or-less systemic treatment of the Physical-Morphic Body as a totality may be required. In advanced, advancing or systemic disease states - cancer, for example - the whole Physical-Morphic Body may be affected in some way.

An underlying assumption is that the sub-fields of a particular Location are in a nested, or vertical, hierarchy. An example is the Gastro-Intestinal Tract, which here is broken down to 8 sub-fields. Each sub-field in turn, will contain the fields which correspond to the details of its local micro-anatomy, e.g. villi (small intestine); goblet cells (stomach etc); subdivisions of the colon (ascending, transverse, descending), and so on.

Apart from the vertical correspondences, there are also horizontal correspondences; cells, for example, are common to the entire anatomy. It should be remembered that there is nothing to stop further micro-analysis and treatment of microstructures if appropriate Codes are available. However, this moves away from the holistic bias of Radionics, and in general

The right-hand column, Quality, serves as a basic reminder as to the basic role of the Locations and their Subdivisions:

LOCATION	SUBDIVISION	BASIC FUNCTION
PHYSICAL-MORPHIC BODY		THE SUM TOTAL OF THE STRUCTURAL COUNTERPART FIELDS
SENSORIUM	VISUAL SYSTEM AUDITORY SYSTEM VESTIBULAR SYSTEM SENSES & RECEPTORS	CONTACT WITH THE EXTERNAL & INTERNAL ENVIRONMENTS
NERVOUS SYSTEM	CENTRAL NERVOUS LIMBIC SPINAL CORD AUTONOMIC SYMPATHETIC PARASYMPATHETIC SENSORY (PERIPHERAL) MOTOR (PERIPHERAL) HYPOTHALAMUS	RECEPTION, PROCESSING & TRANSMISSION OF VOLUNTARY & INVOLUNTARY NERVOUS SIGNALS; RECEPTION, PROCESSING OF PERCEPTIONS RECEIVED FROM HIGHER SUBTLE BODIES; PRODUCTION OF 'NORMAL' CONSCIOUSNESS (MIND & EMOTIONS)
ENDOCRINE SYSTEM	PINEAL GLAND PITUITARY GLAND THYROID GLAND PARATHYROID GLAND ADRENAL GLANDS; OTHER HORMONE-PRODUCING TISSUE	PRODUCTION & RECEPTION OF SIGNALS USING HORMONES
GASTRO-INTESTINAL TRACT	MOUTH TEETH	INGESTION, DIGESTION &

	OESOPHAGUS STOMACH DUODENUM SMALL INTESTINE COLON RECTUM	ASSIMILATION OF NUTRIENTS & ELIMINATION OF WASTE
ABDOMINAL VISCERA	PANCREAS LIVER GALL BLADDER BILE DUCT KIDNEYS	FUNCTIONS RELATED TO DIGESTION & ASSIMILATION OF NUTRIENTS; PRODUCTION OF ENZYMES, CATALYSTS, ETC; ELIMINATION OF WASTE
CARDIO-VASCULAR SYSTEM	PULMONARY CIRCULATION SYSTEMIC CIRCULATION HEART ARTERIES VEINS CAPILLARIES	CIRCULATION OF BLOOD
RESPIRATORY SYSTEM	SINUSES & AIRWAYS LARYNX & TRACHEA BRONCHI LUNGS	OXYGEN PROCESS
SKELETAL SYSTEM	SPINAL COLUMN BONE & CARTILAGE JOINTS & ARTICULATIONS TENDONS & LIGAMENTS	SUPPORT & STRUCTURE
CONNECTIVE TISSUE		SUPPORT & STRUCTURE
MUSCULAR SYSTEM	VALVES & SPHINCTERS CONNECTIVE TISSUE	MOVEMENT & STRUCTURE

IMMUNE SYSTEM	IMMUNE CELLS - ALL BONE MARROW THYMUS SPLEEN	DEFENCE
LYMPHATIC SYSTEM		DEFENCE & ELIMINATION
BLOOD		TRANSPORT
FLUIDS		PROTECTION & ELIMINATION
SKIN		PROTECTION
EXOCRINE GLANDS		PRODUCTION, MAINTENANCE & REMOVAL
URINARY TRACT	URINARY BLADDER	ELIMINATION
REPRODUCTIVE SYSTEM (F)	OVARIES FALLOPIAN TUBES UTERUS & CERVIX GENITALS MAMMARY GLANDS	
REPRODUCTIVE SYSTEM (M)	TESTES PROSTATE GLAND GENITALS	
CELLS & CELLULAR REPRODUCTION	CELLS STEM CELLS CELL MEMORY DNA RNA CHROMOSOMES	BASIC UNIT OF PHYSICAL FORM
TISSUES		GROUPS OF CELLS PERFORMING SPECIFIC FUNCTIONS

APPENDIX 3: FACTORS GROUPED INTO TWELVE CATEGORIES

CATEGORY	FACTORS
1. **FLOW**	CONGESTION; OVERSTIMULATION; UNCO-ORDINATION; CO-ORDINATION BETWEEN; TIME-BASED CYCLES & FUNCTIONS
2. **STRUCTURE & INTEGRITY**	DAMAGE; DISTORTION; DISLOCATION; CLEAVAGE; INTEGRITY (VARIOUS SUB-CATEGORIES), PHASE, ANGLE
3. **PATHOLOGICAL INHIBITION**	a. CLASSICAL MIASMS: PSORA; SYCOSIS; SYPHILIS; TUBERCULOSIS; CANCER b. ACUTE MIASMS & SEQUELAE: ACUTE INFECTIOUS & EPIDEMIC DISEASES AND THEIR AFTER-EFFECTS c. ENVIRONMENTAL MIASMS: PETROCHEMICAL; HEAVY METAL; RADIATION; STELLAR d. DERIVED INDIVIDUAL MIASMS: ARTICULATED MIASM, WHICH MAY TYPICALLY INCLUDE SPECIFIC DISEASE FORMS DESCRIBED BY ORTHODOX MEDICINE, CONSIDERED AS NEGATIVE ENERGETIC PRINCIPLES
4. **POLLUTION**	POISONS, TOXINS, TOXAEMIA
5. **INVASION**	BACTERIA; VIRUSES & RETROVIRUSES; PARASITES & PROTOZOA; FUNGAL; OTHER INFECTIOUS ORGANISMS; INFECTION - MULTIPLE; INFESTATION
6. **REACTION**	a. *DEFENSIVE*: INFLAMMATION; AUTO-IMMUNE RESPONSE; AUTO-INTOXICATION; NON-LIVING DEPOSITS b. *AUTO-GENERATED*: ALLERGY; FOOD

	INTOLERANCE; MALABSORPTION; NON-LIVING DEPOSITS; HYPERSENSITIVITY - CHEMICAL; HYPERSENSITIVITY (SPECIFIC LOCATION); HYPERSENSIBILITY
7. **MORBID**	MALIGNANCY; TUMOURS & NEOPLASMS; CANCER
8. **STRESSORS - RELATIONAL & EXTERNAL**	a. *RELATIONAL*: FUNCTIONAL; PSYCHOLOGICAL; EMOTIONAL; PSYCHOSOMATIC; SHOCK; REACTIVE RELATIONSHIP; PREGNANCY b. *EXTERNAL*: ENVIRONMENTAL, ELECTROMAGNETIC, GEOPATHIC, IATROGENIC, VACCINATION
9. **DEPLETION & IMBALANCE**	NUTRITIONAL DEFICIENCY; VITAMIN & MINERAL DEFICIENCY; ENZYME & CATALYST DEFICIENCY; OTHER DEFICIENCY; HORMONE IMBALANCE; ELECTROLYTE IMBALANCE; ACID-BASE; DEHYDRATION; MALABSORBTION
10. **MORTAL , ACUTE & SUB-ACUTE**	(for example) ABSCESS; ADDICTION; ADHESIONS; ANEURYSM; CYST; EMBOLISM; FISTULA; FRACTURE; HAEMORRHAGE; HERNIA; HIATUS HERNIA; OEDEMA; PERFORATION; PROLAPSE; SCAR TISSUE; SCLEROSIS; SPASM; THROMBOSIS; ULCER
11. **OCCULT**	PSYCHIC INTERFERENCE; PSYCHIC ATTACK; ACTIVATED SHELL; POSSESSION; BLACK MAGIC ATTACK
12. **TRANSITIONAL**	ASTROLOGICAL DISTURBANCE; HEALING AGGRAVATION; KARMIC CAUSATION; IRREVERSIBLE PATHOLOGY; DEATH APPARENT

APPENDIX 4: INTEGRITY - LOCATIONS

This special category concerns the quality and calibre of linkages between the various fields, Locations and structures of the Subtle Anatomy.

LOCATION	SUB-LOCATIONS
PRANIC TRIANGLE	
PRANIC TRIANGLE - ETHERIC BODY	
CHAKRA - GLAND INTEGRITY	(*basically and subject to further clarification*) CROWN CHAKRA - PINEAL BROW CHAKRA - PITUITARY GLAND THROAT CHAKRA - THYROID GLAND HEART CHAKRA - THYMUS SOLAR PLEXUS CHAKRA - PANCREAS SACRAL CHAKRA - GONADS BASE CHAKRA - PARATHYROID GLANDS BASE CHAKRA - ADRENALS
CHAKRA - NADI INTEGRITY	NADIS EMANATE FROM ALL MAJOR CHAKRAS AND INTERCONNECT WITH THE PHYSICAL NERVOUS SYSTEM
CHAKRA - SUBTLE BODY INTEGRITY	• CHAKRAS INTERFACE WITH EACH OF THE PLANES FROM WHICH THE SUBTLE BODIES ARE DERIVED. • LEVELS OF CONSCIOUSNESS FOUND ON EACH PLANE OR SUBPLANE ARE AVAILABLE TO THE INDIVIDUAL ACCORDING TO THE ABILITY TO RECEIVE, UNDERSTAND AND PROCESS THEM. • ACCESS TO THESE VARIOUS LEVELS OF CONSCIOUSNESS IS GAINED THROUGH THE MAJOR CHAKRAS. • EACH OF THE MAJOR CHAKRAS WILL INTERFACE APPROPRIATELY WITH THE RELATED SUBTLE BODY. • FOR EXAMPLE, THE ASTRAL PLANE WILL (TO VARYING DEGREES IN EACH INDIVIDUAL) CONNECT TO THE CROWN, BROW, HEART, THROAT,

	SOLAR PLEXUS AND OTHER MAJOR CHAKRAS.
	• THESE IN TURN WILL INTERCONNECT WITH THE ASTRAL BODY.
	• SIMILAR RELATIONSHIPS EXIST BETWEEN THE OTHER PLANES, e.g., ATMIC, BUDDHIC, MENTAL AND THE MAJOR CHAKRAS AND THE OTHER SUBTLE BODIES.
ETHERIC BODY - PHYSICAL BODY INTEGRITY	THE ETHERIC BODY AND ITS SUBSTRUCTURES - THE PHYSICAL-MORPHIC AND PARAPHYSICAL STRUCTURAL COUNTERPART FIELDS - MUST INTEGRATE CORRECTLY WITH THE PHYSICAL BODY PROPER
SUBTLE BODY INTERFACE POINTS	A COMPLEX OF LINKAGES WHICH INTEGRATE THE SUBTLE BODIES ONE TO THE OTHER RESULTING IN AN ALIGNED AND CO-ORDINATED SYSTEM. For example, THE MENTAL BODY MUST INTEGRATE WITH THE ASTRAL BODY AND ETHERIC BODY CORRECTLY, and so on.

BIBLIOGAPHY

Abrams, Albert 1916: *NEW CONCEPTS IN DIAGNOSIS AND TREATMENT* reprinted by Borderland Sciences, www.borderlands.com

Archdale, F.A. 1966: *ELEMENTARY RADIESTHESIA AND THE USE OF THE PENDULUM* The Society of Dowsers

Avalon, Arthur (Sir John Woodroffe) 1958: *THE SERPENT POWER THE SECRETS OF TANTRIC AND SHAKTIC YOGA* Dover Publications Inc., New York, NY 10014, USA ISBN 0-486-23058-9

Backster, Cleve (2003): *PRIMARY PERCEPTION* White Rose Press ISBN-13: 978-0966435436

Bailey, Alice 1953: *ESOTERIC HEALING* LUCIS PRESS Ltd, London SW1A 2EF   ISBN 0-85330-121-2

Bailey, Alice 1951 (first printing 1925): *A TREATISE ON COSMIC FIRE* LUCIS PRESS Ltd, London SW1A 2EF   ISBN 0-85330-117-4

Barrett, Sir William and Besterman, Theodore 1926: *THE DIVINING ROD AN EXPERIMENTAL AND PSYCHOLOGICAL INVESTIGATION* Methuen & Co, London WC, UK

Beal, James: *ORGANISM SENSITIVITIES TO ELECTRIC AND MAGNETIC FIELDS: PROPOSED INTERACTING BIOSYSTEM MECHANISMS* published by James B. Beal, PO Box 2112, Wimberley, TX www.emfinterface.com

Bhattacharyya, Benoytosh 1988: *THE SCIENCE OF COSMIC RAY THERAPY OR TELETHERAPY THEORY AND PRACTICE* Firma KLM Private Ltd, Calcutta, India

Bird, Christopher 1993: *THE DIVINING HAND: THE 500-YEAR OLD MYSTERY OF DOWSING* Whitford Press, USA ISBN 0924608161

Bohm, David 1957: *CAUSALITY & CHANCE IN MODERN PHYSICS*, University of Pennsylvania Press, Philadelphia, 19104-4011 USA   ISBN 0-8122-1002-6

Bohm, David 1980: *WHOLENESS AND THE IMPLICATE ORDER* Routledge, London EC4P 4EE ISBN 0-415-11966-9

Burr, Harold Saxton 1972: *BLUEPRINT FOR IMMORTALITY THE ELECTRIC PATTERNS OF LIFE* C W Daniel Company Limited, Saffron Walden, Essex, UK   SBN 85435-281-3

Campbell, Joseph 1968: *THE HERO WITH A THOUSAND FACES* Princeton University Press, Princeton, NJ, USA ISBN 0-691-01784-0

Coles, Peter 1998: *THE ICON CRITICAL DICTIONARY OF THE NEW COSMOLOGY* Icon Books Ltd., Cambridge CB2 4QF, UK   ISBN 1-874166-64-1

Coyle, James F. 2010: *BEYOND BELIEF* Vivid Publishing, Fremantle, WA 6959, Australia ISBN 9781921787171

Cumbey, Constance 1985: *THE HIDDEN DANGERS OF THE RAINBOW THE NEW AGE MOVEMENT AND OUR COMING AGE OF BARBARISM* Huntington House Inc., US   ISBN-13: 978-0910311038

Darwin, Charles 1985: *THE ORIGIN OF SPECIES* Penguin Books, London W8 5TZ, UK ISBN 0-14-043205-1

DeMeo, James 1989: *THE ORGONE ACCUMULATOR HANDBOOK* Natural Energy Works, Oregon 97520, USA ISBN 0-9621855-0-7

Dennett, Daniel C. 1995: DARWIN'S *DANGEROUS IDEA EVOLUTION AND THE MEANINGS OF LIFE* Penguin Books, London W8 5TZ, UK ISBN 0-14-016734-X

Dormandy, Thomas 1998: *THE WHITE DEATH: A HISTORY OF TUBERCULOSIS* The Hambledon Press, NW1 8HZ, UK ISBN 1-85285-169-4

Drown, Ruth B. 1982: *THE THEORY AND TECHNIQUE OF THE DROWN RADIO THERAPY AND RADIO-VISION INSTRUMENTS* distributed in the UK by R.M. Denning, Surrey GU15 2NX, UK ISBN 0-9507861-1-X

Fest, Joachim C: *THE FACE OF THE THIRD REICH* Penguin Books, London W8 5TZ, UK ISBN 0-14-016694-7

Freud, Sigmund edited by Philips, Adam 2006: *THE PENGUIN FREUD READER* Penguin Books, London W8 5TZ, UK ISBN 0-141-18743-3

Fortune, Dion 1935: *THE MYSTICAL QABALAH* Aquarian Press, London W6 8JB ISBN 0-85030-355-4

Gerrard, Don 1990: *THE PAPER DOCTOR A VIBRATIONAL MEDICINE CABINET* ISBN 0-9629704-1-7

Gleick, James 1998: *CHAOS THE AMAZING SCIENCE OF THE UNPREDICTABLE* Vintage, London SW1V 2SA, UK ISBN 9780749386061

Gribbin, John 2000: *Q IS FOR QUANTUM AN ENCYCLOPEDIA OF QUANTUM PHYSICS* Touchstone, New York, NY 10020, USA ISBN-13: 978-0-684-85578-3

Gurudas 1985: *GEM ELIXIRS AND VIBRATIONAL HEALING Vol I* Cassandra Press, San Rafael, California 94915, USA ISBN 0-961-58750-4

Gurudas 1986: *GEM ELIXIRS AND VIBRATIONAL HEALING Vol II* Cassandra Press, San Rafael, California 94915, USA ISBN 0-961-58751-2

Hahnemann, Samuel, edited by Wenda Brewster O'Reilly 2001: *THE ORGANON OF THE MEDICAL ART* Birdcage Books, Washington 98073-2289 USA ISBN 1-889613-01-0

Hahnemann, Samuel 1993: *THE CHRONIC DISEASES* B. Jain Pvt. Ltd, Delhi 110 055 India ISBN 81-7021-016-X

Herbert, Nick 1985: *QUANTUM REALITY BEYOND THE NEW PHYSICS AN EXCURSION INTO METAPHYSICS AND THE MEANING OF REALITY* Doubleday, New York 10036 USA ISBN 0-385-23569-0

Holland, Tom 2003: *RUBICON THE TRIUMPH AND TRAGEDY OF THE ROMAN REPUBLIC* Abacus, London WC2E 7EN ISBN 0-349-11563-X

Huxley, Aldous 1954: *THE DOORS OF PERCEPTION* Penguin Books Ltd, Middlesex, UK ISBN 0140013512

Jahn, Robert G. And Dunne, Brenda J. 2011: *CONSCIOUSNESS AND THE SOURCE OF REALITY* ICRL Press, Princeton, NJ 08540-3530 ISBN 1-936033-03-8

Jawer, Michael A. with Micozzi, Marc S. 2009: *THE SPIRITUAL ANATOMY OF EMOTION* Park Street Press, Rochester, Vermont 05767, USA ISBN 978-1-59477-288-7

Jung, Carl G. 1995: *MEMORIES, DREAMS, REFLECTIONS* Fontana Press, London W6 8JB ISBN 0-00-654027-9

Jung, Carl G. 2009: *ON THE NATURE OF THE PSYCHE* Routledge, Abingdon OX14 4RN, UK   ISBN 0-415-25391-8

Jung, Carl G. 2009: *THE ARCHETYPES AND THE COLLECTIVE UNCONSCIOUS* Routledge, East Sussex BN3 2FA ISBN 978-0-415-05844-5

Jung, Carl G. Introduced by Storr, Anthony 1983: *THE ESSENTIAL JUNG SELECTED WRITINGS* Princeton University Press, Princeton, NJ, USA ISBN 0-691-08615-X

Jung, Carl G. 1973: *SYNCHRONICITY AN ACAUSAL CONNECTING PRINCIPLE* Princeton University Press, Princeton, NJ, USA ISBN 0-691-01794-8

Jung, Carl G. and Pauli, Wolfgang edited by C.A. Meier 2011: *ATOM AND ARCHETYPE THE PAULI-JUNG LETTERS 1932-1958* Routledge, East Sussex BN3 2FA, UK ISBN 978-0-415-12078-4

Kilner, Walter J. 1965: *THE HUMAN AURA* University Books Inc., N.J. 07094, USA ISBN 0-8065-0545-1

Kostro, Ludwik 2000: *EINSTEIN AND THE ETHER* Apeirion, Quebec H2W 2B2, Canada   ISBN 0-968-3689-4-8

Kuhn, Thomas S. 1996: *THE STRUCTURE OF SCIENTIFIC* REVOLUTIONS University of Chicago Press ISBN 0226458083

Laurie, Duncan 2009: *THE SECRET ART A BRIEF HISTORY OF RADIONIC TECHNOLOGY FOR THE CREATIVE INDIVIDUAL* Anomalist Books, San Antonio, TX 78209, USA   ISBN 1933665424

Lipton, Bruce H. 2008: *THE BIOLOGY OF BELIEF* Hay House Inc., USA ISBN 978-1-4019-2312-9

MacIvor, Virginia and LaForest, Sandra 1979: *VIBRATIONS HEALING THROUGH COLOR HOMEOPATHY AND RADIONICS* Samuel Weiser Inc., Maine 03910, USA ISBN 0-87728-393-1

Maslow, Abraham H. 1999: *TOWARDS A PSYCHOLOGY OF BEING* John Wiley & Sons, NY 10158-0012, USA ISBN 0-471-29309-1

Maury, Marguerite 2008: *HOW TO DOWSE - EXPERIMENTAL AND PRACTICAL RADIESTHESIA* ISBN 978-1-44377-286-0

McTaggart, Lynne 2001: *THE FIELD THE QUEST FOR THE SECRET FORCE OF THE UNIVERSE* HarperCollins Publishers, London W6 8JB ISBN 0-7225-3764-6

Mermet, Abbé translated from the French by Mark Clement 1959: *PRINCIPLES AND PRACTICE OF RADIESTHESIA* Vincent Stuart Publishers Ltd, London W1, UK

Merz, Blanche 1995: *POINTS OF COSMIC ENERGY* C W Daniel Company Limited, Essex CB10 1JP   ISBN 0-85207-194-9

Oschmann, James L. 2000: *ENERGY MEDICINE THE SCIENTIFIC BASIS* Churchill Livingstone, a division of Elsevier, Philadelphia, USA   ISBN 978-0-443-06261-2

OXFORD DICTIONARY OF MEDICINES, 2000: Oxford University Press, Oxford OX2 6DP, UK   ISBN 0-19-280059-0

OXFORD REFERENCE CONCISE MEDICAL DICTIONARY, 1994: Oxford University Press, Oxford OX2 6DP, UK   ISBN 0-19-280001-9

Pagels, Heinz R. 1983: *THE COSMIC CODE* Michael Joseph Ltd., London WC1, UK ISBN 0-7181-22178-8

Pauwels, Louis and Berger, Jacques 2001: *THE MORNING OF THE MAGICIANS* Souvenir Press Ltd., Great Russell Street, London WC1B 3PA ISBN 978 0 285 63583 8

Reyner, J H 2001: *PSIONIC MEDICINE* C W Daniel Company Limited, Essex CB10 1JP ISBN 0-85207-342-9

Rose, Dr. Barry 1992: *THE FAMILY HEALTH GUIDE TO HOMOEOPATHY* Dragon's World Ltd, Surrey RH8 0DY, UK ISBN 1-85028-164-5

Sahni, Dr. B. 1992: *TRANSMISSION OF HOMOEO DRUG ENERGY FROM A DISTANCE* B. Jain Publishers Pvt. Ltd., New Delhi-11005, India ISBN 81-7021-135-2

Sankaran, Dr. Rajan 1994: *THE SUBSTANCE OF HOMOEOPATHY* Homoeopathic Medical Publishers Bombay 400 054, India

Saraydarian, Toro 1990: *OTHER WORLDS* TSG Publishing Foundation Inc., AZ 85327, USA ISBN 0-929874-05-6

Scofield, Tony 2003: *HORIZONS OF RADIONICS* Trencavel Press, Kent CT20 2JT ISBN 0-6545786-0-0

Sharamon, Shalila and Baginski, Bodo J. 1991: *THE CHAKRA HANDBOOK* Lotus Light Publications, WI 53192, USA ISBN 0-941524-85-X

Sheldrake, Dr. Rupert 2009: *A NEW SCIENCE OF LIFE* Icon Books Ltd, London N7 9DP, UK ISBN:978-184831-042-1

Sheldrake, Dr. Rupert 2012: *THE SCIENCE DELUSION* Hodder & Stoughton Ltd, 338 Euston Road, London NW1 3BH ISBN 978-1 444 72795 1

Stapledon, Olaf 1937: *STAR MAKER* Victor Gollancz Books, Orion House, 5 Upper St Martin's Lane, London WC2H 9EA

Steiger, Brad 2007: *SHADOW WORLD TRUE ENCOUNTERS WITH BEINGS FROM THE DARKSIDE*, Anomalist Books, San Antonio, Texas 78209, USA ISBN 1933665270

Stevens, Anthony 2001: *JUNG A VERY SHORT INTRODUCTION* Oxford University Press, Oxford OX2 6DP, UK ISBN 978-0-19-285458-2

Susskind, Leonard 2008: *THE BLACK HOLE WAR MY BATTLE WITH STEPHEN HAWKING TO MAKE THE WORLD SAFE FOR QUANTUM MECHANICS* Back Bay Books, New York, NY 10017 ISBN 978-0-316-01641-4

Talbot, Michael 1996: *THE HOLOGRAPHIC UNIVERSE* HarperCollins Publishers, London W6 8JB ISBN 0-586-09171-8

Tomlinson, H. 1958: *THE DIVINATION OF DISEASE A STUDY IN RADIESTHESIA* Health Science Press, Hindhead, Surrey, UK

Tansley, David 1984: *CHAKRAS RAYS AND RADIONICS* C W Daniel Company Limited, Essex CB10 1JP ISBN 0 85207 161 2

Tansley, David (in collaboration with Malcolm Rae and Aubrey T. Westlake) 1992: *DIMENSIONS OF RADIONICS* Brotherhood of Life, Inc., Albuquerque, NM87106, USA

Tansley, David 1972: *RADIONICS AND THE SUBTLE ANATOMY OF MAN* C W Daniel Company Limited, Saffron Walden, Essex, UK ISBN 0-85032-089-5

Tansley David 1975: *RADIONICS INTERFACE WITH THE ETHER FIELDS* C W Daniel Company Limited, Saffron Walden, Essex, UK   ISBN0-85032-129-8

Tzu, Lao 1963: *TAO TE CHING* Penguin Books Ltd Middlesex England ISBN 0-14-044131-X

THE MERCK MANUAL, SIXTEENTH EDITION, 1992 MERCK & CO., Inc., Rahway, N.J. USA   ISBN 0911910-16-6

Vermeulen, Frans 1996: *SYNOPTIC MATERIA MEDICA II*, Merlin Publishers, 2023 WE Harlem, Netherlands ISBN 90800845-9-X

Wachsmuth, Gunter 1932: *THE ETHERIC FORMATIVE FORCES IN COSMOS, EARTH AND MAN* Anthroposophic Press, New York

Watkins, Alfred 1925: *THE OLD STRAIGHT TRACK*

Wesson, Robert 1997: *BEYOND NATURAL SELECTION*, MIT Press, Cambridge, Massachusetts, USA   ISBN 0-262-73102-9

Wethered, Vernon D. 1987: *AN INTRODUCTION TO MEDICAL RADIESTHESIA AND RADIONICS* C W Daniel Company Limited, Saffron Walden, Essex CB10 1JP, UK   SBN 85207-109-4

Zukav, Gary 1979 : *THE DANCING WU LI MASTERS* Rider and Co/Hutchinson and Co (Publishers)

INDEX

instruments, Radionics without, 275
INTEGRITY, 165
Intellect, 109
Intelligent Design, 120
intention and methods in healing, 273
Interaction of cosmic rays with local fields, 185
interference patterns, 48, 185
Intuition, Higher and 'Instinct', 108
INVASION, 168
Inverse-Square Law, 4
irreversible pathology, 19
IRREVERSIBLE PATHOLOGY, 203
ISOMORPHS, 270
Itchycoo Park, 166
Jahn and Dunne, 4, 21
Jawer and Micozzi, 12
Jeremiah 1:11, 56
Josephson, Professor Brian D., 298
Joyce, James, Finnegan's Wake, 59
Jung
Jung, Carl, 45
Jung adaption of homoeostasis to concepts of
    psychology, 49
Jung Archetypes, Theory of, 50
Jung, archetypes as the bridge to matter, 50
Jung, Carl, 120
Jung, Carl, 9, 50, 57, 59, 67, 86, 109, 110, 114,
    119
Jung, Carl, 120
Jung, Carl and objective of alchemy, 51
Jung, Carl and the materialist hypothesis, 121
Jung, Carl and unconscious mediated by
    archetypes, 133
Jung, Carl, and individuation, 91
Jung, Carl, archetypes, definition, 111
Jung, Carl, complexes, 271
Jung, origins of neurosis, 226
Jungian psychology and the shadow, 202
kama-manas, 114
karma, concept in vogue in the West, 203
KARMIC CAUSATION, 202
key to manifestation, 301
Kilner, Aura case history, 155
Kilner, Dr Walter, and the Aura, 154
King Crimson, 24
Kirlian, Semyon Davidovich and
    Khrisanovna,Valentina, 28
Kostro, Ludwik, 305
Kuhn, Thomas S.
The Structure of Scientific Revolutions, 60
Kundalini, 88
Lakhovsky, Georges, 170
Lakhovsky, Georges, soil and cancer, 185
language
as a primary means of expression of contents of
    consciousness, 59

Language as a coding system, 6
Lao Tzu, 108, 309
Lao-Tzu describes the process of manifestation,
    139
Laurie, Duncan, 35
Laws of Gravity, analogy with, 145
Leibniz,Monads of, 51
Lethbridge
T.C., 24, 26
life force, 66
life force, repair of as objective of Radionics
    according to Tansley, 83
life force, specific quantum of, 11
Lipton, Bruce Ph.D., 150
list,dowsing in a list, 76
Location - Factor system proposed by Malcolm
    Rae, 14
Location-Factor combinations, some sample, 253
Location-Factor disturbances, need for large
    range of, 255
LOCATIONS, definition, 230
Lord Rees, former President of the Royal Society
    and Astronomer Royal
comments on nature of the Universe, 85
LRI Analysis Chart 1, 77
LRI instrument and use of Analysis Chart 1, 77
Luciferian-Illuminati world conspiracy and Alice
    Bailey, 100
luck, 67
Luminiferous Aether', 116
MacIvor and Laforest, 196
Magneto-Geometric Applications, 7
Magneto-Geometric cards, three examples, 285
Magneto-Geometry, 14
MALABSORPTION, 172
MALABSORPTION, 191
Malcolm Rae, 20
Malcolm Rae visited by Soviet delegation, 29
Man, in essential essence
according to Bailey, 86
Mantra as a waveform, 151
Mantra as an *externalization in sound of a
    process in consciousness. We become what
    we think we are.*, 152
Mantra, human body as a, 151
Mantras, Bailey describes, 151
manufactured objects, energetic presence of,
    277
map dowsing, 47, 65
Maslow, Abraham H., 86, 91
Maslow, Abraham H. and loss of self, 113
Maslow, heirarchy of needs correlated with
    Chakras, 144
material world influenced or not by human
    thoughts, 20

NOTES ON COLOUR PLATES

The first 4 plates show instruments developed by the author. In general these can be described as Coherent Energy Transfer Instruments, and one of the functions they perform is to enable Radionic actions such as those described in this book.

The ALPHA-NUMERIC TRANSDUCER v3 (ANT v3) was introduced in 2002 and has been developed through several versions. The instrument has 8 card slots. Each slot will read a variety of Codes, including the author's Alpha-Numeric and related cards; Magneto-Geometric (Rae) cards; Radionic Rates printed on white card, etc. The output from each slot can set over a wide potency range, variable from 0 - 100MMM. DIRECT mode allows transfer of the energy without any potency setting. In treatment applications the ANT v3 is pulsed with an external trigger signal which can be sourced from either a CD player or .mp3 player.

The ANT v3 has an External Well input. The External Well, when plugged in, overrides card slot 5 and its output can be varied with the potency setting controls. The External Well can be used for copying or transfer purposes and its output can also be mixed in with that from the other card slots.

ALPHA-NUMERIC TRANSDUCER SCMFP   - Single Card, Multi-Function Potentiser, also known as the ANT 'Remedy Maker'. This is a single card version of the ANT v3 and is very similar in function except that the range LM1 - 9 has been added to the potency setting control. The ANT SCMFP also has an External Well input.

Note that the internal construction system of the ANT instruments does not use magnetism or electricity and they are in no sense a copy of a Rae Potentiser.

LRI (Large Radionic Instrument) - introduced in 2004 this instrument is for both Analysis and Treatment purposes and is for the experienced user. Four Charts are provided with the instrument which assist in Analysis of the patient according to the general methodology set out in this book and a fifth is to indicate possible treatments. The LRI instrument can give a range of treatments when so initiated by the operator.

MRI (Midi Radionic Instrument) - this instrument allows use of up to 8 codes with a witness, the central plate being subdivided into 9 sections. Its basic use is to give treatment, but it can be used for remedy copying.

SRI (Small Radionic Instrument) is a credit-card sized unit which allows basic Radionic treatments to be given.

The author has a range of other instruments under development.

There follow a number of plates which show elaborate code diagrams in various stages of development but for example Sulphur and Arsenicum Album can be considered complete for all applications. The basic use for each diagram is indicated by the adjoining label.

These diagrams are designed to depict the indicated Command or Preset to a very high degree of accuracy; each one may have many layers, sometimes hundreds of layers, which are reduced to the final 2-dimensional image. Many of the code diagrams have taken several years or even longer to develop. In addition a background field is being build up as the ground from which the entire 'visible' coding system can be derived. This entails the creation of many pages of alpha-numeric code, sometimes running into the hundreds of thousands of pages for a particular objective.

The basic units used in developing this psychoactived symbology are shape, number, colour and the Latin alphabet. The original diagrams are developed on an artwork approximately 1.25 metres square, but the final product is reduced to the size of an MGA Card (7.5 x 6.5cm including title header). Numerical parameters (for example) such as dimensions or angle of rotation of shapes are typically described to a very high degree of resolution, sometimes to four or more decimal places.

The cards are only intended for use in instruments developed by the author. Those shown are for illustration purposes and should not be used in any application.